Chemical Engineering for the Food Industry

Chemical Engineering for the Food Industry

Edited by

P.J. FRYER
School of Chemical Engineering
University of Birmingham
Birmingham, UK

D.L. PYLE
Department of Food Science and Technology
University of Reading
Reading, UK

and

C.D. RIELLY
Department of Chemical Engineering
University of Cambridge
Cambridge, UK

BLACKIE ACADEMIC & PROFESSIONAL
An Imprint of Chapman & Hall
London · Weinheim · New York · Tokyo · Melbourne · Madras

Published by Blackie Academic and Professional,
an imprint of Chapman & Hall, 2–6 Boundary Row, London SE1 8HN, UK

Chapman & Hall, 2–6 Boundary Row, London SE1 8HN, UK

Chapman & Hall GmbH, Pappelallee 3, 69469 Weinheim, Germany

Chapman & Hall USA, 115 Fifth Avenue, New York, NY 10003, USA

Chapman & Hall Japan, ITP-Japan, Kyowa Building, 3F, 2-2-1 Hirakawacho, Chiyoda-ku, Tokyo 102, Japan

DA Book (Aust.) Pty Ltd, 649 Whitehorse Road, Mitcham 3132, Victoria, Australia

Chapman & Hall India, R. Seshadri, 32 Second Main Road, CIT East, Madras 600 035, India

First edition 1997

© 1997 Chapman & Hall

Typeset in 10 on 12 pt Times by Best-set Typesetter Ltd., Hong Kong

Printed in Great Britain by Hartnolls Ltd, Bodmin, Cornwall

ISBN   0 412 49500 7

A catalogue record for this book is available from the British Library

Library of Congress Catalog Card Number: 96-85315

Printed on acid-free text paper, manufactured in accordance with ANSI/NISO Z39.48-1992 (Permanence of Paper)

Contents

9   Thermal treatment of foods   331
P.J. FRYER

10 Mixing in food processing   383
C.D. RIELLY

11 Process design: an exercise and simulation examples   434
C.A. ZAROR and D.L. PYLE

Contributors

H.A. Chase   Department of Chemical Engineering, University of Cambridge, Pembroke Street, Cambridge CB2 3RA, UK.

P.J. Fryer   School of Chemical Engineering, University of Birmingham, Edgbaston, Birmingham B15 2TT, UK.

A.N. Hayhurst   Department of Chemical Engineering, University of Cambridge, Pembroke Street, Cambridge CB2 3RA, UK.

R.M. Nedderman   Department of Chemical Engineering, University of Cambridge, Pembroke Street, Cambridge CB2 3RA, UK.

D.L. Pyle   Department of Food Science and Technology, University of Reading, Whiteknights, PO Box 226, Reading RG6 6AP, UK.

C.D. Rielly   Department of Chemical Engineering, University of Cambridge, Pembroke Street, Cambridge CB2 3RA, UK.

J. Varley   Department of Food Science and Technology, University of Reading, Whiteknights, PO Box 226, Reading RG6 6AP, UK.

C.A. Zaror   Department of Chemical Engineering, University of Concepcion, Casilla 53-C, Correo 3, Concepcion, Chile.

Preface

Industrial food processing involves the production of added value foods on a large scale; these foods are made by mixing and processing different ingredients in a prescribed way. The food industry, historically, has not designed its processes in an engineering sense, i.e. by understanding the physical and chemical principles which govern the operation of the plant and then using those principles to develop a process. Rather, processes have been 'designed' by purchasing equipment from a range of suppliers and then connecting that equipment together to form a complete process. When the process being run has essentially been scaled up from the kitchen then this may not matter. However, there are limits to the approach.

- As the industry becomes more sophisticated, and economies of scale are exploited, then the size of plant reaches a scale where systematic design techniques are needed.
- The range of processes and products made by the food industry has increased to include foods which have no kitchen counterpart, such as low-fat spreads.
- It is vital to ensure the quality and safety of the product.
- Plant must be flexible and able to cope with the need to make a variety of products from a range of ingredients. This is especially important as markets evolve with time.
- The traditional design process cannot readily handle multi-product and multi-stream operations.
- Processes must be energetically efficient and meet modern environmental standards.

The problems of the food industry at the moment are very similar to those faced by the chemical process industries forty years ago. Design techniques which had proved able to cope with a small number of processes, based on well-tried plant units, were not able to cope with the requirements for new materials and more efficient production techniques. Chemical engineering is the profession which evolved to solve the design problems of the process industries. Chemical engineers have developed design techniques for continuous process plant, both individual plant items such as heat exchangers and reactors, and whole flowsheets. Although the materials used by the food industry are more complex than those commonly used in the chemical industry and the product safety requirements are different from those required of chemical plant, the principles used in the analysis and design of food and chemical plant are the same.

Once a process has been designed, it must be operated and controlled in an efficient way. Chemical engineers have developed ways to monitor and analyse the behaviour of process plant. In conjunction with modern developments in information technology, these concepts can be used to optimize the running of process plant.

An increasing number of chemical engineers are being employed by the food industry, and thus a large number of people working in the industry are coming into contact with chemical engineering design techniques. The aim of this book is to outline the basic principles on which chemical engineering works and to develop those ideas into ways of studying food process plant.

The book has its origin in a successful course which has been run in the Chemical Engineering Department at Cambridge since 1989, designed to give an introduction to chemical engineering principles to people working in the food industry but without a degree in chemical engineering. Over the years, the material in the book, first given as lectures and examples on the course, has evolved in response to the needs of the industry and to specific comments from the individuals on the course.

There are two things that this book does **not** set out to do.

- It does not aim to give a list of the processes used by the food industry and the equipment used to carry out those processes. Such a list is always out of date, as equipment is modified, and, more importantly, as novel processes are introduced. **Rather, we seek to outline the physical principles which underpin processing, such as heat, mass and momentum transfer and reaction engineering.**
- It does not describe the whole of chemical engineering. It is no longer possible to put the whole of chemical engineering into one book! Each chapter introduces topics on which whole books have been based. **By reading this book and doing the worked examples, a good basic understanding will be obtained; references are included so that those with specific needs can go further.**

The book is aimed at two groups: it will be useful both for those who are not chemical engineers and who are working in the food industry, and as a refresher for chemical engineers in the food industry. Using the written material, it is possible to examine food processing plant and to understand the design principles involved in heat transfer, mass transfer, mixing and reaction, which can be found in all plants. The aim of engineering, however, is efficient and economic design. We have included at the end a lengthy worked design example, which develops a flowsheet and plant items from an outline of a process. The example comes with supporting information on computer disk; increasingly, all design is computer based, and all professionals in the food industry must be computer literate. The programs which come with this book allow a further demonstration of the physical principles which we are trying to get over and reinforce the practical aspects of the subject.

A note on units

We have tried wherever possible throughout this text to conform to the SI system of units. Sometimes data has come in such a form that we have fallen below the standards which are imposed by the 'strict' SI system, and we have justified that to ourselves by noting that the 'real world' often appears ignorant of the SI system. Note that $kJ\,kg^{-1}K^{-1}$ are the same numerically as $J\,kg^{-1}°C^{-1}$ etc. The important point is to be consistent and, above all, **always** to check that equations and formulae are dimensionally correct.

Acknowledgements

This book has been developed over a number of years by the authors of the individual chapters in response to discussions with the many people in the food industry who have been on our course. We are deeply grateful for the feedback given, which has enabled us to improve the relevance of the material to industry needs.

The Editors wish to thank all of the authors for spending so much time developing this course, and transferring a vague idea into first a successful course, and then this book. They also thank all those who have suffered during its preparation.

List of symbols

Symbol	Definition	Units
A	area	m^2
A_o	area of orifice	
A	area under C-curve	$kmol\,s\,m^{-3}$
A	pre-exponential factor	–
a	specific area per unit volume	m^2/m^3
B	baffle width	m
Bi	Biot number	–
b	thickness	m
C	annual cash flow (Chapter 1)	£/yr
C	constant of integration	
C	cook value	min
C	impeller clearance (Chapter 10)	m
C_c	contraction coefficient	
C_D	discharge coefficient	
C_{max}	maximum cook value	min
C_v	velocity coefficient	
c	concentration	$kmol\,m^{-3}$
$\bar{c}$	mean concentration	$kmol\,m^{-3}$
c_A	concentration of species A	$kmol\,m^{-3}$
c_b	bulk concentration	$kmol\,m^{-3}$
c_e	concentration of tracer in exit stream from reactor	$kmol\,m^{-3}$
c_{film}	solubility in film	$kmol\,m^{-3}$
c_i	interfacial concentration	$kmol\,m^{-3}$
c_{in}	concentration of tracer in inlet stream to reactor	$kmol\,m^{-3}$
c_s	surface concentration	$kmol\,m^{-3}$
c^*	dimensionless concentration	–
c_∞	final concentration	$kmol\,m^{-3}$
c_0	initial concentration	$kmol\,m^{-3}$
c_D	drag coefficient	
c_f	friction factor	
$\bar{c}_P$	mean specific heat capacity	$J\,kg^{-1}K^{-1}$
c_P	specific heat capacity at constant pressure	$J\,kg^{-1}\,K^{-1}$

Symbol	Definition	Units
c_V	specific heat capacity at constant volume	$J\,kg^{-1}\,K^{-1}$
D	decimal reduction time	min
D	large diameter, such as pipe; common distance scale in dimensionless calculations	m
$\mathcal{D}$	diffusion coefficient	$m^2\,s^{-1}$
D_a	axial diffusion coefficient	$m^2\,s^{-1}$
D_e	effective diffusion coefficient	$m^2\,s^{-1}$
D_H	hydraulic mean diameter	m
d	small diameter, such as particle	m
d_{max}	maximum bubble size	m
d_{32}	Sauter mean diameter	m
Da	Damköhler number	–
E	electric field strength	$V\,m^{-1}$
E	energy (Chapter 1)	J
E	extract flowrate	$kg\,s^{-1}$
E_a	activation energy	$J\,kmol^{-1}\,K^{-1}$
$E(t)$	residence time distribution	–
e	equivalent roughness size	m
e	error signal	
F	F-value: integrated lethality	min
F	flow rate	$m^3\,s^{-1}$
F	force	N
F	imposed forcing function	
F	fouling factor	$K\,m^2\,W^{-1}$
F_j	molar flowrate of compound j	$kmol\,s^{-1}$
F_P	required process integrated lethality	min
$F(t)$	cumulative residence time distribution	
Fr	Froude number	–
FV	future value	
G	shear modulus for elastic deformation	Pa
G	transfer function	
G'	storage modulus	Pa
G''	loss modulus	Pa
Gr	Grashof number $= \rho\Delta\rho g L^3/\mu^2$	–
g	acceleration due to gravity	$m\,s^{-2}$
H	closed-loop transfer function	
H,h	height	m
H	Henry's law constant	$Pa\,m^3\,kg^{-1}$
$\mathcal{H}$	humidity	kg/kg
ΔH	loss of head	m
ΔH_f	standard heat of formation	$J\,kmol^{-1}$
ΔH°_R	standard heat or enthalpy of reaction	$J\,kmol^{-1}$

Symbol	Definition	Units
h	film heat transfer coefficient	$W\,m^{-2}\,K^{-1}$
h	specific enthalpy (Chapter 1)	$J\,kg^{-1}$
h_{fi}	latent heat of fusion	$J\,kg^{-1}$
h_{fg}	latent heat of evaporation	$J\,kmol^{-1}$
I	current (electrical)	A
i	fractional interest or discount rate	–
J	mass transfer rate	$kmol\,s^{-1}$
j	mass flux	$kg\,m^{-2}s^{-1}$
j_D	j-factor for mass transfer	
j_H	j-factor for heat transfer	
K	equilibrium constant	
K	overall mass transfer coefficient	$m\,s^{-1}$
K	partition coefficient	
K	power law consistency index (Chapter 5)	$Pa\,s^n$
K_c	controller gain	
K_m	Michaelis constant for enzyme-catalysed reaction	$kmol\,m^{-3}$ or $kg\,m^{-3}$
K_o	Monod constant	$kmol\,m^{-3}$ or $kg\,m^{-3}$
K_p	static gain (Chapter 7)	
k	film mass transfer coefficient	$m\,s^{-1}$
k_L	liquid mass transfer coefficient	$m\,s^{-1}$
k_r	rate constant	s^{-1}
k_n	rate constant for reaction of order n	
k_s	solid mass transfer coefficient	$m\,s^{-1}$
L	Open loop transfer function	–
L_d	detector length scale	m
L_E	energy lost per unit mass	$J\,kg^{-1}$
L, l	length	m
M	flux of momentum	$kg\,m\,s^{-2}$
M	mass	kg
M	mean molecular mass	
M	mixing index	–
m	Distribution coefficient	–
m_0	initial mass	kg
N	total molar flux	$kmol\,m^{-2}s^{-1}$
N	impeller speed	rps
N_A	aeration number	
N_{po}	ungassed power number	–
NPV	Net Present Value	£
N_Q	flow number	–
N_1	first normal stress difference	Pa

Symbol	Definition	Units
N_2	second normal stress difference	Pa
Nu	Nusselt number $= hL/\lambda$	–
n	number	–
n	power-law exponent in eqn (5.7)	–
P	power input	W
P	productivity	$kg\,m^{-3}\,s^{-1}$
P	total pressure	Pa
P	wetted perimeter of duct	m
P_a	atmospheric pressure	Pa
P_o	ungassed power unit	W
ΔP	pressure drop	Pa
Pr	Prandtl number $= \mu c_P/\lambda$	–
PV	present value	
p	partial pressure	Pa
p°	equilibrium vapour pressure	Pa
Q	heat flow	W
Q	Oxygen transfer rate (Chapter 4)	$kg\,m^{-3}\,s^{-1}$
Q_C	process cooling (Chapter 6)	W
Q_c	heat content	J
Q_G	heat generation rate (Chapter 9)	$W\,m^{-3}$
Q_T	Total heat (Chapter 1)	J
Q_g	gas volumetric flowrate	$m^3\,s^{-1}$
Q_H	process heating (Chapter 6)	W
Q_L	liquid volumetric flowrate	$m^3\,s^{-1}$
q	heat flux	$W\,m^{-2}$
R	large radius	m
R	rate of oxygen consumption or demand	$kg\,s^{-1}$
R	electrical resistance (Chapter 9)	Ω
R_F	fouling resistance	$K\,m^{-2}\,W^{-1}$
R_g	gas constant	$J\,mol^{-1}\,K^{-1}$
R_s	radius of sphere	m
r_A	rate of reaction per unit volume (described in terms of production of A)	$kmol\,m^{-3}\,s^{-1}$
r	small radius	m
Re	Reynolds number $= \rho u_m D/\mu$ (different types defined in text)	
S	selectivity	
S	solvent flowrate	$kg\,s^{-1}$
s	pressure gradient	$Pa\,m^{-1}$
Sc	Schmidt number $= \mu/\rho D$	
Sh	Sherwood number $= kd/\theta$	–
St	Stanton number $= h/\rho u_m c_P$	

Symbol	Definition	Units
T	tank diameter (Chapter 10)	m
T	temperature	K or °C
T_0	initial temperature	K
T_i	interface temperature	K
T_L	liquid temperature	K
T_m	mean temperature of fluid	K
T_{ref}	reference temperature	K
T_s	surface temperature	K
T_w	wall or water temperature	K
ΔT_{lm}	logarithmic mean temperature difference	K
ΔT_{min}	minimum approach temperature	K
ΔT	temperature difference	K
T_D	derivative action time (Chapter 7)	
T_I	integral action time (Chapter 7)	s
t	time	s
$\bar{t}$	average of the residence time distribution	s
t_o	residence time along the axis	s
U	internal energy (Chapter 1)	$J\,kg^{-1}$
U	overall heat transfer coefficient	$W\,m^{-2}\,K^{-1}$
U°	clean heat transfer coefficient	$W\,m^{-2}\,K^{-1}$
u	velocity of flow through a quasitubular reactor	
V	voltage (Chapter 9)	V
V	volume	m^3
V_m	maximum reaction rate for an enzyme-catalysed reaction	$kmol\,m^{-3}\,s^{-1}$
V_r	volume of liquid in reactor	m^3
v	velocity	$m\,s^{-1}$
v_1	centreline velocity	
v_m	mean velocity	$m\,s^{-1}$
v_∞	terminal velocity	$m\,s^{-1}$
v_p	velocity of particle	$m\,s^{-1}$
v_r	velocity ratio	–
W	blade width (Chapter 10)	m
W	work	J
W_g	additional resistance of gel layer (Chapter 4)	$m\,s^{-1}$
W_m	hydraulic resistance of membrane (Chapter 4)	$m\,s^{-1}$
w	mass flowrate (Chapter 1)	$kg\,s^{-1}$
w_1, w_2	total material flows or flowrates (Chapter 1)	$kg\,s^{-1}$
w_L	volumetric flowrate	$m^3\,s^{-1}$
w	width	m
We	Weber number	–

Symbol	Definition	Units
X	mixedness fraction	–
X_A	fractional conversion of component A	
x,y,z	deviation/perturbation variable (Chapter 7)	
x,y,z	distance	m
x,y,z	mass or mole fraction or concentration (Chapters 1 and 4)	
x	output (Chapter 7)	
Y	yield coefficient	kg/kg
z_c, z_F	Z value: slope of the lethality or cooking curve	K
α	solids volume fraction	–
α	thermal diffusivity $= \lambda/\rho c_P$	$m^2 s^{-1}$
β	shear rate constant	–
Γ	torque	N m
$\dot{\gamma}$	shear rate or strain rate	s^{-1}
γ	strain	–
δ	disturbance (Chapter 7)	
δ	thickness	m
δ	loss angle	rad
ε'	dipole density	
$\dot{\varepsilon}$	elongational strain rate	s^{-1}
ε	gas volume fraction	–
ζ	damping coefficient	
η_∞	upper Newtonian viscosity	Pa s
θ	angle	rad
θ	controller output (Chapter 7)	
θ	temperature	K
θ_W	fraction of water in the material	
ϑ	dimensionless time	
κ	electrical conductivities in the x and y directions	$s\,m^{-1}$
λ	relaxation time $= \mu/G$ (Chapter 5)	s
λ	thermal conductivity	$W\,m^{-1}K^{-1}$
μ_m	maximum growth rate for a microbial fermentation	h^{-1}
μ	viscosity	Pa s
μ_a	apparent viscosity	Pa s
μ_E	elongational viscosity	Pa s
μ_0	lower Newtonian viscosity	Pa s
$|\mu^*|$	magnitude of complex viscosity	Pa s
ν	kinematic viscosity $= \mu/\rho$	$m^2 s^{-1}$
ρ	density	$kg\,m^{-3}$
σ^2	variance	–

Symbol	Definition	Units
σ	normal stress	Pa
σ	surface tension (Chapter 10)	$N\,m^{-1}$
τ	shear stress	Pa
τ	system time constant	s
τ_w	wall sheer stress	Pa
τ_y	yield stress (Chapter 5)	Pa
Φ	constant value of N_{po}	–
$\phi_{C,F}$	cook and sterility ratio	
ϕ	dispersed phase volume fraction	
ϕ	phase shift	
ω	frequency	$rad\,s^{-1}$

1 Introduction to process design

D.L. PYLE

Introduction

At the core of chemical engineering is design, frequently of continuous processes. A food process plant will consist of a series of process units, each of which carries out some specific job, such as mixing, fermentation, sterilization, or separation. Each of these units is designed using physical and chemical principles; later chapters of this book will consider the principles which underpin these designs. However, to produce an efficient process it is necessary to consider the whole process, to understand the way in which material moves around the plant and to calculate the heating and cooling duties needed.

Chemical engineers begin design by constructing a **flowsheet** for a plant, on which a **Material Balance** can be carried out to define all the flows in and out of the system and individual units. This balance enables a preliminary idea of the best flowsheet to be obtained; for example, if only 5% of the inputs in a process unit are actually used, then it will probably be necessary to add a recycle stream to return unreacted material to the unit. In addition to the mass balance, an estimate of the heating and cooling loads on the plant, the **Thermal Balance**, can be developed. Material and thermal balances can be carried out before going into detail about the sizes of individual units; the preliminary flowsheet incorporates all the key elements of the process without specifying the details of the design, such as the size of any pumps, pipes and heat exchangers needed.

This chapter introduces techniques for the analysis of flowsheets and processes which will be used throughout this book. It also introduces the key problem of food process engineering, of ensuring that the process is economically viable. The profitability of a given process is, in practice, very difficult to estimate. However, the use of ideas such as the net present value of a project can be used both to estimate the success of the project and to compare it to possible other investments. A series of examples are provided to illustrate the concepts developed in this chapter; these will be taken up and developed in depth in the rest of the book.

Chemical Engineering for the Food Industry. Edited by P.J. Fryer, D.L. Pyle and C.D. Rielly. Published in 1997 by Blackie A & P, an imprint of Chapman & Hall, London. ISBN 0 412 49500 7.

The aim of design is to arrive at a precise specification of all the material and energy requirements, and the equipment, pipework, instrumentation and control schemes necessary for a process to be constructed and operated efficiently, safely and economically. This involves consideration of the whole process and of the individual units that comprise it. The first stage in process design is to generate possible schemes that might meet the requirements of the process in question. This involves considering alternative **operations** (such as direct or indirect sterilization, filtration or centrifugation, co- or counter-current spray drying) and **sequences** of these operations. It results in a qualitative process description, which is usually presented as a schematic diagram, or flowsheet, of the whole process. For example, Fig. 1.1 shows a simplified outline of a hypothetical process for semi-batch extraction from a solid using supercritical carbon dioxide. In this case, the engineer would certainly consider other alternatives with a view to improving energy efficiency and process economics.

In many ways flowsheet development is the most creative part of the design process and the most difficult to pin down in terms of standard or rote procedures. Here, we won't focus on this preliminary phase of overall process design, although we shall consider some alternatives, and how to evaluate them, on the basis of selected examples. First, however, consider how alternative flowsheets could be evaluated. The first point, clearly, is to determine whether the process is technically feasible. It may not be feasible for a variety of reasons: for example, one of the process operations might be fraught with difficulties, or require unrealistically large material or energy inputs. Invariably there will be several technically feasible options, but some will certainly be more efficient – in technical terms – than others, and in order to discriminate between them it is necessary, in the next stages of evaluation, to estimate the flows of materials and energy. A further stage in the appraisal process would be to consider the relative economic merits of the various alternatives. All these stages of process design and evaluation are quantitative, even if they do not involve very accurate calculations early on in the design process. Some of the methods that underpin these stages

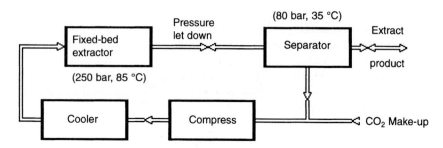

Fig. 1.1 Simplified flowsheet of semi-batch extraction with supercritical carbon dioxide.

will be developed in this chapter, which is divided into three sections dealing with the quantification of the flows of material, energy and cash respectively.

Chapter 11 outlines a more extended design of an integrated cheese-making plant. This is presented as a problem to be worked through; the solution will be found to draw heavily on material from this chapter. Readers are strongly urged to attempt to solve this problem. A simplified spreadsheet solution of this problem is also given in the computer disk attached to this text.

1.1 Material requirements and flows

1.1.1 Mass balances

We first consider the ideas and techniques of 'mass balancing', which are used at the design stage to estimate material flows throughout a process. The same principles have another important application in their use to check, from operating data, that processes are operating as desired. Figure 1.2 shows a simplified flowsheet of a milk spray drying plant. In order to specify the process equipment units it is necessary, *inter alia*, to estimate the flows of dried product and gaseous exhaust per tonne or m^3 of milk fed to the process. We can confidently assert that, in spite of any chemical or biochemical changes, matter is neither formed nor destroyed during the process so that, provided all the flows in and out of the process – or in and out of an individual process unit – are accounted for, we can, in principle, set up a material balance.

Consider a time interval t of process operation. Then the total mass of material accumulated within the process will be the net difference between all the flows into and out of the process during the time interval:

$$\text{Accumulation} = \Sigma(\text{Inlet flows}) - \Sigma(\text{Outlet flows})$$

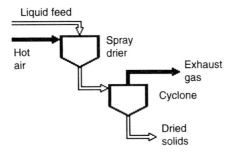

Fig. 1.2 Schematic of spray drier.

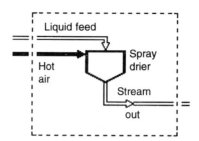

Fig. 1.3 Spray drier unit and system boundary.

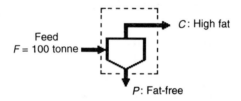

Fig. 1.4 Example 1.1: fat separator.

where Σ indicates summation. For example, a balance over the spray drier unit (Fig. 1.3) would start from

Accumulation in drier = Milk in + Hot air in − Hot stream out

Similarly, a balance over the cyclone would start from:

Accumulation in drier = Hot stream in − Dry milk out − Gas stream out

Often the accumulation term will be zero. There should be no build-up of product inside a continuously operating spray drier, for example. Thus, if we consider a *steady* continuous process:

$$w_1 = w_2 \tag{1.1}$$

where w_1 and w_2 are the total material flows in and out respectively. This equation also holds for a batch process, where w_1 and w_2 are identified with the totals of the starting and final materials. It also holds for a steady process if w_1 and w_2 are average flowrates (e.g. in $kg\,s^{-1}$) rather than total flows (i.e. in kg). Note that in general this equation is only true for **mass** flows. With liquids and where density changes are small it may hold in volumetric units (e.g. in m^3); where gas flows are involved, changes in the conditions between the inlet and outlet mean that volumetric flows are rarely appropriate. For example, there is no reason in general why the volumetric flows of milk and air into the spray drier should equal the volumetric flows of dried product and exhaust air. Nor, where there are chemical changes, will overall balances written in molar units satisfy equation (1.1).

If there are no chemical/biochemical changes, equation (1.1) will also apply to **individual components** or **compounds** in the process streams. For example, the flow of milk solids into the drier must balance the flow of solids in the dried product and any losses in the gas exhaust.

As it is often necessary to convert between different measures, a few basic definitions are summarized in Appendix 1.A.

1.1.2 Choosing a basis

In order to carry out a material balance calculation it is necessary to define a basis, such as an operating time period or a reference quantity. Suppose you are designing a plant that produces 10000 140 g pots of yoghurt per day; it isn't hard to see that for calculation purposes this might not be the most convenient starting point. It would probably be easier to take a defined quantity of milk (that is, a starting material) and then to scale the results to the real operating conditions at the end of the calculation.

The following three rules will be found useful:

- Choose the basis that is most convenient for calculation.
- Specify the basis explicity.
- Don't change the basis during the calculation.

The following example illustrates some of the basic principles mentioned above.

EXAMPLE 1.1

Consider a separator in which a liquid containing 5 wt% fat is concentrated to 35 wt%; the other product stream, P, is to be fat-free. The separator produces 195 t day^{-1} of the high-fat product, C. What are the flows of the streams involved?

Basis: 100 tonne of feed. This is chosen for convenience of calculation; we shall subsequently convert the result to correspond to the specified product flow. The process is represented in Fig. 1.4.

Thus an overall balance gives

$$F = 100 = P + C \tag{1.2}$$

A balance on fat gives

$$0.05F = 5 = 0.35C \tag{1.3}$$

and solving equations (1.2) and (1.3) gives

$$C = 14.29 \text{t}$$

and

$$P = 85.71\,t$$

In other words, for every 100t of feed, there are 14.29 and 85.71 t of high-fat and fat-free product respectively.

However, the 100t feed assumed for the calculation doesn't correspond to the daily production of 195t of product C. To convert the answer to a daily basis we must multiply all the streams by 195/14.29 (= 13.646), to give the daily flows through the plant:

	In (tonnes)	Out (tonnes)
F	1364.6	–
C	–	195.0
P	–	1169.6
Total	1364.6	1364.6

Note that, considering the feed to comprise fat and fat-free liquid, we could write another equation by setting up a balance on the fat-free liquid (on the original basis):

$$0.95F = 95 = 0.65C + P \tag{1.4}$$

However, adding equations (1.3) and (1.4) gives equation (1.2), so that the additional equation is redundant. The reason is that as F is specified, there are only two unknowns (P and C) and thus there can be only two independent equations in the set (1.2)–(1.4). Once two of these are solved, the third is automatically satisfied. In some cases the choice of which independent equations to use makes a considerable difference to the ease of calculation.

EXAMPLE 1.2: MULTICOMPONENT SEPARATION

Suppose that in Example 1.1 the aqueous phase contained some dissolved components, such as lactose and salts. How would these components be distributed following separation? Let us suppose that they are not bound to the fat in any way; in this case they should be distributed in the same proportions in the water phase of the two outlet streams as in the inlet. In particular, suppose that in addition to the fat, the inlet stream contains 5% lactose and 2% salt.

If, as suggested, there is no preferential fractionation of the lactose and salt between the fat-rich and fat-free streams, we can take advantage of the fact that the lactose, salt and water must therefore be in the same proportions (5:2:88) throughout, by eliminating fat from the calculation. The table below shows the composition of the feed on two different bases:

	Mass (kg)	Mass fraction	Mass fraction (fat-free basis)
Fat	5	0.05	–
Lactose	5	0.05	0.0526
Salt	2	0.02	0.0211
Water	88	0.88	0.9263

On a fat-free basis the total flows of feed, streams C and P are thus 95, 9.29 ($= 14.29 - 5$), and 85.71 tonnes respectively. The fractions of lactose, salt and water in each of these are given in the table above. Therefore, for example, the quantity of lactose in stream C must be $0.0526 \times 9.29 = 0.489$ t.

On a fat-free basis, the compositions of streams F, C and P are (in kg):

Stream	F	C	P
Lactose	5	0.489	4.511
Salt	2	0.196	1.804
Water	88	8.605	79.395
Total	95	9.290	85.710

Note that this summary table allows one to check that all the component and total balance requirements are satisfied.

A further example will help to illustrate some other closely related concepts, and in particular it will show the way in which many problems can conveniently be solved algebraically.

EXAMPLE 1.3: ALGEBRAIC FORMS, WET AND DRY BASIS, TIE SUBSTANCES

Consider a fruit from which the juice is extracted by pressing. The fruit enters with a juice content of 70 wt% and soluble sugars comprise 15% of the juice. At the end of the pressing process the pressed solid (pomace) contains 10% juice and the clear extract juice contains 15.5% sugars. All

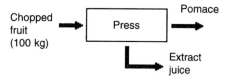

Fig. 1.5 Example 1.3: juice extraction.

percentages are on a weight basis. We wish to complete the mass balance around the extractor.

Basis: 100 kg fruit

There are several unknowns, and it is convenient to denote each by an algebraic symbol. Then a table of inputs and outputs is:

	In (kg)	Out (kg) Pomace	Out (kg) Juice
Insoluble dry matter	30	T	0
Juice			
Soluble sugars	10.5	a	x
Water	59.5	b	y
Total	100	$T + a + b$	$x + y$

We now proceed to calculate T, a, b, etc., using the information on compositions and the same principles as before. In particular, for each component, the input (that is, the entry in the second column) must equal the sum of the outputs (the entries in columns 3 and 4). Note that as there are five unknown variables, five independent equations or relationships will be needed for a unique solution.

1. As the insoluble dry matter can only appear in the pomace, $T = 30$. A component such as this, which is carried unchanged across a process, often provides a useful check or vehicle for establishing a mass balance. It is called a **tie substance.**

2. As the pomace contains 10% juice (i.e. soluble sugars and water):

$$\frac{a+b}{30+a+b} = 0.1 \tag{1.5}$$

i.e.

$$a + b = 3.333 \tag{1.6}$$

3. Balances on sugar and water:

$$10.5 = a + x \tag{1.7}$$

$$59.5 = b + y \tag{1.8}$$

and

$$70 = a + b + x + y \qquad (1.9)$$

The three independent equations (1.6), (1.7) and (1.8) are insufficient to solve uniquely for a, b, x and y. Equation (1.9) is not independent, as it is the sum of (1.7) and (1.8), and therefore does not provide any further information.

A further equation may be written, as the extract juice is known to contain 15.5% sugars, or

$$0.155 = \frac{x}{x + y} \qquad (1.10)$$

so that

$$x = 0.1834y \qquad (1.11)$$

From equations (1.9) and (1.6):

$$x + y = 66.667$$

so that

$$x = 10.33$$

and

$$y = 56.337$$

From (1.7) and (1.8):

$$a = 0.27$$

$$b = 3.063$$

It will be seen that these values satisfactorily complete the input/output table:

	In (kg)	Out (kg) Pomace	Out (kg) Juice
Insoluble dry matter	30	30	0
Juice			
Soluble sugars	10.5	0.27	10.33
Water	59.5	3.063	56.337
Total	100	33.333	66.667

In Example 1.2 we showed how the compositions might be defined on a fat-free basis. In a similar way we can distinguish here between a **wet** and a **dry** basis. For example, in the problem statement the pomace juice was defined as a percentage of the total pomace: that is, on a **wet basis**. On this basis the juice is 10%, which is of course consistent with the final table, column 2: 3.333/33.333. On a dry, juice-free, basis its fraction is 3.333/30 = 0.111.

In the general case where a stream contains a, b, c and w kg of components A, B, C and water respectively the mass fractions on an overall (wet) and dry basis are summarized in the table below. It is often convenient to be able to convert between different bases in this way.

	Mass (kg)	Mass fraction	Mass fraction (dry basis)
A	a	$a/(a + b + c + w)$	$a/(a + b + c)$
B	b	$b/(a + b + c + w)$	$b/(a + b + c)$
C	c	$c/(a + b + c + w)$	$c/(a + b + c)$
Water	w	$w/(a + b + c + w)$	–

In example above, the percentage of juice in the pomace on a wet basis is 10%:

$$\frac{a+b}{30+a+b} = 0.1$$

From this we can readily calculate its composition on a dry basis:

$$\frac{a+b}{30} = 0.1/0.9 = 0.111$$

Many problems are more complex than the ones considered so far. Sometimes there are many components to account for, as in processes to recover complex flavour components. Sometimes the topology of the process is more complex. Figure 1.1 includes an additional complication over the first three examples because solvent (the carbon dioxide) is recycled; recycle streams and complex linkages between process units are very common in the process industry. Often the individual components of the feed are not conserved in the same form over the process. In cheese-making, for example, a series of microbial or enzymatic processes lead to the transformation of milk into cheese, butter, ethanol etc. In this latter case we need to know something about the stoichiometry of the process, while recognizing that this is invariably more complex with bioprocesses than with chemical processes. Before considering this latter aspect, let us first consider some of the issues concerned with the process topology.

1.1.3 The system boundary

In the examples above it was tacitly assumed that the separation took place in one unit. However, it wouldn't make any difference to the overall answer if several concentration and separation stages were involved to give the same result. In other words, the boundary box shown in Fig. 1.4 (Example 1.1) merely defines the system over which the material balance is established. Whether the 'box' contains one or several process stages is immaterial provided the boundary is drawn correctly so as to cut all entering and leaving streams. Nor does it matter how the stages within the box are connected to each other. We could, then, draw a system boundary around the whole of a flowsheet, and provided all the material flows into and out of the process (but not necessarily those within the process) are correctly represented on the flowsheet we could then use this to set up an overall balance.

EXAMPLE 1.4

Suppose that the fat separation process in Example 1.1 was carried out in two stages, as illustrated in Fig. 1.6; the intermediate concentrate S *contains 25% fat. Calculate the unknown streams and their compositions.*

Three possible 'systems' over which balances could be established are identified in Fig. 1.6 by the dotted lines defining the system boundaries. In particular, boundary A delineates the overall process: the only streams relevant are *F*, *C* and *P*. Boundaries B and D define the boundaries appropriate to balances over the individual units, from which *S*, P_1 and P_2 can, in principle, be calculated.

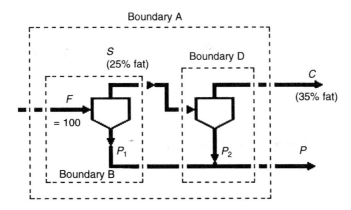

Fig. 1.6 Example 1.4: two-stage separation.

Basis: 100 tonnes F

1. Overall balance (i.e. boundary A):
   Two balances only are needed to yield the flows C and P. Here we use the total and one component balances:

   Total flows:
   $$F = 100 = P + C \qquad (1.12)$$

   Fat:
   $$0.05F = 5 = 0.35C \qquad (1.13)$$

   so that
   $$C = 14.29$$
   $$P = 85.71$$

   which is, of course, identical to the solution of Example 1.1. This confirms the point made above about the irrelevance of the internal structure to the overall balance.

2. Balance over first separator (i.e. boundary B):
   Again, as the input is specified, there are two unknowns only, S and P_1, and thus two balances or relations are needed:

   Total flows:
   $$F = 100 = S + P_1 \qquad (1.14)$$

   Fat:
   $$0.05F = 5 = 0.25S \qquad (1.15)$$

   so that:
   $$S = 20$$
   $$P_1 = 80$$

3. Balance over second separator (boundary D):
   This is formally identical to the problem posed by the first separator, as the input S is now known. The solution is straightforward:

   Total:
   $$20 = C + P_2 \qquad (1.16)$$

   Fat:
   $$5 = 0.35C \qquad (1.17)$$

   so that:
   $$C = 14.29$$
   $$P_2 = 5.71$$

Note however that there is some redundancy here, as C was already calculated from the overall balance, and

$$P_2 = P - P_1 = 5.71 \tag{1.18}$$

In this example the topology was not complex: the calculations were straightforward, as it was possible to complete the solution by marching forward from the inlet. However, an attempt to solve the problem 'backwards', by solving around separator 2 first, would be unsuccessful: it is often found preferable for the directions of the material and information flows to coincide. Note that the balances on the individual units must always be consistent with the overall balance.

1.1.4 Recycles

Recycle streams are very common in process technology. They are used for various reasons and, in particular, to conserve material and to increase process efficiency. The carbon dioxide loop in Fig. 1.1 is a good example; note, too, that the solvent may also recycle valuable extracted components. In a similar way, the efficiency of a continuous fermenter (as used in ethanol production, for example) can often be increased, for example by recycling cells and unconsumed nutrients.

We illustrate the effects of recycling and the method of solving material balance problems with recycle in the next example.

EXAMPLE 1.5

One important bioprocess where recycling allows significant improvements in process efficiency is the enzymatic isomerization of glucose:

Glucose $\rightleftharpoons$ Fructose

This reaction is reversible, and the equilibrium constant is close to 1. Thus the best that can be achieved is a product stream containing 50% each of glucose and fructose. However, fructose and glucose can be partially separated (by using a chromatograph, for example), so that the process flowsheet in Fig. 1.7 may allow higher yields of fructose by recycling unreacted glucose to the reactor.

In practice the glucose feed is always contaminated with a small percentage of inert oligosaccharides, and this has an important bearing on the recycle process.

As an example consider a simplified process in which the fresh feed contains 98% glucose and 2% oligosaccharides; all percentages are on a weight basis.

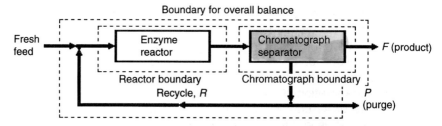

Fig. 1.7 Example 1.5: glucose isomerization process.

*The reaction products are at equilibrium. The chromatograph is as-
sumed to achieve perfect separation of the fructose and glucose: that is,
the product stream is glucose-free; the recycle is fructose-free; all the
oligosaccharide leaves the separator in the glucose stream. We now
consider how the process yield varies with recycle, R.*

Basis: 100 kg fresh feed

At steady state, there is no change in any composition or flow; then an
overall balance (see Fig. 1.7) where the system boundary is cut only by
the feed, product and purge streams, gives

$$100 = F + P \qquad (1.19)$$

and an overall balance on inerts yields

$$2 = (1 - x)P \qquad (1.20)$$

where x is the fraction of glucose in stream P.

Notice that, without the purge stream, inert oligosaccharides would build
up in the process.

Specifying x fixes P and F. Thus if $x = 0.9$ (i.e. the inerts comprise 10%
of the stream), $P = 20$ and $F = 80$ kg. If $x = 0.95$, $P = 40$ and $F = 60$ etc. In
order to see what this implies for the recycle we must consider what
happens inside the process.

First consider a balance over the reactor (Fig. 1.7). The flows of glucose, fructose, and inerts (all in kg) are:

	In	Out
Glucose	98 + 0.9R	49 + 0.45R
Fructose	0	49 + 0.45R
Inert	2 + 0.1R	2 + 0.1R
Total	100 + R	100 + R

where the equilibrium condition (i.e. that the glucose and fructose concentrations are equal) has been used to calculate the glucose and fructose

exit concentrations in column 3. Note that, as in the previous examples, the overall total acts as a check on the calculation.

Although this balance doesn't itself yield the recycle (in fact it holds for all possible values of R) we can follow through one or more of the components to check that the internal and overall balances coincide, and to complete the solution of the problem. That is, the solution must ensure that the flows of all components in the outlet stream from the reactor equate to their flows in the exit stream from the chromatograph, and thus to the flows in the purge and recycle. The easiest component to use is fructose, as the fructose leaving the reactor all ends up in stream F after the separator. Thus a balance on fructose over the chromatograph (see boundary illustrated in Fig. 1.7) gives

$$49 + 0.45R = F = 80 \tag{1.21}$$

so that $R = 68.9\,\text{kg}$.

There is only one value of the recycle flow consistent with the predetermined value of x. You can readily check that as x, the fraction of glucose in the recycle stream, decreases so must R increase. The object of recycle in this case was to increase the yield of fructose on glucose. In the absence of recycle the fractional conversion of glucose would be 0.5. Here the fractional conversion is

$$y = \frac{80}{98} = 0.816$$

Again you can check that increasing the recycle rate (which must be increasingly dilute in glucose) would give an increased conversion of glucose. For example, at $x = 0.2$, $R = 485\,\text{kg}$, and $y = 0.995$.

Of course, this increased conversion is not realized at zero cost: there is an increasingly large volume of material to recirculate and the reactor must be redesigned to achieve the chosen efficiency (which here is to reach equilibrium).

Finally, return to the balance over the separator (Fig. 1.7). The glucose and inerts entering from the reactor enter the recycle stream and a purge split is then taken to maintain the inerts balance. The mass balance on glucose and inerts over the split must satisfy the requirements imposed. Thus:

	Leaving separator	Leaving in P	Recycle
Glucose	$49 + 0.45R$	$0.1P$	$0.1R$
Inerts	$2 + 0.9R$	$0.9P$	$0.9R$

which, since $F = 100 - P$, are both consistent with equation (1.21).

You should check that all the individual and total flows in and out of each process unit balance.

1.1.5 Solving problems that include recycles

Invariably, the first step in trying to solve any problem should be to establish an overall balance, as was done in Example 1.5 by equations (1.19) and (1.20). As the example shows, problems involving recycle loops are sometimes tractable analytically. Sometimes, however, it is then necessary to resort to trial-and-error methods, and many computer-aided design packages incorporate efficient algorithms for this.

In Example 1.5 the recycle flow necessary to reconcile the component balances could be arrived at by such a process: that is, by repeated trials with different values of R. The method is illustrated below.

EXAMPLE 1.6: NUMERICAL SOLUTION OF RECYCLE PROBLEM

The same values of the feed flow (100 kg) and glucose concentration in the purge ($x = 0.9$) are assumed as in Example 1.5. Thus, from the overall balance (equations (1.19) and (1.20)), $P = 20$ kg and $F = 80$.

The calculation procedure is as follows:

1. Guess R.
2. With $x = 0.9$, calculate glucose (g) and inerts (i) in recycle ($= A$ in Table 1.1).
3. Using feed content 98 kg glucose and 2 kg inerts, calculate g and i at entry to reactor ($= B$ in Table 1.1).
4. Using equilibrium condition, calculate g and f at reactor exit ($= C$ in Table 1.1).
5. Calculate fructose product, F_c, and compare with target stream $F (= 80)$.
6. Calculate g and i leaving separator ($= D$).
7. Calculate g and i in recycle from $D - P$ and compare with target ($= A$).

If the calculated values do not match with the design or assumed values (i.e. in steps 5 and 7) try a new R and repeat until answers converge.

The procedure is illustrated in Table 1.1 for two iterations. The correct result can be converged on readily using a simple algorithm.

1.1.6 Reaction stoichiometries

Although Example 1.5 involves a reaction, it is relatively simple to handle because of the simplicity of the reaction stoichiometry: one mole (or kg) of glucose gives one mole (or kg) of fructose. Thus it is easy to keep track of the flows.

Table 1.1 Example 1.6

First iteration, $R = 50$

	A	B	C	F_c	F	D	P	D–P
g	45	143	71.5	0	0	71.5	18	53.5
f	0	0	71.5	71.5	80	0	0	0
i	5	7	7	0	0	7	2	5
T	50	150	150	71.5	80	78.5	20	58.5

Result: Calculated fructose product (F_c) < Design value
Calculated glucose in recycle ($D–P$) > Assumed value
∴ Try higher R

Second iteration, $R = 80$

	A	B	C	F_c	F	D	P	D–P
g	72	170	85	0	0	85	18	67
f	0	0	85	85	80	0	0	0
i	8	10	10	0	0	10	2	8
T	80	180	180	85	80	95	20	75

Result: Calculated fructose product (F_c) > Design value
Calculated glucose in recycle ($D–P$) < Assumed value
∴ R too high: try new value in range $50 < R < 80$

Many situations, however, are more complex. In food and bioprocess operations involving more than blending, the raw materials are transformed (bio)chemically into new products, and these processes may be too complicated to represent by a simple chemical equation. Consider for example the processes involved in transforming milk into cheese and whey, or the set of reactions involved in extrusion cooking. Nonetheless, however complex the chemical processes, we can be sure that:

1. a total overall mass balance must close;
2. balances on the chemical elements (C, N etc.) must close;
3. a balance on inert components must also close.

For example, in a typical microbial process we have

C–, N–, H–, O–, etc. sources + cells = more cells and products

The usual approach taken in attempting to describe these processes is to write an overall pseudo-chemical equation. For example, the production of single cell protein (SCP) from an n-alkane carbon source (assuming an average composition $C_{10}H_{20}$) has been described by:

$$0.168C_{10}H_{20} + 1.4O_2 + 0.18NH_3$$
$$= CH_{1.84}O_{0.41}N_{0.18} + 0.674CO_2 + 1.039H_2O \qquad (1.22)$$

Note that, while this equation does not pretend to give a mechanistic description, it must satisfy various consistency requirements, as follows.

Each element should balance on the left- and right-hand sides of the equation. Thus:

	LHS	RHS
C	1.68	1.674
H	3.90	3.878
O	2.8	2.797
N	0.18	0.18

It will be seen that, to a fair degree of accuracy, the balance is achieved.

The total **mass** on the right- and left-hand sides of the equation must also be equal. If the individual elemental balances are satisfied then the overall balance must also be automatically satisfied. Thus:

$$LHS = 0.168 \times 140 + 1.4 \times 32 + 0.18 \times 17 = 71.38$$
$$RHS = 22.92 + 0.674 \times 44 + 1.039 \times 18 = 71.28$$

Here the 'molecular mass' of the microbial cells is 22.92: to avoid ambiguity it is conventional to define the molecular mass of a 'carbon mole' of cells: that is, of cells defined with the number of C atoms set arbitrarily to 1. Note that the overall cell composition simply represents the relative proportions between the elements. Different organisms or the same organism under different growth conditions will have (slightly) different compositions.

In general, **moles** are not conserved, where (bio-)reactions occur. In the example above there is an increase of almost one mole over the reaction. Usually, therefore, in dealing with biological processes it is more convenient to work in mass units. It must be emphasized that all components that are not transformed in the process (i.e. elements or inerts) are conserved.

It is noteworthy that the closure of the mass balance in this example is not perfect. One reason is that the overall stoichiometry does not have the same fundamental significance as a typical single chemical equation, such as $N_2 + 3H_2 \rightarrow 2NH_3$. The equation quoted above is the net result of many simultaneous and parallel reactions, not just one; moreover, a C-mole of cells is a very different concept from a mole of a chemical or biochemical compound, and must be empirically determined. In practice, instrument errors and inaccuracies, variations in flows and hold-ups in a process conspire to make the accurate closure of material balances extremely difficult. Nevertheless, the use of experimental data to attempt to establish elemental or overall material balances is a most important diagnostic tool for the process engineer.

1.1.7   Stoichiometric and yield coefficients

The premultipliers in the stoichiometric equation (1.22) (0.168, 1.4 etc.) are the **stoichiometric coefficients**. They represent the molar proportions between the various components involved in the reaction. By convention the coefficient of one of the reagents or products is set to 1: it is immaterial which is chosen. Thus in section 1.1.6, 1.4 moles of oxygen are consumed per C-mole of cells produced (and per 0.18 moles of ammonia consumed, etc.). Given the molecular masses of the components these coefficients are readily transformed into mass units. Consider equation (1.22):

$$0.168 C_{10}H_{20} + 1.4 O_2 + 0.18 NH_3 = CH_{1.84}O_{0.41}N_{0.18} + 0.674 CO_2 + 1.039 H_2O$$

Mol mass:

| 140 | 32 | 17 | 22.92 | 44 | 18 |

The mass of cells per unit mass of C-source is

$$Y = \frac{22.92}{0.168 \times 140} = 0.974 \tag{1.23}$$

Y is known as a **yield coefficient** and has the units of $kg\,kg^{-1}$ (here, kg cells kg^{-1} *n*-alkane). Yield coefficients can be defined for each pair of products and substrates.

Thus for the reaction

$$A + bB + cC + \ldots = pP + qQ + rR + \ldots$$

we can write the yield coefficient between product P (molecular mass M_P) and substrate B (molecular mass M_B):

$$Y_{PB} = \left(\frac{p}{b}\right)\left(\frac{M_P}{M_B}\right) \tag{1.24}$$

The stoichiometric and yield coefficients represent the ratios between components **consumed and produced**; it is quite rare for all the components to be fed in the same proportions as their coefficients (that is, in stoichiometric proportions), and care must be taken in handling these real problems.

1.1.8   Use of stoichiometric and yield coefficients in design

Consider a complex process:

$$A + bB + cC + \ldots = pP + qQ + rR + \ldots$$

where A, B etc. represent the compounds participating as substrates in the reaction. For convenience suppose that P is the primary product. Yield coefficients are defined, for example:

Y_{PA} = kg P produced kg^{-1} A consumed $(= p.M_P/M_A)$,
Y_{PB} = kg P produced kg^{-1} B consumed $(= p.M_P/bM_B)$ etc.

Table 1.2 Use of stoichiometric and yield coefficients in design

	In (kg)	In (kmol)	Out (kmol)	Out (kg)
A	w_A	w_A/M_A	$(1-x)w_A/M_A$	$(1-x)w_A$
B	w_B	w_B/M_B	$w_B/M_B - xbw_A/M_A$	$w_B - xbw_A M_B/(M_A)$
...				
P	0	0	xpw_A/M_A	$xpw_A M_P/(M_A)$
Q	0	0	xqw_A/M_A	$xqw_A M_Q/(M_A)$
Σ	$w = w_A + \ldots$			w

Now consider a process with feed comprising $w_A, w_B, \ldots$ kg of A,B etc. Suppose a fraction x of A is converted by the reaction above: what are the quantities of A,B, $\ldots$ P,Q, $\ldots$ leaving in the product streams?

We illustrate how an overall balance can be arrived at in terms of the stoichiometric coefficients: from the reaction stoichiometry, w moles of A react with (wb) moles of B (etc.) to produce wp moles of P, etc.; similarly, y kg of A react with ybM_B/M_A kg of B. Thus we can construct a table of inputs and output. In Table 1.2 the calculation sequence goes from left to right across the columns. The totals of columns 1 and 4 must balance.

The fractional conversions of the feed components are equal (i.e. to x) only when their molar flows are in the same ratio as the stoichiometric coefficients: that is, they are fed in stoichiometric proportions. This can be seen by considering the entries for component B in the table above. The fractional conversion z is defined by $(1-z)(\text{column 2}) = (\text{column 3})$:

$$\frac{(1-z)\,w_B}{M_B} = \frac{w_B}{M_B} - \frac{xbw_A}{M_A}$$

so that

$$(1-z) = (1-x)$$

when

$$\frac{w_B}{M_B} = \frac{bw_A}{M_A}$$

In many processes of practical importance the feed components are not fed in stoichiometric proportions; the substrate that would first disappear if the process went to completion is called the **limiting reagent**. (This is not necessarily the limiting substrate in the language of fermentation technology.)

The same type of calculation as shown in Table 1.2 can be carried though using yield rather than stoichiometric coefficients, as illustrated in the following example.

EXAMPLE 1.7

We take as an example the (BP) process for SCP production based on n-alkanes. Details are summarized below. The aim is to establish a complete mass balance over the whole process.

Basis: 100 kg *n*-alkane

Data

C-source: C-10 (i.e. $C_{10}H_{20}$)
O-source: air; supplied in 20% excess over stoichiometric requirement
N-source: ammonia; supplied in 5% excess over the stoichiometric requirement
Salts: added in aqueous solution, neglect in balance
Cell concentration in product stream: $30\,g\,l^{-1}$
Yield: 90% of alkane converted

Yield coefficients

On the basis of the stoichiometry above (equation (1.22)):

$$0.168C_{10}H_{20} + 1.4O_2 + 0.18NH_3$$
$$= CH_{1.84}O_{0.41}N_{0.18} + 0.674CO_2 + 1.039H_2O$$

the yield coefficients (Table 1.3) are readily calculated from equation (1.24), which in its most general form is

$$Y_{ij} = \left(\frac{a_i}{a_j}\right)\left(\frac{M_i}{M_j}\right)(\text{kg component } i)(\text{kg component } j)^{-1}$$

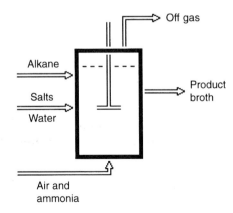

Fig. 1.8 Example 1.7: fermenter.

Table 1.3 Example 1.7: Yield coefficients

Compound	Molecular mass	Stoichiometric coefficient	Cell yield coefficient, Y_{xi} (kg cells) (kg compound i)$^{-1}$
n-Alkane	140	0.168	0.9745
Oxygen	32	1.40	0.5116
Ammonia	17	0.18	7.49
Carbon dioxide[a]	44	0.674	0.7729
Water[a]	18	1.039	1.226
Cells	22.92	–	–

[a] Denotes product

Table 1.4 Example 1.7: Calculation of mass balance

Component	In: feed (kg)	Consumed or produced (kg)	Out in product Stream (kg)
Alkane	100	99	1
Oxygen	200	188.6	11.4
Nitrogen[a]	658.4	–	658.4
Ammonia	13.66	12.87	0.79
Cells	–	96.48	96.48
Carbon dioxide	–	124.74	124.74
Water[b]	–	78.71	78.71
Total	972.06	0.54	971.52

[a] Assuming air to be 23.3 wt % oxygen
[b] Excluding water added to fermenter

where a_i, M_i and a_j, M_j are the stoichiometric coefficients and molecular masses associated with 'i' and 'j'.

The ratio of quantities consumed or produced between any pair of substrates and products i and j is given in terms of the cell yield coefficients in Table 1.3 by

$$Y_{ij} = \frac{Y_{xj}}{Y_{xi}} (\text{kg } i)(\text{kg } j)^{-1}$$

For example, between oxygen and alkane:

$$Y_{oa} = \frac{0.9745}{0.5116} = 1.905 \text{ kg oxygen (kg alkane)}^{-1}$$

On the basis of 100 kg n-alkane the theoretical requirements for oxygen and ammonia can be calculated:

Theoretical oxygen requirement = 1.905 × 100 = 190.5 kg
Theoretical ammonia requirement = 0.130 × 100 = 13.0 kg

The actual flows are 1.2 and 1.05 times these values, respectively. As 99 kg alkane are consumed per 100 kg fed to the fermenter, the actual masses of oxygen and ammonia consumed are 0.99 times the theoretical requirements. The amounts of cells, carbon dioxide and water produced are calculated in a similar way to give the results in Table 1.4. The slight errors in the table reflect the inaccuracy in the stoichiometric equation.

This calculation does not include the water added to the fermenter. The final cell concentration in the aqueous phase is 3 wt%: the broth therefore is 3216 kg, which implies addition of 3039.81 kg of water in the feed. Neglecting the solubility of the gases in water and assuming the gas product stream is dry, the overall balance can be represented (after rounding):

In (total)	4012 kg
Out	
Gas	795 kg
Liquid	3216 kg
Total	4011 kg

1.1.9 Algebraic representation

In order to generalize these results it is often convenient to represent the balances in algebraic form. Indeed, other chapters in this book, particularly that on reactor design (Chapter 8), use this method.

Consider a continuous steady process with feed and outlet flowrate w and inlet and outlet concentrations of a chosen species s_i and s_o. For a particular species, the amount of that species consumed per unit time is

$$w(s_i - s_o) \qquad (1.25)$$

Considering the fermenter process above, for example, we can write balances on substrate and cells, with concentrations s and x respectively, in terms of the yield coefficient of cells Y_{xs} on substrate, as:

$$\text{Cells produced} = Y_{xs} (\text{Substrate consumed})$$

to give

$$w(x_o - x_i) = Y_{xs} \, w(s_i - s_o) \qquad (1.26)$$

or, as x_i is often zero (corresponding to a sterile feed):

$$x_o = Y_{xs} \, (s_i - s_o) \qquad (1.27)$$

1.1.10   Conclusions

In this section we have introduced some of the basic ideas of mass balances and their application to design and operational control in the process industry. Today many of the calculation procedures mentioned above are carried out routinely by computer, using one of the many flowsheeting or design programs that are now available. We should not allow ourselves to be mystified by the apparent sophistication and power of these methods: the fundamental principles are based on the laws of conservation, which have been introduced here. From a consideration of the conservation of mass we next move on to the conservation of energy.

1.2 Energy balances

1.2.1 Introduction

Energy is a vital and often expensive input into the process industries. The simpler sorts of question that commonly arise in the context of process design or operation are to calculate the heating or cooling requirements for a thermal process, such as sterilization, or the power requirements for a mixing or pumping operation. Sometimes energy will be required in the form of heat (typically as process steam) or sometimes as shaft power from a motive or electrical source. From a conceptual point of view, the energy source or sink may not be important, but it will have a considerable bearing on the process efficiency. This brings us to the second sort of question: is a particular method of heating or cooling the most efficient method? What is the best option? How can the energy efficiency of a process or part of a process be maximized?

Many of the more elementary, but none the less important, questions of the first type can be answered on the basis of the first law of thermodynamics. Others, such as the calculation of theoretical limits, may need the second law. Here we will confine ourselves to the first law, which is essentially a statement that energy is conserved. The second law analysis of processes is outlined in Chapter 6. The first task is to clarify what we mean by energy.

1.2.2 Energy: units and datum levels

In a system with basic units of mass, length and time there are three important derived units: **force**, **energy** (or **work**, as these are synonymous) and **power**. In the SI system, where the unit of force, with the dimensions of mass times acceleration, is the newton (N), defined as $1\,kg\,m\,s^{-2}$, energy or work has the units of joules (J) where $1\,J = 1\,N\,m$; power, which is the rate of doing work, is defined in watts, where 1 watt $(W) = 1\,J\,s^{-1}$.

Consider an object of mass $1\,kg$ held stationary $1\,m$ above the floor. This object then has a potential energy of $9.81\,J$. Note that it is necessary to define a reference level: in this case the floor. If some other reference or

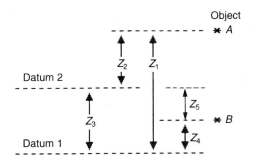

Fig. 1.9 Energy datum levels.

datum level had been chosen the energy of the object would of course be different. However, it is straightforward to relate the various energy levels to one another as illustrated by Fig. 1.9, in which A and B indicate two positions of the object. The table below summarizes the potential energies of the 1 kg objects with reference to various datum levels:

Object	Datum	Energy
A	1	$E(A,1) = 9.81Z_1$
A	2	$E(A,2) = 9.81Z_2 = 9.81\{Z_1 - Z_3\}$
B	1	$E(B,1) = 9.81Z_4$
B	2	$E(B,2) = -9.81Z_5 = 9.81\{Z_4 - Z_3\}$
A	B	$E(A,B) = 9.81\{Z_1 - Z_4\}$
B	A	$E(B,A) = 9.81\{Z_4 - Z_1\}$

Note, for example, that $E(A,B) = E(A,1) - E(B,1)$ or $E(A,2) - E(B,2)$; $E(A,B) = -E(B,A)$. The signs associated with the E-values are important. A negative sign corresponds to an object whose energy level is *below* the datum. Provided the datum levels are defined unambiguously, the calculation of energy levels with respect to other datum levels is a trivial matter. Moreover, the route by which the object reaches its stationary level A or B is irrelevant: energy is a function of **state** and not of path.

This brief discussion has been in terms of the very familiar concept of **potential energy**, whose application to many thermal problems in process engineering is relatively limited. Materials and objects have energy as a result of attributes other than position, such as velocity, temperature, pressure, physical state and chemical composition. Just as with potential energy, it is important to define datum levels unambiguously; energy is always a function of state and the simple rules of additivity etc. seen above can be transferred whatever the form of energy involved. Of course it is also important to work in the same and consistent units; then the question as to whether heating comes from an electrical source or steam, say, becomes irrelevant to the energy balance (but not to efficiency or cost). This still begs the question of how we define energy levels for the situations relevant to process engineering. We shall return to that issue after considering a more abstract formulation of the laws of energy conservation.

1.2.3 Conservation of energy

While we believe that energy is conserved in all cases of practical importance in the food and biological process industries, there are of course several important constraints, many of which derive from the ways in which energy can be converted from one form to another. In flow problems a mechanical energy balance is adequate when the interconversion of thermal and mechanical energy is negligible: Bernoulli's equation (equation (2.5)) is then the appropriate form of the energy balance. In other situations the interchange may be represented as a loss term, even though energy is not really 'lost'. In mixing vessels the shaft power to drive the process is converted into motion and, ultimately, through viscosity into heat. Thermal energy or heat can only be transferred down a temperature gradient, so that while a cooling water stream may retrieve the energy being dissipated from a high-temperature process vessel, the energy will be low quality because of its temperature, and it will require ingenuity and money to upgrade its quality (see Chapter 6). Many of these very important features are concealed by the first law of thermodynamics, which simply asserts that energy is conserved across all these processes of transformation. In the real world many of the transformation processes are irreversible (it is easier to convert mechanical energy into heat than vice versa).

1.2.4 Application of the laws of conservation of energy

As with material balances it is important to have a clear definition of the system over which the balance is constructed. We must also differentiate between systems that are **closed** and those that are connected to the wider environment by material flows, such as the thermal sterilizing system in Fig. 1.10, which is an example of an **open** system. An example of a closed system would be a batch mixing vessel, such as a butter maker, in which the only transfers of energy across the boundary of the system during operation are in the non-material forms of heat and shaft power. In an open system the flowing streams have work done on them in entering, and do work on the fluid ahead in leaving. (see Chapter 2, section 2.2.3).

For a **closed system** the formal statement of the first law is very simple. Consider a process operated over a given time interval (Fig. 1.11), in which the total net flows of heat and work are Q_T ($= Q_{T1} + Q_{T2} - Q_{T3}$) and W (defined positive for flows **into** the system). Then the increase (decrease) in

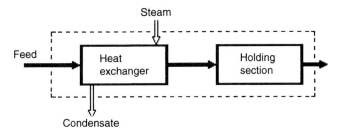

Fig. 1.10 Steam sterilization by indirect exchange: an open system.

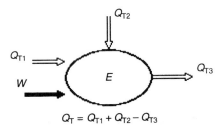

$$Q_T = Q_{T1} + Q_{T2} - Q_{T3}$$

Fig. 1.11 Closed system.

energy stored in the system must, because of the conservation rule, equal the net transfer of energy into (out of) the system, or

$$\Delta E = Q_T + W \qquad (1.28)$$

If ΔE is not zero then the final system contents must differ from the starting contents in some way, such as changed composition, temperature, physical state or internal surface area. For example, if the system represented a device for stirring and heating a liquid, the increase in energy resulting from stirring would be entirely accounted for by an increase in temperature of the contents. For a butter maker, however, chemical and physical changes including the generation of an emulsion would need to be accounted for. Clearly, equation (1.28) will only be really useful when ΔE can be related to these physical and chemical changes.

In the limit, equation (1.28) can also be written in terms of the **rates** of energy change and transfer so that instantaneously

$$\frac{dE}{dt} = Q + w \qquad (1.29)$$

where Q and w are the instantaneous rates of input of energy and work into the system, $\left(\text{i.e. } \dfrac{dQ_T}{dt} \text{ and } \dfrac{dW}{dt}\right)$ so that the right-hand side of equation

(1.28) is the net power input. Equation (1.28) will normally have the units of joules, while (1.29) will be in watts.

Note that by writing these equations in terms of energy **changes** there is no need to define an explicit datum level from which to measure the stored energy in the system.

Now consider the more general case of an **open system**, which we represent in an abstract way (Fig. 1.12). Here m represents a flowrate; Q and w are the net rates (normally in watts) of heat and work input (i.e. power as heat and mechanical energy). M, Q_T and W represent total (integrated) quantities over a period of time.

The net change in stored energy within the system boundary over a given period of operation must, if energy is conserved, exactly balance the net energy input by heat and work and the net energy difference between all the inflowing and outflowing streams. Thus, if we call the energy per unit mass of each stream E_1, E_2, etc. (where the energy levels must now be defined with reference to consistent datum levels) the energy balance becomes

$$\Delta E_s = Q_T + W + (M_1 \times E_1 + M_2 \times E_2 + \dots) \\ - (M_{O1} \times E_{O1} + M_{O2} \times E_{O2} + \dots) \tag{1.30}$$

where ΔE_s is the **change** in stored system energy over the operating period in question. As before, equation (1.30) can be written in terms of instantaneous rates in the form

$$\frac{dE_s}{dt} = Q + w + \left(m_1 \times E_1 + m_2 \times E_2 + \text{K}\right) \\ - \left(m_{O1} \times E_{O1} + m_{O2} \times E_{O2} + \text{K}\right) \tag{1.31}$$

In what follows we shall write more compactly:

$$\sum_{in} ME = \left(M_1 \times E_1 + M_2 \times E_2 + \dots\right) \tag{1.31a}$$

$$\sum_{in} mE = \left(M_1 \times E_1 + m_2 \times E_2 + \dots\right) \tag{1.31b}$$

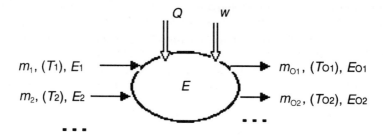

Fig. 1.12 A generalized open system.

etc.

Equations (1.30) and (1.31) represent the general and abstract case of an **unsteady open system**: unsteady because they include changes in the stored energy of the system with time. The start-up of a liquid heater would be unsteady while the contents build up and the temperatures are established. However, once the system has achieved a steady state in which all flows and temperatures are constant with time, the stored energy is then constant so that equations (1.30) and (1.31) become respectively

$$Q_T + W + \sum_{in} ME - \sum_{out} ME = 0 \qquad (1.32)$$

and

$$Q + W + \sum_{in} mE - \sum_{out} mE = 0 \qquad (1.33)$$

which are the general equations for a **steady open** system.

1.2.5 Stored and internal energy, enthalpy

As we have noted before, the stored energy within a process stream includes contributions from a variety of sources, such as kinetic and potential energies, electrical and magnetic potential, surface energy, the temperature, composition, physical conditions and state of the stream. In any particular situation some or most of these terms will be negligible: thus, in situations involving only a single phase, surface forces can be forgotten. It is important to remember that all the contributions must be measured with respect to a defined but usually arbitrary datum.

In many applications we can work in terms of the specific enthalpy of a component or mixture of components. The **enthalpy** (which is simply a measure of energy content) is the sum of **internal energy** U (reflecting temperature, physical state, etc. in relation to a defined datum), and a **flow work** term PV (where P is pressure and V is volume), also in joules. The origin of this term is discussed in Chapter 2 (section 2.2.3). This term is only relevant to **open** systems.

Values of the internal energy U and enthalpy h of pure components are readily calculated and are often tabulated, always with respect to a defined datum. For example, the steam tables tabulate the internal energies and enthalpies of water as liquid and vapour over a wide range of conditions, with reference to liquid water at its triple point. These tabulated values do not include the contribution to the internal energy of water that comes from its chemical composition. This latter term is only relevant if water is decomposed or generated by a chemical reaction during the process. If this term were to be included we would need to change the datum from liquid water to its elements.

Values of specific enthalpy are usually given the symbol h (kJ kg^{-1}); in chemical and biochemical applications enthalpies are often defined per mole. Specific enthalpy is defined by

$$h = U + PV$$

where U is the specific internal energy and V is the specific volume (i.e. $1/\rho$).

In summary, the integrated form of the first law for a closed system containing total mass M is:

$$Q_T + W = M[U_{\text{final}} - U_{\text{start}}] \qquad (1.34)$$

and for a steady open system:

$$Q_T + W + \sum_{\text{in}} Mh - \sum_{\text{out}} Mh = 0 \qquad (1.35)$$

1.2.6   Values of enthalpy

We now briefly consider some simple situations where internal energy and enthalpy values can be readily calculated.

Pure component with no change of phase.   The specific heat capacities at constant volume and pressure c_V and c_P are defined as the energy required for a single degree change in temperature; in particular,

$$c_P = \frac{\partial h}{\partial T} \qquad (1.36)$$

where the derivative is taken at constant pressure. Thus the enthalpy of a pure component at T_2 with reference to itself in the same physical state at T_1 is *mean specific heat capacity*

$$h_{21} = \int_{T_1}^{T_2} c_P \, dT = \bar{c}_P \left(T_2 - T_1 \right) \qquad (1.37)$$

where $\bar{c}_P$ is the mean specific heat capacity over the temperature range T_1 to T_2.

Thus, for example, liquid water has a mean heat capacity of $4.19\,\text{kJ}\,\text{kg}^{-1}\,\text{K}^{-1}$ over the range 0–$100\,°C$; taking its enthalpy as zero at $0\,°C$, the enthalpy of water at $50\,°C$ is thus approximately $50 \times 4.19 = 209.5\,\text{kJ}\,\text{kg}^{-1}$. The energy to heat $100\,\text{kg}$ of water from 25 to $50\,°C$ is, from equation (1.37):

$$Q_T = 100 \times 4.19 \times (50 - 25) = 104\,750\,\text{kJ}$$

This assumes that the mean heat capacity over the temperature ranges in question remains constant; it is not constant, but the errors involved here are small.

Pure component with change of phase.   A phase change occurring at a given temperature and pressure invariably requires or liberates an amount of energy: the specific latent heat or enthalpy. Consider a pure component with enthalpy datum T_1, liquid phase. The component evaporates at T_2 and is then superheated to T_3. The heat capacities of the liquid and vapour over the temperature ranges in question are c_f and c_g respectively; then the enthalpy at T_3 is

$$h_{3,1} = \int_{T_1}^{T_2} c_f \, dT + h_{fg}\left(T_2\right) + \int_{T_2}^{T_3} c_g \, dt \tag{1.38}$$

$$= h_{f2,1} + h_{fg}\left(T_2\right) + h_{g3,2} \tag{1.39}$$

where $h_{fg}\left(T_2\right)$ is the specific latent heat at T_2, and the other two terms are the enhalpy of the liquid at T_2 with reference to liquid at T_1 and of vapour at T_3 with reference to vapour at T_2.

Because energy and enthalpy are state functions it will be seen that in fact the final enthalpy is independent of the path between the reference at T_1 and the final state at T_3; in other words, the temperature T_2 need not correspond to the actual temperature at which the phase change occurs.

EXAMPLE 1.8

Consider the continuous sterilization process illustrated in Fig. 1.13 with the temperatures indicated. The process is to handle 36 000 kg h⁻¹ of liquid medium. All heat losses may be neglected. Energy is to be supplied by condensing steam at 180 °C; there is no subcooling of the condensate, i.e. the condensed steam leaves at 180 °C. Assume the mean specific heat capacity of the liquid = 4.2 kJ kg⁻¹ K⁻¹ and assume that the liquid has the same properties as liquid water.

Calculate:

(a) the rate of heat transfer between steam and medium, and the required steam flowrate;

(b) the rate of heat transfer between the liquid and the cooling water, and the required cooling water flow.

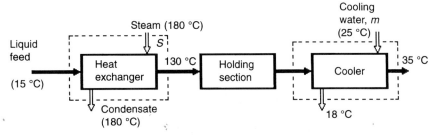

Fig. 1.13 Example 1.8: steam sterilization with product cooling.

From steam tables:

T (°C)	h_f (kJ kg^{-1})	h_{fg} (kJ kg^{-1})	h_g (kJ kg^{-1})
180	763.1	2014.9	2778.0

where h_f and h_g have the same datum and (see equation (1.39)) $h_g = h_f + h_{fg}$.
Basis: $36\,000\,\text{kg h}^{-1} = 10\,\text{kg s}^{-1}$
Datum: Liquid water/medium at 0 °C.

Energy balance around the first unit

Assume steady conditions. Considering the whole heat exchanger, there are no flows of heat or power other than those associated with the material flows, so that

$$\sum_{\text{in}} m \times h = \sum_{\text{out}} m \times h$$

where:

Inputs: $\displaystyle\sum_{\text{in}} m \times h = 10 \times 4.2 \times 15 + S \times 2778 \ (kW)$

Outputs: $\displaystyle\sum_{\text{out}} m \times h = 10 \times 4.2 \times 130 + S \times 763.1 \ (kW)$

whence:

$$10 \times 4.2 \times 115 = S \times 2014.9 \quad (= S \times h_{fg})$$

so that

$$S = 2.397\,\text{kg s}^{-1}$$

The rate of heat exchange between the condensing steam and the liquid medium is $2.397 \times 2014.9 = 4829.7\,\text{kW}$. Notice that in this case the energy balance states that the change in enthalpy of the liquid stream exactly balances the change in enthalpy on the steam side; the datum values disappear from the calculation.

The balance is summarized in the table below:

Stream in	Flow (kg s^{-1})	T (°C)	$m \times h$ (kW)	Stream out	Flow (kg s^{-1})	T (°C)	$m \times h$ (kW)
Water	10	15	630	Water	10	130	5460
Steam	2.397	180	6658.9	Cond.	2.397	180	1829.1
Total	12.397		7288.9		12.397		7289.1

It would have been possible to draw system boundaries around the two separate streams (Fig. 1.14). In this case it would be necessary to solve first for q (= 4830 kW) before completing the calculation of the steam flow.

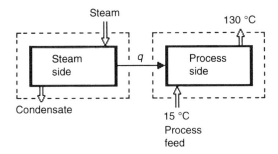

Fig. 1.14 Example 1.8: indirect steam sterilization (alternative representation).

Energy balance around the cooler (Fig. 1.13)

This is very simple. Using the same method as above we obtain

$$10 \times 4.2 \times (130 - 35) = m \times 4.2 \times (25 - 18)$$

so that the cooling water flowrate m is

$$\frac{10 \times 95}{7} = 135.7 \, \text{kg s}^{-1}$$

with rate of transfer to the coolant stream = $135.7 \times 4.2 \times 7 = 3989.6$ kW.

Generalizing to a heat exchanger at steady state with no heat losses in which stream 1, flowrate m_1, undergoes a temperature change ΔT_1 and stream 2, flowrate m_2, undergoes a change ΔT_2:

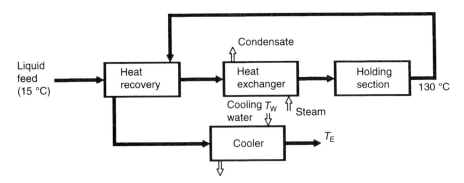

Fig. 1.15 Example 1.8: steam sterilization with heat recovery.

$$m_1 c_{P1} \Delta T_1 = m_2 c_{P2} \Delta T_2$$

where c_{P1} and c_{P2} are the mean specific heat capacities.

The flowsheet used in this problem is very inefficient from an energy conservation point of view, as the energy transferred from the steam is rejected into the cooling water stream at a temperature of only 25 °C, with no attempt at recovery. A more efficient scheme might be as shown in Fig. 1.15. Note that in practice there can never be complete recovery, as there must always be a finite driving force for heat transfer, so that the exit and inlet temperatures on the heat exchanger may approach to within typically 10 °C. Further discussion of this point is given in Chapter 6.

1.2.7 Enthalpies of mixtures

In practice most process streams comprise mixtures of components, whether dissolved or suspended. Sometimes these mixtures are far from ideal, so that enthalpy and other data must be gathered from the literature or measured directly. Usually, a reasonable first approximation in the situations that arise in the context of food and bioprocessing is to assume ideal behaviour: that is, that the enthalpy of a mixture is the weighted sum of the specific enthalpies of the various components, just as adding mixtures of mass m_1 and m_2 with solute concentrations c_1 and c_2 gives a total solute quantity equal to $m_1 c_1 + m_2 c_2$. This assumption will often break down where there are strong solutions, or significant heat effects on mixing etc. Three heat effects in particular can invalidate the assumption of ideality: due to dissolution, mixing and dissociation. In many cases it is reasonable and justifiable for the purposes of establishing an energy balance to treat a complex stream as if it were a single component with empirically determined physical and thermodynamic properties.

1.2.8 Chemical and biochemical reactions

So far all this discussion of energy balances has been concerned with essentially physical changes. Clearly, however, there are many situations of great importance where chemical or biochemical changes occur. We now consider how the treatment may be extended to cover such eventualities. Consider an energy balance about a biscuit-baking line. Suppose the datum level is taken as the raw material ingredients (flour, fat, water etc.) at 0 °C. The materials fed to the dough mixer will then have positive enthalpy values because their temperatures will generally be greater than the datum. (Sometimes enthalpies deriving only from temperature effects are called 'sensible' enthalpies.) At the end of the dough-making cycle the dough will also have a positive 'sensible' enthalpy by virtue of its temperature, but its enthalpy or energy value must also reflect the fact that the dough is not simply an ideal mixture of the datum ingredients. In practice some of the energy input into the mixer will have gone into the creation of new chemical bonds, and the dough's enthalpy will reflect this. Indeed, if we wished to measure the standard enthalpy of formation of dough from its ingredients we would carry out an experiment in which the ingredients would start at 25 °C, the dough would be made, while monitoring the net energy input by mixing and cooling, until the end of the process when the dough would be returned to 25 °C. The net energy input over this whole process would be the enthalpy of the final product with respect to the starting materials under isothermal conditions. This would be the standard enthalpy or heat of formation of the dough; the sign convention adopted is that **exothermic** processes have a **negative** heat of formation or reaction, corresponding to the removal of heat from the process to maintain isothermal conditions.

In principle, food and biological operations can be handled in just the same way as chemical reactions, for which the necessary thermodynamics is well established. In practice, as with complex mixtures, many unknown transformations may occur, in which case the process can be handled as a pseudo-reaction (compare the brief description of the stoichiometry of biochemical processes in section 1.1.6 above); alternatively it may be possible to identify the most important or limiting processes to help quantification.

We shall confine ourselves here to a steady continuous system as sketched in Fig. 1.16. Here, m_{ji}, m_{ko} are mass flowrates (kg s^{-1}); n_{ji}, n_{ko} are the corresponding molar flowrates (kmol s^{-1}); T_{ji} etc. are temperatures (K or °C); and h_{ji} are the corresponding specific enthalpies (kJ kg^{-1}) (see below for the datum levels). Subscripts i and o refer to input and output streams respectively.

Non-reacting system. Datum: 25 °C; all components in their standard states.

Then from equation (1.35)

$$\sum_j m_{ji} \times h_{ji} + Q + w = \sum_k m_{ko} \times h_{ko} \tag{1.40}$$

($\sum_j$ implies that the summation is carried out over all inputs, i.e. $j = 1,2....$)

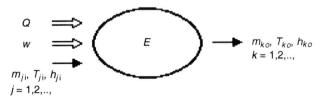

Fig. 1.16 Steady continuous open system.

Reacting systems. First we must clarify the definition of standard enthalpies of formation and reaction.

By convention standard heats or enthalpies are defined at 25 °C (298 K); the physical states of all reagents and products **must** be specified.

The standard enthalpy of formation of a compound is the change in enthalpy when 1 kmol of the compound is formed from its elements in stoichiometric proportions, beginning and ending at 25 °C and 1 bar (10^5 Pa), with specified states of the elements and compound.

In this case the enthalpy datum is the **elements** at 25 °C.

The standard enthalpy of any reaction is defined in an exactly corresponding way as the enthalpy change that results from a reaction beginning and ending at 25 °C and 1 bar; again, the physical states of all the reagents must be specified.

In this case the change in enthalpy is defined with respect to the **reagents** at 25 °C.

By virtue of the fact that enthalpies are function of state we can readily relate the standard heats of **formation** of the reagents and products (ΔH_{fr}, ΔH_{fp}) to the standard heat or enthalpy of **reaction**, ΔH°_R:

$$\Delta H^{\circ}_R = \Sigma a \Delta H_{fp} - \Sigma b \Delta H_{fr} \qquad (1.41)$$

where a, b are the stoichiometric coefficients of products and reagents respectively. Thus for the reaction

$$xA + yB \rightarrow C$$

$$\Delta H^{\circ}_R = \Delta H_{fC} - x\Delta H_{fA} - y\Delta H_{fB} \text{ per kmol C} \qquad (1.42)$$

We now consider how these definitions can be used in setting up energy balances.

Energy balance over a reacting system. The balance can be written in various complementary ways, depending on the choice of datum. It is possible to write the balance using the **elements** as the datum level, in which case all enthalpies of reagents and products must be defined relative to their elements (i.e. to include contributions from the heat of formation and the 'sensible' enthalpy). For complex biological processes this is usually less convenient than choosing the **inputs** (i.e. reagents and other feed materials) as the datum. As the qualitative discussion of the dough-making process illustrates, in this latter case:

- the enthalpy of the input stream(s) is simply the sum of the sensible enthalpies of all the feed materials, i.e. allowing for temperature and possibly phase changes from the standard state taken as datum;
- the enthalpy of the ouput stream(s) has two components that are to be added:
  - (a) the 'sensible' enthalpy, which measures the enthalpy of the output materials with respect to themselves at 25 °C (to account for the fact that the output streams are not at the datum temperature), and

(b) the enthalpy of the output compounds at 25 °C with respect to the feed materials, also at 25 °C. This second term is of course the standard enthalpy of reaction. For a single reaction in which x kmol of product are formed this latter term will be $x\Delta H°_R$; in the general case we can write the overall energy balance

$$\sum_j n_{ji} \times h_{ji} + Q + w = \sum_r x \times \Delta H°_R + \sum_k n_{ko} \times h_{ko} \qquad (1.43)$$

where the summations are carried out over all inputs ($j = 1,2,\ldots$), all reactions ($r = 1,2,\ldots$) and all outputs ($k = 1,2,\ldots$) respectively. The specific enthalpies h are all measured/calculated relative to the same compound at 25 °C as datum (i.e. the h terms are the 'sensible' enthalpies referred to above).

As equation (1.43) is written in terms of flowrates, Q and w will be in kW; the balance can of course be written in terms of quantities, in which case Q_T and W will be in energy units.

It will be seen that equation (1.43) reduces trivially to the earlier balances for non-reacting systems (i.e. equation (1.40)).

In the chemical industry it is relatively rare to encounter reactors in which the work input (w) is significant in comparison with the thermal input or output, but this is not the case in the food and biotechnology sectors. Extrusion cookers and many fermenters involve considerable work inputs, which must be included in the energy balance.

EXAMPLE 1.9

Torula yeast (C. utilis) is a food grade yeast that can be produced by fermentation of complex sugars. The yeast is produced continuously in a fermenter of capacity 50 m³ operating at 35 °C. The liquid feed contains 10 wt% substrate and is fed at 50 kg min⁻¹. The yeast yield is 0.5 kg/kg substrate fed. The oxygen requirement is 0.6 kg/kg yeast consumed and is supplied as air at twice that rate.

The conditions in the fermenter are indicated in Fig. 1.17. The mixer has a power drive of 100 kW: neglecting losses in the motor and shaft we assume that 100 kW of (shaft) work is put into the fermenter contents. The overall apparent enthalpy of the reaction (which, being aerobic, is highly exothermic) is − 16 000 kJ (kg yeast formed)⁻¹. Assume the respiratory quotient (moles CO₂/O₂) = 1. With the data below calculate the cooling requirements for the fermenter.

Data

Assume the medium and broth have the same specific heat capacity as water = 4.2 kJ kg⁻¹ K⁻¹.

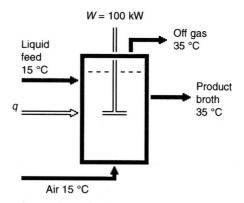

Fig. 1.17 Example 1.9: yeast fermenter.

Air:
   Assume comprises 21 vol% (23 wt%) oxygen,
   Mean density: $1.29\,kg\,m^{-3}$,
   Mean specific heat capacity: $1\,kJ\,kg^{-1}\,K^{-1}$.
Water vapour at 35 °C:
   Saturated vapour pressure: 0.062 bar,
   Enthalpy: $2450\,kJ\,kg^{-1}$ referred to liquid water at 25 °C,
   Density: $0.804\,kg\,m^{-3}$.

Solution

Basis: feed rate of $50\,kg\,min^{-1}$
Datum: 25 °C; inputs at their standard states; liquid water.

(a)   Mass balance (approximate)

Assuming complete conversion of the carbon source:
Yeast production rate = $2.5\,kg\,min^{-1}$

Gas feed:
Oxygen consumed = $0.6 \times 2.5 = 1.5\,kg\,min^{-1}$
As the actual supply rate is twice the demand,
air supplied = $(2 \times 1.5)/0.23 = 13.0\,kg\,min^{-1}$
and, as the RQ = 1,
carbon dioxide produced = $1.5 \times 44/32 = 2.06\,kg\,min^{-1}$

Gas exit stream:
Total dry gas leaving = $13.0 - 1.5 + 2.06 = 13.06\,kg\,min^{-1}$
Assuming this gas is saturated with moisture:
Water in exit gas $\approx 0.062 \times 13.56 \times 0.804/1.39$
                  $= 0.486\,kg\,min^{-1}$

Liquid stream out ≈ 50 − 2.5 − 0.5 = 47 kg min⁻¹ (assuming all substrate consumed).

(b) Energy balance

(i) Enthalpy of inlet streams (datum = 25 °C):

$$\frac{-(50 \times 4.2 \times 10 + 13 \times 10)}{60} = -37.17 \text{ kW}$$

(ii) Sensible enthalpy of outlet streams (datum = 25 °C):

This comprises respectively (i) the liquid product, (ii) the 'sensible' enthalpy of the gas stream, and (iii) the latent heat of the water vapour in the outlet gas stream:

$$\frac{47.0 \times 4.2 \times 10 + 13.56 \times 10 + 0.486 \times 2450}{60} = 55 \text{ kW}$$

(c) Net heat of reaction

$$\frac{2.5 \times 16\,000}{60} = 666.7 \text{ kW}$$

(d) Overall balance (here written in mass units; compare equation (1.43))

$$\sum_j m_{ji} \times h_{ji} + Q + w = \sum x \times \Delta H^\circ_R + \sum_k m_{ko} \times h_{ko}$$

substituting from above:

$$-37.2 + Q + 100 = -666.7 + 55.0$$

so that

$$Q = -674.5 \text{ kW}$$

The results of the calculation are summarized in the table below, with the same datum of 25 °C and the reagents.

Input	Flow (kg s⁻¹)	T (°C)	Enthalpy (kW)	Output	Flow (kg s⁻¹)	T (°C)	Enthalpy (kW)
Liquid	0.833	15	−35	Liquid	0.783	35	32.9
Air	0.217	15	−2.17	Gas	0.226	35	22.1
Mixer			100	Cooling			674.5
ΔH°_R			666.7				
Total			729.53				729.5

EXAMPLE 1.10

As a second example we consider the glucose isomerization process whose material balance implications were discussed in Example 1.5. Here we consider the reactor only. Glucose enters in 40% aqueous solution at 60 °C; there is no recycle. The reactor is operated adiabatically (i.e. Q = 0). It is assumed that the specific heat capacity of the liquid stream is the same as water (c_P = 4.18 kJ kg^{-1} K^{-1}). Heat-of-solution effects are neglected. The standard enthalpy of the isomerization reaction at 25 °C, $\Delta H°_R$, is 5730 kJ kmol^{-1}; the equilibrium constant for the reaction (which is 1.04 at 60 °C) follows the van't Hoff equation (Atkins, 1990, p. 219):

$$\frac{d(\ln K)}{dT} = \frac{\Delta H°_R}{R_g T^2} \tag{1.44}$$

or

$$\frac{d(\ln K)}{d(1/T)} = -\frac{\Delta H°_R}{R_g}$$

where R_g = 8314 J kmol^{-1} K^{-1}; T is in K.

Assuming that the products are in equilibrium at the end of the reactor we wish to calculate the temperature and composition of the product stream.

The special feature of this problem is that the mass balance cannot be calculated *ab initio*, because the exit composition depends on the equilibrium constant, which itself depends on temperature through equation (1.44). As the reaction is (mildly) endothermic, the exit temperature will presumably be below 60 °C; moreover, the heat absorbed by the reaction depends on the number of moles of glucose isomerized, so the equations for conservation of mass and energy are coupled together.

Basis: 1 kmol glucose in the feed.
Datum: 25 °C; liquid water; glucose in solution.

(a) Material flows and composition

As the inlet stream contains 40 wt% glucose the total inlet flow corresponding to the chosen basis is 180/0.4 = 450 kg.

Let the fractional conversion of glucose = *f*. Then the outlet stream contains 1 − *f* kmol glucose and *f* kmol fructose respectively.

By definition

$$\frac{f}{1-f} = K(T) \tag{1.45}$$

where $K(T)$ may be deduced from equation (1.44).

(b) Equilibrium constant, K

Integrating equation (1.44):

$$\ln K = -\frac{\Delta H^\circ_R}{R_g T} + C \qquad (1.46a)$$

where C is the constant of integration.
  Using the fact that $K = 1.04$ at $60\,^\circ$C gives $C = 2.109$. Thus

$$\ln K = -\frac{5730}{R_g T} + 2.109 \qquad (1.46b)$$

(c) Energy balance

As the reactor is operated adiabatically, $Q = 0$, and equation (1.43) becomes

Total enthalpy of inlet stream = Net enthalpy of reaction + Total
                                    enthalpy of output stream   (1.47)

where the enthalpy terms in equation (1.47) are

Inputs: $450 \times 4.18 \times (60 - 25)$
Reaction: $5730 \times f$
Outputs: $450 \times 4.18 \times (T - 25)$
whence:

$$T = 60 - \frac{5730 \times f}{450 \times 4.18} \qquad (1.48)$$

The exit conditions from the reactor, i.e. f and T, are given by solving equations (1.45), (1.46b) and (1.48) simultaneously or by trial and error. This can be represented graphically (Fig. 1.18).
  Solving by trial and error gives:

$$T = 58.45\,^\circ\text{C}$$
$$f = 0.5073$$
$$K = 1.03$$

The result – that the temperature is so close to the inlet of $60\,^\circ$C and the equilibrium constant is very close to 1.04 – is not surprising, as the reaction here is only weakly endothermic, and there would be little loss of accuracy in assuming that the system was isothermal and adiabatic.

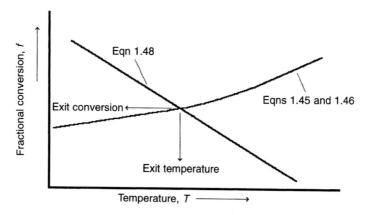

Fig. 1.18 Example 1.10: mass and energy balance solution.

1.2.9   Coupled heat and mass balances

Example 1.10 illustrates the fact that mass and energy balances cannot always be carried out independently, by computing first a mass balance and then an energy balance. In practice many processes depend on the simultaneous resolution of the two balances. The final example of a spray drier exemplifies the issues involved, this time in a system without reaction.

EXAMPLE 1.11

100 kg h⁻¹ of spray milk powder containing 4% moisture are produced in a continuous cocurrent spray drier. The feed solution contains 45 wt% milk solids and enters at 15°C. Atmospheric air with humidity ℋ = 0.005 kg water/kg dry air is heated to 150°C before entering the drier.

The air stream leaves the drier at 95°C, and the solids product leaves at 70°C.

Neglecting any heat losses, calculate the inlet liquid flow, the air flow and the exit humidity of the air stream.

Set up an overall summary mass and energy balance.

Data

Mean specific heat capacity of dry air = 1 kJ kg⁻¹ K⁻¹
Mean specific heat capacity of water vapour = 1.67 kJ kg⁻¹ K⁻¹
Mean specific heat capacity of dry solids = 1.6 kJ kg⁻¹ K⁻¹
Mean specific heat capacity of liquid water = 4.2 kJ kg⁻¹ K⁻¹
Latent heat of evaporation of water at 0°C = 2500 kJ kg⁻¹

Solution

Basis: 100 kg spray dried product
Datum: 0 °C; liquid water.

Process diagram (Fig. 1.19)
(All flows in kg h^{-1})
L = liquid feedrate
g = **dry** air rate
G_i = total airflow in
G_o = total airflow out
S = product rate = 100 kg h^{-1}

Balance on dry solids

$$\begin{aligned}
\text{Solids in} &= \text{Solids out}\\
0.45\,L &= 100(1 - 0.04) = 96\\
L &= 213.3\,\text{kg h}^{-1}\\
\text{Water in feed} &= 0.55\,L\\
&= 117.3\,\text{kg h}^{-1}
\end{aligned}$$

Balance on dry air

$$\text{Dry air in} = g = \text{dry air out}$$

Water balance

$$\text{Water in} = \text{Water out (in exit air + solids)}$$

i.e.:

$$0.005\,g + 117.3 = \mathscr{H}g + 4$$

where $\mathscr{H}$ = humidity of exit stream. Thus

$$g(\mathscr{H} - 0.005) = 113.3 \qquad (1.49)$$

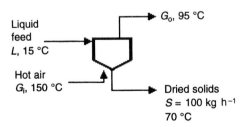

Fig. 1.19 Example 1.11: spray drier.

Enthalpy balance

Neglecting heat losses, the energy balance (equation (1.35)) becomes

Enthalpy of L + Enthalpy of G_i = Enthalpy of G_o + Enthalpy of S

where the total enthalpies of these streams are given by:

L: $(117.3 \times 4.2 + 96 \times 1.6)15 = 9693.9\,kJ$
G_i: $150\,g + 0.005\,g(1.67 \times 150 + 2500) = 163.75\,g\,kJ$
G_o: $95\,g + g\mathscr{H}(1.67 \times 95 + 2500) = (95 + 2658.65\,\mathscr{H})g\,kJ$
S: $(96 \times 1.6 + 4 \times 4.2)70 = 11\,928\,kJ$

Thus

$$9693.9 + 163.75\,g = 11\,928 + (95 + 2658.65\,\mathscr{H})g$$

i.e.:

$$g(2658.65\mathscr{H} - 68.75) = -2234.1 \qquad (1.50)$$

Solution for g and $\mathscr{H}$

Equations (1.49) and (1.50) can now be solved simultaneously for g and $\mathscr{H}$, to give

$$g = 5472.0\,kg \text{ dry air } h^{-1}$$
$$\mathscr{H} = 0.025705\,kg\,kg^{-1} \text{ dry air}$$

so that

$$G_i = 5472(1 + 0.005) = 5499.4\,kg\,h^{-1}$$
$$G_o = 5472(1 + 0.025\,705) = 5612.7\,kg\,h^{-1}$$

Summary of overall mass and energy balances – basis 1 h; datum 0 °C

Stream	In (kg)	Enthalpy in (kJ)	Out (kg)	Enthalpy out (kJ)
Liquid, L	213.3	9693.9	–	–
Air, G_i	5499.4	896040	–	–
Air, G_o	–	–	5612.7	893799.8
Solids, S	–	–	100	11928
	5712.7	905733.9	5712.7	905727.8

1.2.10   Conclusions

In this section we have encountered some of the basic principles and methods that can be used to apply the first law of thermodynamics (the principle of energy conservation) to selected food and bioprocess problems. The discussion has largely centred on problems involving thermal changes and energy inputs in the form of shaft work, such as in mixing. The application of 'mechanical' energy balances is considered in Chapter 2; Chapter 3, on heat transfer and heat exchanger design, also draws implicitly on the material of this chapter. Chapter 6 addresses some questions of energy efficiency and the use of analyses based on the second law of thermodynamics.

Finally, in the following section of this chapter we consider briefly some elementary aspects of process economics.

1.3   Process economics

There is surely no need here to emphasize the importance of economics in determining the viability of a process or product. In just the same way that a fully detailed mass and energy balance can only be elaborated when the detailed process design is complete, so the full details of the process economics will only be revealed when the process is up and running and the product has entered the market. Nevertheless, it is clearly important to be able to make realistic estimates of the process economics during the design and development stages. It is often not fully appreciated how much light an economic analysis can shed on the priorities for research and development and process engineering. In this section we shall very briefly discuss some of the factors that contribute to the cost of a product and then some of the basic concepts of economic appraisal. These concepts can be applied at any stage of the process cycle.

1.3.1   Processes, products and time

No process was ever built in a day; any manufacturing plant in the food industry will be the result of many years of research, development and operating experience. An idealized and simplified picture of the way such a process comes into being would start with the preliminary idea of an integrated plant; an outline preliminary flowsheet and estimates of the main material and energy flows would then be developed with a first very preliminary assessment of the likely economics. There would then be a period – perhaps several years – of research and development and pilot-scale testing, as existing technology is adapted and new technology created. At this stage a detailed design of the whole process can be finalized, leading (assuming the future for the process and its economics still look favourable) to the fabrication, construction and commissioning of the plant. Plant start-up is invariably followed by a period of running-in as bottlenecks are removed and unforeseen problems are resolved. It is usually some time before the plant reaches anything like its design capacity and its operating phase, which if all goes well ought then to extend over several years.

Figure 1.20 shows, in a simplified way, and not to scale, how the patterns of expenditure and revenue vary during this process development and production cycle.

Another way of representing this flow of expenditure and revenues is in the form of a cumulative cash picture, in which the origin is an arbitrarily chosen date for the start of the project (Fig. 1.21). Among the points that can made about this picture are the following.

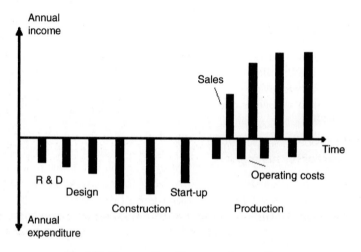

Fig. 1.20 Time profile of income and expenditure.

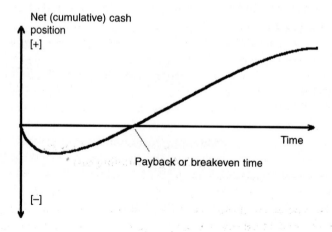

Fig. 1.21 Cumulative cash-flow diagram.

- Flows of expenditure and revenue are spread over considerable periods of time.
- Expenditure and revenue may often be shared with other projects and operations.
- The picture is inherently subject to variations (markets, prices, quality, availability etc.). Apart from the difficulties of forecasting these variations, the accuracy of technical and economic design parameters should improve during the design and development cycle; early projections of plant cost are likely only to be accurate to within around 25–30%, but later projections must be much more accurate.
- Expenditure is likely to be allocated to different heads during the cycle. In the earlier phases it will be allocated to R&D and design. There will be a period of considerable capital expenditure during the construction phase. During the production phase the principal items of expenditure will be on people, materials and services, maintenance and taxes. The allocation of R&D and design expenditure is a matter for industry policy. In what follows we shall assume that the capital costs include an agreed contribution.

We shall consider a simplified picture in which the time origin corresponds with the start of the major capital expenditure. First we consider briefly the ways in which costs are conventionally allocated.

1.3.2   Costs: capital and operating; fixed and variable

Suppose we are designing a cheese-making plant. Among the major costs associated with the process are the following:

1. the cost of the equipment and plant, pipework, instrumentation, buildings etc. (the total installed cost will probably be up to 3.5–4 times the total cost of the major equipment items);
2. the cost of material inputs to the process – milk, starters, etc.;
3. power, steam, cooling water and services;
4. labour;
5. laboratories and other overheads;
6. maintenance;
7. taxes, insurance etc.

Conventionally these costs are often grouped into **capital**-related costs (essentially item 1 above) and **operating** or **running costs**: that is, those costs directly attributable to the day-to-day running of the plant.

An alternative division is between **fixed** and **variable** costs. In this scheme, fixed costs are those that are **necessarily** incurred no matter what the extent of capacity utilization; variable costs are those that depend on the actual scale of production or the capacity utilization. For example, raw material costs can be expected to depend on the level of production. This division does not generally exactly correspond to that between capital and operating costs; it can be a powerful and useful way of analysing process economics. The first part of the discussion here will use the capital/operating scheme. The use of fixed and variable costs will be illustrated later.

1.3.3 Building up a cost picture

If a process is to be assessed for its viability during the design phase it will be necessary to estimate the capital and operating costs. Capital costs will of course depend on the detailed design and configuration of the equipment. Detailed estimation is a highly specialized job, and we shall assume that acceptably accurate estimates are available. Operating costs depend on the results of the mass and energy balances, which, given unit costs, will permit the calculation of the costs of supplying materials and services. They will also include other costs, such as labour and services. It will also be necessary to estimate the likely market prices for any products and by-products. The same items will, of course, occur in an evaluation carried out during the project lifetime, at which stage they will be available and not estimated.

EXAMPLE 1.12

As an example consider a design study of a fermentation plant to produce ethanol (and feed yeast by-product) from sugar cane juice. The plant is to produce 200 m³ day⁻¹ of 95% ethanol. It should be noted that the figures used in this example are rather optimistic.

Capital

The total installed cost of the plant is estimated to be around £7.5 m. A scrap value at the end of the project of £2.0 m is assumed. The plant is assumed to be in full production for 11 years.

Annual costs

The operating costs and revenue on an annual basis at full capacity include the following major elements:

Operating costs	£m
Raw materials (sugar etc.)	21.48
Water, power, steam	3.14
Labour, laboratories, overheads etc.	0.46
Taxes, insurance, maintenance	0.68
Total	25.76

Revenues:

Ethanol sales (at £390 m^{-3})	27.3
Yeast by-product sales	3.63
Total	30.93

Notes:

- 350 days operation per year are assumed.
- Material, services, products estimated from mass balance and unit costs.

Summary table

	£m
Installed capital cost	7.5
Annual operating costs	25.76
Annual sales revenue	30.93

Annual profile of costs and revenues

Although as we have seen a typical process has several years in gestation and start-up to full production, we shall simplify matters here by assuming that the capital investment period extends over two years only (in two equal instalments) and that the plant comes into full production in the following year. The following year-by-year picture can then be built up (all in £m):

Year	Capital, K	Running, O	Sales, R	Net income, $R-O-K$	Cumulative income
0	3.75	0	0	-3.75	-3.75
1	3.75	0	0	-3.75	-7.50
2	0	25.75	30.93	5.17	-2.33
3	0	25.75	30.93	5.17	+2.84
4	0	25.75	30.93	5.17	8.01
:	:	:	:	:	
12	(−)2.0	25.75	30.93	7.17	51.37

The picture above would seem to be very satisfactory: the cumulative cash flow becomes positive between years 2 and 3 of the project, presumably implying that the project would thereafter show a profit. However, a key assumption built into the table is that the net annual surpluses can be added together to give the running cumulative total. We need to consider whether this assumption is correct.

1.3.4 Discounting and the time value of money

The construction of a cumulative total assumes that $1 or £1 spent or earned in any year is identical in value to $1 or £1 in any other year. There are two reasons for questioning this: one is inflation, which clearly undermines the value of the currency; the other relates more fundamentally to the potential value of the currency. Consider the assumption that £1 earned today is the same as £1 in 10 years' time. In fact the £1 earned today could be used for investing or lending. If the interest rate were a constant 10% per annum, £1 today invested would yield £1.1 in 1 year, £1.1 × 1.1 in 2 years, and so on. In general, at a constant annual fractional interest rate $= i$ and over a time period of n years:

$$£X \text{ today} \rightarrow £X(1 + i)^n \text{ in } n \text{ years' time} \tag{1.51}$$

Alternatively

$$£Y \text{ in } n \text{ years' time} \rightarrow \frac{Y}{(1+i)^n} \text{ today} \tag{1.52}$$

In these relationships, equation (1.51) represents the **future value** (FV) and equation (1.52) the **present value** (PV) of X and Y respectively.

This suggests that to make the annual cash flows commensurable we should work in terms of **either** future **or** present values. The table below shows a simplified example of the application of the formulae for FV and PV, with $i = 0.1$.

Year	Income	FV at end year 3	PV at year 0
0	100	133.1	100
1	100	121	90.91
2	100	110	82.64
3	100	100	75.13
Total	400	464.1	348.68

In practice it is common to work in terms of present values, and we shall conform to that in what follows. The technique is called **discounting**. Clearly our assumption of constant interest rate is not essential; it merely simplifies the arithmetic.

Thus the present value at year zero of a cash flow £C in year n with a fractional interest or discount rate i is

$$PV = \frac{C}{(1+i)^n} \tag{1.53}$$

Applying the technique of discounting to the alcohol process example (Example 1.12) with values of $i = 0.1$ and 0.2 (i.e. interest rates of 10% and

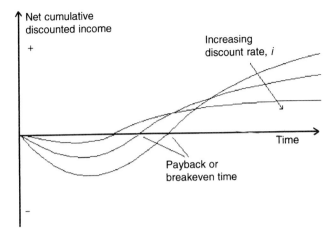

Fig. 1.22 Effect of discounting on cash flow.

Table 1.5 Results of applying discounting to Example 1.12

Year	Net income	PV $i = 0.1$	ΣPV $i = 0.1$	PV $i = 0.2$	ΣPV $i = 0.2$
0	−3.75	−3.75	−3.75	−3.75	−3.75
1	−3.75	−3.41	−7.16	−3.125	−6.875
2	5.17	4.27	−2.89	3.59	−3.285
3	5.17	3.88	0.99	2.99	−0.295
4	5.17	3.53	4.52	2.49	2.195
. . .	. . .	. . .	. . .	. . .	. . .
. . .	. . .	. . .	. . .	. . .	. . .
12	7.17	2.28	23.98	0.80	11.99
Total	51.37		23.98		11.98

20% p.a.) respectively we obtain the results listed in Table 1.5. The sum of the discounted net revenues (i.e. ΣPV in columns 4 and 6 in the table) is called the **net present value** (NPV) of the project.

Note that the effect of discounting is to reduce the real values of the cash flows and their sums. In general the higher the interest rate, the more significant is the effect of discounting, as is illustrated by Fig. 1.22. The breakeven point (also known as the discounted payback time) is also increased.

1.3.5 Significance

What are the implications and use of the method sketched out above? The interest (or discount) rate is a measure of the rate of return that the owners or managers of the project could realize from an alternative investment.

If it is to be a guide towards the most profitable use of the investment sums, then it should reflect the interest rate that would be realized from the **best** alternative investment: which need not, of course, be in the same sort of project or sector. The discount rate is thus the **opportunity cost** of capital, reflecting the value of the funds to be deployed or the rate of borrowing.

When the market is the only determinant, if the effective return on the project is less than i, it shouldn't go ahead. In other words, provided the correct value of discount rate is used, projects for which NPV < 0 should not proceed; projects with NPV > 0 should go ahead.

The discount factors $1/(1 + i)^n$ that occur in the expression for the NPV can also be regarded as temporal weighting factors: that is, as allocating differential weights to future returns on a project. For example, if I and E are the income and expenditure in any particular year we can write

$$\text{NPV} = (I - E)_0 + w_1(I - E)_1 + w_2(I - E)_2 + w_3(I - E)_3 + \ldots \quad (1.54)$$

where

$$w_1 = \frac{1}{(1+i)} \quad (1.55)$$

$$w_2 = \frac{1}{(1+i)^2} \quad (1.56)$$

etc.

High values of the discount rate imply a strong preference for early returns; future benefits are given a very low weight as can be seen from the tabulated NPVs in the alcohol project.

With discount rates above 10 or 15% per annum, what happens to the project beyond year 10 becomes relatively unimportant. In assessing industrial projects the lifetime is usually taken in the range 10–15 years.

1.3.6 Internal rate of return (IRR)

Some companies have a preference for using the IRR rather than the NPV as a measure. As the alcohol production example suggests, the value of the NPV at the end of the project (i.e. after 13 years) will become negative at high values of the discount rate. The internal rate of return is defined as the value of the discount rate at which the NPV becomes zero: which usually must be computed by trial and error. If the IRR is greater than the company target (which may be the bank rate, for example) then the project should proceed. If the IRR is lower than the the target, the project should not go ahead. Usually the IRR and NPV methods give the same result in terms of project ranking.

1.3.7 Payback time

Another measure of profitability is the time to recover the investment, or the payback time. On the cumulative cash-flow diagram this is the point at which the curve cuts the axis. Clearly it is important to differentiate between the discounted and undiscounted values of the payback time.

1.3.8 Inflation

It must be emphasized that all the discussion above relates to an inflation-free world; in this picture the time value of money stems from its earning capacity or its cost to the borrower. In the real world inflation does occur and the calculations must be adjusted accordingly so that a reference constant-value currency is adopted. Inflation at a constant annual rate of f further reduces the present value of the unit of currency by $1/(1 + f)^n$. Strictly this should be handled separately from the discounting operation; in practice, if the discount and inflation rates are low, they are sometimes compounded into an effective discount rate $= i + f$.

1.3.9 Risk

New projects always involve a degree of risk. This may be due to over-optimism about the technology, inaccuracies and uncertainties in forecasts of costs and market conditions, and so on. At the very least this implies that any analysis of economic viability should include a study of its sensitivity to the key parameters. In some sectors it is conventional to include some hedging against risk by using artificially high values of the discount rate.

1.3.10 Depreciation

Depreciation should **not** be included as a cost in the calculation of net present value. It does not represent a genuine cost to the project, but only a transfer of funds within the operating entity. It does of course influence the tax regime, and this 'knock-on' effect should be included in the calculations.

1.3.11 Summary of the procedure

When the objective is to calculate the viability of a project or process the procedure outlined above may be summarized as follows.
    Given actual or estimated values of:

- capital costs;
- operating costs;
- revenue;
- interest/discount rate;

calculate:

- net annual cost flows;
- NPV;
- if NPV > 0, go ahead;
- if NPV < 0, do not proceed.

1.3.12   Unit cost of production

Amongst the data needed in the procedure described above is the market cost of the product. Often it is useful to be able to calculate explicitly the actual cost of producing a given amount of product under a defined set of operating conditions. It will be recognized that the same information on capital and operating costs as used above is also needed for this calculation. The net cost of production is the resultant of the contribution of the capital investment, other production costs, and any revenues. The simplest and most direct, but approximate, way of carrying out this calculation is to consider a typical period (say a year) of operation. The annual operating costs and revenues can be calculated as usual; the contribution to the overall cost from the capital investment, which may have been completed several years before, can be estimated by assuming that these costs are spread evenly over the project lifetime. This is equivalent to assuming straight-line depreciation over the project life.

For example, considering the alcohol production process in Example 1.12, the average capital charge per year, neglecting interest payments and the scrap value, is £7.5m/13 = £0.577m per year, and the net annual cost of production allowing for by-product credits is £22.13m per year. Thus, the average net annual cost of production on this basis is £(0.577 + 22.13)m or £22.707m per year, and the unit cost of production of ethanol is £22.707m/ (350 × 200) or £324 per m³ of product.

Apart from giving an indication of the operating margin, this type of calculation is also useful in demonstrating interest payments and the relative importance of different cost elements. In this particular example, capital costs are relatively unimportant; the single most important item in the cost of production is the raw material cost. This therefore suggests that a key determinant of economic efficiency will be the yield of product per unit mass of raw material.

1.3.13   Fixed and variable costs

From the example above it will also be clear that some cost elements are independent of the particular conditions of plant operation, and in particular the degree of capacity utilization. For example, the fixed capital investment and many overheads such as labour costs will be the same whether the plant is working at full or 50% capacity. These are called **fixed costs**.

However, other costs – raw materials, medium nutrients, energy, and some taxes – will depend on the particular production level. In the simplest case these **variable costs** will vary directly with the level of production, but in general there is not necessarily a linear relationship between inputs and outputs.

For example, let us drastically simplify the ethanol production example by assuming that the fixed costs comprise the capital costs, labour and overheads, and taxes, insurance and maintenance. It will be assumed that the costs of raw materials and water, power and steam and the revenue from by-products are all variable and directly proportional to the level of production of ethanol.

As before, we take a typical year's production as the basis of the calculation. If the actual scale of production is U m³ ethanol per day (annual production = $350\,U$) then from the cost data of Example 1.12:

$$\text{Annual fixed costs, } F = \text{Capital cost contribution}$$
$$+ \text{ Labour etc.} + \text{ Taxes etc.} \qquad (1.57)$$
$$= 0.577 + 0.46 + 0.68 = £1.717\,\text{m}$$

Annual variable cost is the product of the marginal variable cost of production, V (assumed constant), and the production level, U.

The annual cost for a plant with capacity 200 m³/day from materials and services is £$(21.48 + 3.14)$m = £24.62 m. Per m³/day of product therefore the marginal cost of production is

$$V = £24.62\text{m}/200 = £0.1231\,\text{m}$$

For a plant producing U m³/day, the annual variable cost is:

$$V \times U = £0.1231\,\text{m} \times U \qquad (1.58)$$

and the overall annual cost of production, not including by-product credits, is from equations (1.57) and (1.58)

$$C = F + V \times U = 1.717 + 0.1231 \times U \qquad (1.59)$$

Similarly, assuming sales and production levels are always balanced, the **annual sales revenue** from ethanol and by-products is

$$R = S \times U \qquad (1.60)$$

where S is the unit income (i.e. annual revenue per m³ of ethanol). Here, assuming a uniform ethanol sales price of £390/m³, and using the fact that the annual sales revenue at the design capacity is £30.93 m (see table of costs and revenues, Example 1.12):

$$R = \frac{30.93 \times U}{200} = 0.15465\,U \qquad (1.61)$$

Clearly, for a plant to remain profitable $R > C$; this condition can be shown graphically by plotting C and R versus the level of production, U, as shown

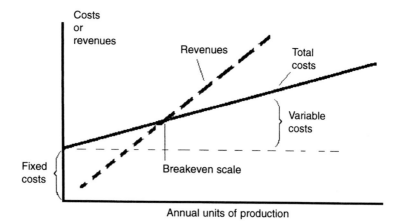

Fig. 1.23 Cost of production and breakeven.

in Fig. 1.23. Breakeven occurs when $R = C$ or, in this example, from equations (1.61) and (1.59), when

$$0.15465 \times U = 1.717 + 0.1231 \times U \qquad (1.62)$$

i.e.

$$U = 54.43 \, m^3 \text{ per day}$$

Thus here, where the unit cost of production of ethanol is considerably lower than the assumed market price, a substantial fall in production from the design level could be sustained. Clearly, if the breakeven were very close to the design level, great care would need to be taken before authorizing the project. The problem was simplified by assuming that marginal costs and revenues were independent of the scale of production and market penetration. However, the same principles apply in the more realistic case where the cost and revenue curves are non-linear in scale of production.

1.3.14   Conclusion

It must be stressed that this account of process economics has been drastically simplified. The real world is more complex than the examples here might suggest. However, it is hoped that the discussion will have clarified some of the basic principles. One point that should be stressed is that any estimation of costs and revenues is subject to considerable uncertainty. It is strongly recommended that any economic analysis involves an exploration of the sensitivity of the result to the principal assumptions. Finally, it should be noted that further issues are involved in building up balance sheets from the basic data incorporated in the cash-flow analysis; those issues have not been addressed here.

Appendix 1.A: Some basic definitions

Composition measures

Consider m kg of a mixture of components A, B, etc., containing m_a kg A, m_b kg B, ... where A, B have molecular masses M_a, M_b etc. Then

$$m = m_a + m_b + \ldots = \sum_i m_i$$

In the SI system the number of kmol of A $= m_a/M_a$, etc.

Then the mass fraction z_a of A = Mass of A/Total mass

$$z_a = \frac{m_a}{m_a + m_b + \ldots}$$

$$= \frac{m_a}{\sum_i m_i}$$

$$= \frac{m_a}{m}$$

The mole fraction

$$x_a = \text{kmol A} / \text{Total kmol}$$

$$= \frac{m_a/M_a}{m_a/M_a + m_b/M_b + \ldots}$$

The mean molecular mass of a mixture, M, is the average in which the weights are the component mole fractions; it is also the ratio between the total mass of the mixture and the number of kmol:

$$M = x_a M_a + x_b M_b + \ldots$$

$$= \frac{m}{m_a/M_a + m_b/M_b + \ldots}$$

Also

$$\frac{1}{M} = \frac{z_a}{M_a} + \frac{z_b}{M_b} + \ldots$$

The mass (molar) concentration is the mass (kmol) of component A per unit volume of mixture. These two measures are related through the molecular mass of A. Concentration measures and mass or mole fractions can be related given the mixture density.

Mixtures: ideal and non-ideal

Although assumptions of ideal behaviour are commonly made, and can drastically simplify calculations, beware that many systems diverge from ideality, particularly at temperatures and pressures different from the ambient.

For example, it can often be assumed that the components of liquid mixtures are additive, so that, for example, the mixture density is estimated as

$$\frac{1}{\rho} = \frac{z_a}{\rho_a} + \frac{z_b}{\rho_b} + K$$

where z_i is the mass fraction of component i. However, even many familiar mixtures deviate from ideality: 50 cm³ of water and 50 cm³ ethanol give a mixture with volume 96.4 cm³.

Gases. Provided ideal behaviour is maintained, the volume and mole fractions of a component in a mixture are identical. Under ideal conditions the partial pressure p can also be directly related to the mole fraction. The partial pressure is defined as the pressure that the individual component would exert at the temperature and total pressure P in question in a defined volume V. For an ideal gas the pressure P is given by

$$PV = nRT$$

where n is the number of moles. With an ideal mixture of ideal gases Dalton's law applies:

$$P = p_a + p_b + \ldots$$

where p_a etc. are the partial pressures. Thus we can also write

$$p_a = y_a P$$

and

$$\frac{p_a}{p_b} = \frac{y_a}{y_b}$$

where y_i is the mole fraction of component i in the gas mixture.

The **equilibrium vapour pressure** $p°$ is defined as the pressure that would be exerted in a closed volume in which pure liquid exists in equilibrium with pure saturated vapour. This pressure is a strong function of temperature.

Consider now a closed system containing two totally immiscible liquids. They will therefore evaporate independently: at equilibrium each will exert its equilibrium vapour pressure so that the total pressure P exerted by the mixture is

$$P = p_a° + p_b°$$

Note that P is quite independent of the quantities of the liquid phases present, provided only that both liquids exist at equilibrium. Under these conditions then the partial pressures of A and B are equal to their equilibrium vapour pressures.

A different result is obtained for an ideal solution of two liquids, an ideal solution being one in which the various molecules are so similar that the solution behaviour is the same as a pure component. The ethanol–water system is not ideal. Under ideal conditions Raoult's law applies, that is the partial pressure of each component will be proportional to its mole fraction in the liquid, x_i, and the total pressure, being the sum of the partial pressures, is thus

$$P = p_a + p_b = x_a \times p_a^o + x_b \times p_b^o$$

and the mole fraction of Λ, say, in the vapour phase is

$$y_a = \frac{x_a \times p_a^o}{P}$$

Non-ideal liquid solutions are ones in which the linearity of Raoult's law between partial pressure and liquid mole fraction does not hold. Usually as one component approaches 100% of the mixture its behaviour will approach Raoult's law. At low concentrations, Henry's law often holds:

$$p_a = H x_a$$

where Henry's constant, H, depends on the mixture components.

Air/water systems: humidification and drying. There are several common definitions that are particularly useful in the analysis of processes involving water/air mixtures.

In many humidification and drying processes it is convenient to use the quantity of bone-dry air as the basis for calculation, since this is often a tie substance (see Example 1.11). Rather than use mole or mass fractions (which are based on the total mixture) it becomes useful to work in terms of humidity:

$$\text{Humidity, } \mathcal{H} = \frac{\text{Mass of water vapour}}{\text{Mass of bone-dry air}}$$

Similarly, the molar humidity is:

$$\mathcal{H}_m = \frac{p_w}{p_a} = \frac{p_w}{P - p_w}$$

where p_w and p_a are the partial pressures of water vapour and dry air respectively, and P is the total pressure.

Clearly $\mathcal{H}$ and $\mathcal{H}_m$ are related through the molecular masses of air and water respectively:

$$\mathcal{H} = \frac{18 \times \mathcal{H}_m}{29}$$

At saturation the water vapour exerts its equilibrium vapour pressure so that the saturation humidity is

$$\mathcal{H}_s = \frac{p_w^o}{P - p_w^o}$$

The percentage humidity and relative humidity should not be confused with each other. The percentage humidity is the ratio of the actual and saturation humidities ($\mathcal{H}_m/\mathcal{H}_s$); the relative humidity is the ratio between the partial pressure of the water vapour and its equilibrium vapour pressure, expressed as a percentage.

The temperature at which a particular air–water vapour mixture becomes saturated so that $\mathcal{H}_m = \mathcal{H}_s$ is the saturation temperature or dew-point. Many of these and related thermodynamic properties are available in graphical form.

Conclusions

Although the emphasis in this first chapter on material, energy and economic balances has been towards their use in process design, the same techniques are vital for analysing process performance. Mass balances are needed in order to assess process yields and efficiency. Energy balances allow one to calculate how effectively energy is being used; economic analysis doesn't just reveal whether a process is or is not viable, but can provide considerable insight into the parts of a process which are most critical. In any real process the fact that measurements are subject to error and that process conditions fluctuate and drift must always be remembered when trying to establish these balances.

After reading this chapter you should understand the importance of correctly defining the system boundary, that is, the parts of the process which form the basis of a material or energy balance. You should know the difference between a steady and an unsteady process and should appreciate the significance of assuming that a continuous process is also steady. The principles of setting up – or checking – mass balances based on the total component flows, or on individual components such as the chemical elements, and their appropriateness to different situations have been introduced. Chapter 11 provides an opportunity for you try out these techniques on a realistic process example. A typical process can involve reactions which are so complex that the traditional stoichiometric methods are not applicable, or where recycle and bypass streams complicate matters. You should appreciate some of the ways of handling these complications.

The second part of the chapter dealt with the application of the law of energy conservation to typical processes; the material in this chapter also serves as an introduction to Chapters 3 and 4 on heat transfer. You should understand the importance of establishing a clear reference or datum level for all such balances and recognize the difference between an open and a closed system. The main practical difference between these two is that the first law of thermodynamics for a closed system is most conveniently set up in terms of internal energies, whilst for open systems it is most convenient to use enthalpies. You should therefore know how these are defined and how they are related. It is worth emphasizing that for liquids and solids the difference between internal energy and enthalpy (or c_P and c_V) is usually small; for gases and vapours, because they are compressible, it is large. After reading this chapter you should be able to solve problems involving energy balances over typical processes, particularly thermal operations. It should also provide a basis for understanding more complicated processes such as compression and refrigeration cycles, and – as outlined in Chapter 6 – the methods of process energy integration.

Like the other sections of this chapter, the methods of economic analysis could themselves be the basis of a whole book. Here we have introduced some very basic ideas, such as the difference between capital and operating (or fixed and variable) costs and how they can be used to construct annual cash flows. One of the most important concepts introduced here is that of discounting, which is the key to ensuring that cash flows in different years can be compared, i.e. made commensurate. Based on these ideas you should understand, and be able to calculate, some of the measures of process viability including the net present value and the internal rate of return. We have not attempted to broach the issues of cost estimation nor of setting up balance sheets and financial statements.

In the real world it is difficult to calculate precise mass, energy and economic balances, because data and measurements are incomplete or error-ridden, or because the future is uncertain. Too often this becomes a counsel of despair and no attempt is made to calculate any balance at all. We hope that, at the end of this book, you will see the importance of carrying out even quite rough calculations: provided the assumptions and uncertainties are recognized, the benefits far outweigh the trouble of doing the calculations. Even when it is not possible to completely solve the material and energy balances, the approach we outline here, of setting a boundary and identifying the flows across it, is always useful. It should be the first stage of every systematic analysis.

Finally, most of the calculations discussed in this chapter are now routinely carried out with spreadsheets or more sophisticated computer-aided design packages. Chapter 11 illustrates a spreadsheet-based procedure. Although some of the calculation algorithms and methods of data generation now available are extremely sophisticated, the basic principles outlined here still apply, and should help you both to check and to understand these more advanced procedures.

Further reading

The material summarized in this chapter is covered at various levels of rigour and comprehensibility in many introductory texts for chemical engineers; one or two food engineering texts also include material on mass and energy balances. Volume 6 of Coulson and Richardson is particularly useful in that it covers mass and energy balances, some aspects of design and process economics in a single volume. It doesn't, however, consider food engineering applications. This bibliography is divided into three parts. The first covers sections 1.1 and 1.2 of this chapter; the second lists a few books that go into more detail of the process operations typical of the process and food industries; the third covers some books on process economics.

Basic texts

Atkins, P.W. (1990) *Physical Chemistry*, 4th edn, Oxford University Press, Oxford.
Charm, S.E. (1978) *The Fundamentals of Food Engineering*, AVI Publishing Co., Westport, CT, USA.
Coulson, J.M., Richardson, J.F. and Sinnott, R.K. (1983) *Chemical Engineering*, Volume 6, *An Introduction to Chemical Engineering Design*, Pergamon, London.
Felder, R.M. and Rousseau, R.W. (1978) *Elementary Principles of Chemical Processes*, Wiley, New York.
Henley, E.J. and Rosen, E.M. (1969) *Material and Energy Balance Computations*, Wiley, New York.
Toledo, R.T. (1980) *Fundamentals of Food Process Engineering*, AVI Publishing Co., Westport, CT, USA.
Whitwell, J.C. and Toner, R.K. (1969) *Conservation of Mass and Energy*, McGraw-Hill, New York.

Unit operations, food engineering applications

Brennan, J.G., Butters, J.R., Cowell, N.D. and Lilly, A.E.V. (1976) *Food Engineering Operations*, Applied Science Publishers, London.
Coulson, J.M. and Richardson, J.F. (1983) *Chemical Engineering*, Volume 2, Pergamon Press, London.
Fellows, P. (1988) *Food Processing Technology*, Ellis-Horwood, Chichester, UK.
Leniger, H.A. and Beverloo, W. (1975) *Food Process Engineering*, D. Reidel Publishing Co., Dordrecht, Holland.
Loncis, M. and Merson, R.L. (1979) *Food Engineering: Principles and Selected Applications*, Academic Press, New York.

Process economics

Allen, D.H. (1972) *A Guide to the Economic Evaluation of Projects*, Institution of Chemical Engineers, London.
Hacking, A.J. (1986) *Economic Aspects of Biotechnology*, Cambridge University Press, Cambridge, UK.
Holland, F.A., Watson, F.A. and Wilkinson, J.K. (1974) *Introduction to Process Economics*, Wiley, London.
Institution of Chemical Engineers (1977) *A New Guide to Capital Cost Estimation*, Institution of Chemical Engineers, London.
Peters, M.S. and Timmerhaus, K.D. (1980) *Plant Design and Economics for Chemical Engineers*, McGraw-Hill, New York.

2 Newtonian fluid mechanics

R.M. NEDDERMAN

Introduction

The previous chapter has shown how plant flowsheets can be constructed and analysed, and how the viability of a project approximately can be costed. In the flowsheets discussed in Chapter 1, no account was made of how food material moves from one plant unit to another. The next stage of design is to make accurate estimates of the size of these units and of the flows between them. The prediction of the way fluids flow is vital in engineering design, for example in the calculation of pipe sizes and pump duties. It is also necessary to have some idea of the history of the fluid during processing; in food systems, as will be seen later, the range of velocities in the flow can affect the amount and range of thermal processing a fluid receives, and thus can affect the safety and quality of the final product.

The study of fluid flow has to be firmly based on physical principles, such as the conservation of energy and momentum, and on sound physical models for the fluid itself. For fluids such as air and water, the science of fluid mechanics is well developed. Food fluids are much more complex, as will be seen in Chapters 5 and 10, but are ruled by the same principles. This chapter outlines the principles, using examples from simple fluids to make the mathematics clear. It is important to be able to distinguish between turbulent and laminar flows; this chapter describes the characteristics of both. Many flowing food fluids are essentially laminar, although their flows are more complex than those of the Newtonian fluids discussed here. The idea of laminar flows is extended to the study of more complex fluids in Chapter 5. One key idea which is introduced here is that of dynamic similarity. If flows have the same characteristics, then experiments carried out in a given geometry at one scale will be representative of results on other scales. There is still no accurate physical model for many practical situations, so the idea of dynamic similarity is invaluable; it allows correlations to be developed for quantities such as pressure drop and heat transfer coefficient in terms of dimensionless groups, which can then be applied to any length scale of equipment. Many such correlations will be seen throughout this book.

Chemical Engineering for the Food Industry. Edited by P.J. Fryer, D.L. Pyle and C.D. Rielly. Published in 1997 by Blackie A & P, an imprint of Chapman & Hall, London. ISBN 0 412 49500 7

2.1 Laminar and turbulent flow

2.1.1 Introduction

Many of the more important processes of the food industry – heating, mixing and transportation – depend on the fluid properties of the food material or its surroundings. Fluid mechanics therefore underpins much of food technology, and the purpose of this chapter is to form a foundation on which subsequent chapters can build.

Food fluids are generally complex and have a flow behaviour that depends both on their structure and on their processing history. Predicting the flow is therefore difficult. However, the principles that govern the flow behaviour of foods are the same as those that describe the flow of simple fluids such as water. This chapter therefore considers the flow of simple Newtonian fluids; more complex materials will be considered later in Chapters 5 and 10.

At low speeds, fluids tend to flow in a steady and reproducible manner. Such flows are said to be **laminar**, as one layer (lamina) flows smoothly over another. Laminar flows are also called **viscous** flows, as viscous forces (see section 2.3) dominate under these conditions. At higher speeds random eddies occur in the fluid and the flow is said to be **turbulent**. The eddies in turbulent flow have a range of sizes, but the average eddy size is often small compared with the size of the duct along which the fluid is flowing. Under these circumstances the velocity fluctuates randomly about a well-defined mean with only a small variation between maximum and minimum values. Sometimes, however, large eddies occur giving widely fluctuating velocities, and it becomes difficult to define a mean velocity. The distinction between these two types of turbulent flow can be appreciated by comparing the flow produced by a fan, with the wind on a gusty day. Figure 2.1 illustrates the variation of the velocity at a point with time in these three situations.

The behaviour of laminar flows can often be predicted from purely theoretical considerations. However, the theory of turbulent flow is less well advanced, and we usually have to resort to correlations of experimental results to predict the behaviour of fluids under these conditions.

2.1.2 Critical Reynolds numbers

In a pipe of diameter D, the transition from laminar to turbulent flow is found to be sudden; it occurs when the group $v_m D \rho / \mu$ equals about 2200, where v_m is the mean velocity of the fluid and ρ and μ are its density and viscosity. This group is known as the **Reynolds number**, after the discoverer of this phenomenon. Each geometry has its own critical Reynolds number, and the value of 2200 is specific for pipes of circular cross-section. Though we have said that the transition is sudden at the critical Reynolds number,

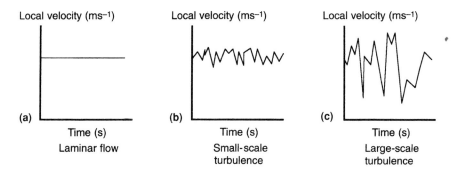

Fig. 2.1 Variation of velocity at a point in different types of flow: (a) laminar; (b) small-scale turbulence; (c) large-scale turbulence.

the behaviour close to that value tends to be unreproducible. Thus it is not always possible to say whether a flow in the Reynolds number range 2000–2400 will be laminar or turbulent, and sometimes it is found that the behaviour switches irregularly between these two states.

2.1.3   Velocity profiles

In laminar pipe flow, it can be shown theoretically (section 2.3) that the velocity profile is parabolic and given by

$$v = v_1\left[1 - \left(\frac{r}{R}\right)^2\right] \qquad (2.1)$$

where v is the velocity at radius r and R is the radius of the pipe, i.e. $D/2$.

In turbulent flow the velocity distribution is well correlated by the so-called **one-seventh power law**, discussed further in section 2.5.6:

$$v = v_1\left(\frac{y}{R}\right)^{1/7} = \frac{60}{49}v_m\left(\frac{y}{R}\right)^{1/7} \qquad (2.2)$$

where v_1 is the centreline velocity, v_m is the mean velocity and y is the distance from the wall, i.e. $y = R - r$.

These profiles are plotted in Fig. 2.2 for the same flowrate. It can be seen that in turbulent flow the velocity is much more uniform than in laminar flow, as a result of the mixing action of the eddies. In laminar flow the centreline velocity is twice the mean velocity, while in turbulent flow the centreline velocity is only $60/49 = 1.22$ times the mean. This has implications for the design of continuous sterilizers, discussed in later sections.

Food fluids generally have high viscosities and thus their flow tends to be laminar. However, in many cases they also show non-Newtonian behaviour

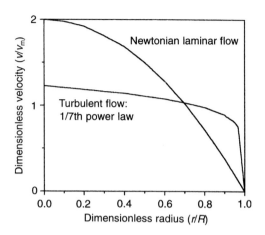

Fig. 2.2 Comparison of velocity profiles in pipe flow.

– that is, variable viscosity – and this will be discussed in Chapter 5. However, there are several low-viscosity fluids of importance in the food industry, such as water and milk, for which the conventional fluid mechanics outlined in this chapter is relevant. Furthermore, a study of these simple fluids provides a firm foundation on which the study of non-Newtonian fluids is traditionally based.

2.1.4 Pressure

It is appropriate at this stage to discuss the concept of **pressure**. This is the force per unit area exerted by the fluid, and acts equally in all directions. In a stationary fluid the pressure increases linearly with depth at a rate ρg where ρ is the density and g the acceleration due to gravity. This result provides a simple means of measuring pressure known as the U-tube manometer. This is a U-shaped tube partially filled with liquid of density ρ_m, with one end connected to the point of interest and the other open to the atmosphere, as shown in Fig. 2.3. The pressure at the measurement point is given by

$$P = P_a + \rho_m g h$$

where P_a is atmospheric pressure and h is the difference in height of the fluid in the two limbs. A U-tube manometer can also be used to measure pressure differences by connecting the two ends to two points of interest between which it is required to measure the pressure difference. Under these circumstances it becomes necessary to make allowance for the weight of the fluid in the tube, and the pressure difference ΔP is given by

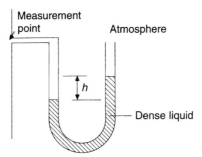

Fig. 2.3 The U-tube manometer.

$$\Delta P = \left(\rho_{m} - \rho_{f}\right)gh$$

where ρ_{m} is the density of the manometer liquid and ρ_{f} is the density of the flowing fluid.

2.2 Ideal fluids

2.2.1 Introduction

Considerable insight can often be gained into the behaviour of fluids in pipes and ducts by assuming that the fluid is ideal: that is, that the velocity is uniform across the duct and that the fluid has zero viscosity (viscosity is defined in section 2.3.1). Although no real fluid conforms to this ideal, these assumptions give rise to little error in many examples of practical importance. As we shall see later (for example, in section 2.5), these assumptions are best for short lengths of pipe. They are therefore appropriate for considering sudden changes such as changes in cross-section, or pipe bends. It can be seen from Fig. 2.2 that the assumption of uniform velocity is more appropriate for turbulent than for laminar flow.

Ideal fluid analysis is based on three basic conservation equations: the conservation of mass, energy and momentum. We shall apply these conservation laws over a short distance between two sections of a generalized duct, which are denoted by section 1 and 2 in Fig. 2.4. F is the force on the wall. The dotted line in this figure represents a **control surface**, which encloses the **control volume**, i.e. that part of the system to which we are paying attention. Very commonly in ideal flows we do not need to consider what happens within the control volume as we can obtain enough information by considering the properties of the fluid as it enters and leaves through the control surface. This is the same principle as that used in Chapter 1.

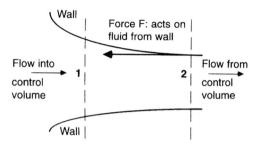

Fig. 2.4 A hypothetical duct. The dotted lines denote the edges of the control surface discussed in the text.

2.2.2 *Conservation of mass: the continuity equation*

If the velocity is constant across any cross-section in the duct, the mass flowrate w is given by

$$w = av\rho \tag{2.3}$$

where v is the velocity of the fluid, ρ is its density and A is the cross-sectional area of the duct. If we consider a duct of varying cross-section as in Fig. 2.4, we can say from the conservation of mass that w is a constant and therefore the flow into the system will equal the flow out in the absence of accumulation. Thus

$$w = A_1 v_1 \rho_1 = A_2 v_2 \rho_2 \tag{2.4}$$

where the subscripts 1 and 2 denote the conditions at the two selected sections.

2.2.3 *The conservation of energy: Bernoulli's equation*

The fluid entering the duct at section 1 of Fig. 2.4 will be subjected to a force equal to the product of the cross-sectional area and the pressure. The boundary dividing this fluid from the fluid behind it will have moved a distance x, and therefore the work done on the fluid entering the duct by the fluid behind it will be PAx, which equals $P_1 V_1$, where P_1 is the pressure at section 1 and V_1 is the volume of fluid entering the duct. For unit mass entering the duct, V will be equal to the reciprocal of the density, i.e. $1/\rho$. Therefore the work done on a unit mass of the fluid entering the duct is P_1/ρ. Similarly, when the fluid leaves, it does work P_2/ρ on the fluid ahead. The fluid had kinetic energy $\frac{1}{2}v_1^2$ per unit mass on entering and has kinetic energy $\frac{1}{2}v_2^2$ on leaving. In the process the fluid has gained potential energy $g(h_2 - h_1)$, where h is height above some arbitrary datum. Assuming that the total energy is conserved between sections 1 and 2, we have as an expression of the conservation of energy

$$\frac{P_1}{\rho} + \frac{v_1^2}{2} + gh_1 = \frac{P_2}{\rho} + \frac{v_2^2}{2} + gh_2 \tag{2.5}$$

This energy balance is known as Bernoulli's equation. It is very useful in the study of flows. Various assumptions have been made in the derivation:

- that the density is constant;
- that the system operates in the steady state, as we have assumed that there is no accumulation of energy between sections 1 and 2;
- that there is no interchange between thermal and mechanical energy, i.e. that the internal energy and hence the temperature of the fluid does not change between sections 1 and 2.

As the two pressure terms in Bernoulli's equation are divided by the same density, we can use either the genuine thermodynamic pressure, known as the **absolute pressure**, or measure the pressure above an arbitrary datum. When measured above atmospheric pressure, the difference is known as the **gauge pressure**.

In low-speed flows, there is little possibility of thermal energy being converted into mechanical energy. However, the converse is possible, especially in the more grossly eddying turbulent flows, and in this case some of the mechanical energy is lost within the section. In all other circumstances a loss term must be included:

$$\frac{P_1}{\rho} + \frac{v_1^2}{2} + gh_1 = \frac{P_2}{\rho} + \frac{v_2^2}{2} + gh_2 + E_L \tag{2.6}$$

where E_L is the energy lost per unit mass between sections 1 and 2. Bernoulli's equation should only be used for the steady flow of constant-density fluids.

2.2.4 Conservation of momentum: the momentum equation

The momentum equation is based on Newton's second law, that the rate of change of momentum is equal to the net applied force. This is often expressed in the form

$$F = ma = m\frac{dv}{dt} = \frac{d}{dt}(mv) \tag{2.7}$$

This form is convenient if we are dealing with a body of finite mass, but in fluid mechanics we are generally concerned with the steady flow of a continuous quantity of fluid. Here is it more convenient to work in terms of a flux of momentum, M, defined as the product of the **mass flowrate** w and the velocity v:

$$M = wv = A\rho v^2 \tag{2.8}$$

Thus if we consider a control volume as shown in Fig. 2.4 we can say that the difference between the flowrates of momentum into and out of the volume will be the rate of change of momentum and hence equal to the net force on the control volume.

The forces on the control volume are the pressure forces at the two cross-sections, which are given by the product of the area and the absolute pressure, $A_1 P_1$ and $A_2 P_2$, and the net force F exerted by the wall of the duct on the fluid. This is equal and opposite to the force exerted by the fluid on the inside surface of the duct. Summing these forces and applying Newton's Law gives

$$A_1 P_1 - A_2 P_2 - F = M_2 - M_1 \qquad (2.9)$$

or

$$F = \left(A_1 P_1 + A_1 \rho_1 v_1^2 \right) - \left(A_2 P_2 + A_2 \rho_2 v_2^2 \right) \qquad (2.10)$$

Note that in the derivation of this equation we have not needed to make the assumption that the density is constant. Unlike Bernoulli's equation, this is valid for compressible as well as incompressible fluids. Furthermore, we have not needed to assume loss-free flow and as a result this equation is more generally valid than Bernoulli's equation. Note also that as the two pressures P_1 and P_2 are multiplied by different areas, it is essential that absolute pressure values are used. This point is considered in greater detail in Example 2.4 below.

We shall illustrate the use of these three basic equations by means of a set of examples.

EXAMPLE 2.1: SMALL ORIFICE IN THE SIDE OF A LARGE TANK

Figure 2.5 shows the system under investigation, in which a fluid is flowing through an orifice at a depth H below the surface of a fluid. Applying Bernoulli's equation from a point on the top surface to the jet emerging from the orifice, we can assemble our data as follows. Consider a control surface extending from the top surface to the jet and let section 1 be a point on the top surface. The pressure here is atmospheric, and as the velocity is small we can say that $P_1 = P_a$, where P_a is atmospheric pressure, $v_1 \simeq 0$. We can take the orifice as our datum of height, and therefore $h_1 = H$.

Within the jet the pressure is again atmospheric, as we can neglect the variation of atmospheric pressure with height as a result of the small density of air. The velocity is the unknown v and the height is at the datum. Hence

$$P_2 = P_a, \qquad v_2 = v \quad \text{and} \quad h_2 = 0 \qquad (2.11)$$

Substituting these quantities into Bernoulli's equation gives

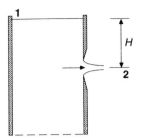

Fig. 2.5 Example 2.1: flow through an orifice at depth H below the surface of fluid in a tank.

$$\frac{P_a}{\rho} + \frac{0^2}{2} + gH = \frac{P_a}{\rho} + \frac{v^2}{2} + 0 \qquad (2.12)$$

or

$$v = \sqrt{2gH} \qquad (2.13)$$

We have calculated this velocity on the assumption that there are no energy losses. In practice there will be some small losses due to drag on the wall near the orifice and rearrangements within the jet. Hence the velocity will be slightly less than the ideal value of equation (2.13). This reduction is commonly expresed in terms of a **velocity coefficient** C_v defined so that

$$v = C_v\sqrt{2gH} \qquad (2.14)$$

Typical values for C_v in this geometry are about 0.98, suggesting that only about 4% of the total energy content is lost.

Observation of the jet shows that there is considerable contraction downstream of the orifice. This is *not* due to surface tension, as it occurs whether the jet is surrounded by air or water. It is due to the momentum of the fluid approaching the orifice from the side and overshooting. The minimum cross-section is known as the **vena contracta** and its area is denoted by $C_c A_o$, where A_o is the area of the orifice and C_c is known as the **contraction coefficient**. For a single orifice, as shown in Fig. 2.5, C_c is often about 0.65 except at very low flowrates.

Equation (2.13) gives the velocity at the *vena contracta*, as it is in the parallel-sided part of the jet that the pressure is atmospheric. Thus the volumetric flowrate is given by

$$w_L = C_c A_o C_v \sqrt{2gH}$$
$$= C_D A_o \sqrt{2gH} \qquad (2.15)$$

where C_D is a **discharge coefficient** defined as the ratio of the actual flowrate to that predicted on the assumption of no energy loss and no contraction. For the simple orifice, $C_D = C_c C_v$ and will be about 0.63.

Thus if we were to consider a hole of diameter 10 mm at a depth of 0.8 m below the top of a tank, we could predict the ideal velocity from equation (2.13) as

$$(2 \times 9.81 \times 0.8)^{0.5} = 3.96 \, \text{m s}^{-1}$$

Assuming a velocity coefficient of 0.98, the actual velocity would be $0.98 \times 3.96 = 3.88 \, \text{m s}^{-1}$. The orifice area is $\pi \times 0.01^2/4 = 7.85 \times 10^{-5} \, \text{m}^2$, so that the area of the *vena contracta* will be about $0.65 \times 7.85 \times 10^{-5} = 5.11 \times 10^{-5} \, \text{m}^2$. The mass flowrate will thus be given by equation (2.3) as $1000 \times 5.11 \times 10^{-5} \times 3.88 = 0.198 \, \text{kg s}^{-1}$.

EXAMPLE 2.2: THE ORIFICE PLATE

One of the commonest ways of measuring the flowrate in a pipe is to insert an orifice plate, as shown in Fig. 2.6. Normally there are three pressure tappings: one some way upstream of the plate, which we will call tapping 1; one near to the *vena contracta*, tapping 2; and one some way downstream of the orifice plate, tapping 3. Unfortunately the UK and US codes of practice do not agree about the best positions for these tappings. The UK code recommends tappings in the corner formed by the junction of the orifice plate with the tube wall, whereas the US code recommends close to the *vena contracta* and a few diameters upstream of the orifice. Whatever their merits for flow measurement, the US tappings are more convenient for theoretical analysis and will be considered here.

Observations using dye traces in transparent tubes show that the flow is smooth as far as the *vena contracta*, suggesting loss-free flow, whereas downstream of the *vena contracta* the jet breaks up, inducing gross eddies with consequential energy losses. It takes some considerable distance before smooth flow is re-established. In the present analysis we shall assume that tapping 2 is at the *vena contracta*, tapping 1 is sufficiently far upstream for the flow to be unaffected by the presence of the orifice, and tapping 3 is sufficiently far downsteam for smooth flow to be re-established.

If the system is ideal we can assume that there are no energy losses between sections 1 and 2 and apply the continuity and Bernoulli equations, giving

$$w = A_1 v_1 \rho = A_2 v_2 \rho \tag{2.16}$$

and

$$\frac{P_1}{\rho} + \frac{v_1^2}{2} = \frac{P_2}{\rho} + \frac{v_2^2}{2} \tag{2.17}$$

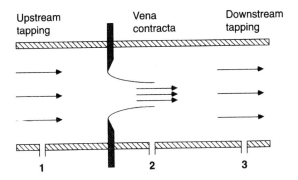

Fig. 2.6 Example 2.2: the orifice plate, showing pressure tappings.

Eliminating v_1 and v_2 between these equations gives

$$w = A_2 \left[\frac{2\rho(P_1 - P_2)}{1 - \left(\dfrac{A_2}{A_1} \right)^2} \right]^{1/2} \tag{2.18}$$

However, we must bear in mind that this analysis neglects the loss of energy, and that A_2 is the area of the *vena contracta* and not the orifice area. As in Example 2.1, the former effect causes little in the way of error, but the jet contraction does have a major effect on the result. The area A_2 can be written as $C_c A_o$, where A_o is the area of the orifice. We could therefore replace A_2 by $C_c A_o$ in equation (2.18), giving

$$w = C_c A_o \left[\frac{2\rho(P_1 - P_2)}{1 - \left(\dfrac{C_c A_o}{A_1} \right)^2} \right]^{1/2} \tag{2.19}$$

but it is more usual to write this equation in the form

$$w = C_D A_o \left[\frac{2\rho(P_1 - P_2)}{1 - \left(\dfrac{A_o}{A_1} \right)^2} \right]^{1/2} \tag{2.20}$$

where C_D is not quite equal to C_c, not only because of the existence of a velocity coefficient due to energy losses, but also because C_c has been omitted from the fraction within the square root. Because the orifice plate is the one of the commonest methods of measuring flowrate, the values of C_D have been determined with the greatest care, and extensive tabulations of C_D as a function of Reynolds number and area ratio can be found in the BSI publication on flow measurement (BS 1042). In conjunction with the values obtained from these tables an orifice plate can give very high accuracy and is often used as the standard for calibrating other flow-measuring devices.

We cannot use Bernoulli's equation to predict the pressure P_3 downstream of the orifice plate as there is considerable eddying as the jet breaks up, with corresponding loss of energy. Instead we can use the momentum equation, together with the assumption that there is negligible longitudinal force on this short section of the pipe. Thus the applied force is given by

$$A_1(P_2 - P_3)$$

which must equal the momentum change, $w(v_3 - v_2) = A_1 \rho v_1 (v_3 - v_2)$. Thus

$$P_3 - P_2 = \rho v_1 (v_2 - v_1) \qquad (2.21)$$

where we have replaced v_3 by v_1 as almost always the pipe diameters before and after the orifice are equal. Note that as $v_2 > v_1$, the pressure rises downstream of the orifice plate. Comparison with equation (2.19) shows that the pressure rise after the orifice plate does not equal the pressure drop between sections 1 and 2. Thus combining equations (2.18) and (2.21) predicts that there is an overall pressure loss given by

$$P_1 - P_3 = \frac{1}{2} \rho (v_2 - v_1)^2 \qquad (2.22)$$

which can alternatively be written as

$$P_1 - P_3 = \frac{1}{2} \frac{w^2}{\rho} \left(\frac{1}{A_2} - \frac{1}{A_1} \right)^2 \qquad (2.23)$$

The overall pressure loss is proportional to the square of the flowrate w, and this is typical of the pressure drop across any item of plant, such as a sudden change in pipe diameter, a pipe bend or a valve.

If we have water flowing with a velocity of $1.5 \, \text{ms}^{-1}$ in a tube of diameter 30 mm fitted with an orifice of diameter 20 mm, we can calculate the relevant areas by $A_1 = A_3 = \pi \times 0.03^2/4 = 7.07 \times 10^{-4} \, \text{m}^2$ and $A_2 = 0.65 \times \pi \times 0.02^2/4 = 2.04 \times 10^{-4} \, \text{m}^2$, assuming a contraction coefficient of 0.65. The velocity v_2 is given from equation (2.16) as $1.5 \times 7.07 \times 10^{-4}/2.04 \times 10^{-4} = 5.20 \, \text{ms}^{-1}$. Thus from equation (2.17) the pressure drop $P_1 - P_2 = 1000 \times (5.20^2 - 1.5^2)/2 = 12.4 \, \text{kN m}^{-2}$ and the pressure recovery downstream of the orifice is, from equation (2.21), $1000 \times 1.5 \times (5.20 - 1.5) = 5.55 \, \text{kN m}^{-2}$. There is therefore an overall pressure loss of $12.4 - 5.55 = 6.8 \, \text{kN m}^{-2}$.

EXAMPLE 2.3: THE VENTURI TUBE

The Venturi tube is a modified version of the orifice plate that has the advantage of a lower overall pressure loss. It consists of a smooth contraction in the cross-section of a pipe followed by a gradual expansion back to the original area. The pressure is measured upstream of the contraction, P_1, and at the throat, P_2, as shown in Fig. 2.7. It is also of interest to predict the pressure P_3 downstream of the Venturi. The expanding part of the Venturi is known as the **diffuser**, and observations show that if the angle of divergence is less than about $10°$ the jet does not break away from the walls of the diffuser, and smooth (and therefore nearly loss-free) flow occurs.

The analysis given in the previous section for the pressure drop $P_1 - P_2$ still applies but now, because of the gradual contraction of the tube, there is little tendency for the jet to contract further and the discharge coefficient differs only slightly from unity, this being due mainly to the effects of wall friction. Furthermore, as the jet does not break away from the edge of the orifice, little energy is lost downstream of the throat and the pressure recovery $P_3 - P_2$ is only marginally less than the pressure drop. Thus there is little overall pressure drop across the device as a whole, and a Venturi tube is therefore to be preferred to an orifice plate whenever there is a need to maintain the presure. However, Venturi tubes are long, owing to the small diffuser angle, and need to be machined with care in order to maintain loss-free flow. Orifice plates are easy to make and, being only a few millimetres in width, can easily be slipped between existing pipe flanges. In many circumstances, particularly for liquids, the extra pumping costs associated with the pressure drop across an orifice plate are quite negligible and the greater ease of construction and convenience of installation make the orifice plate the more popular of the two devices.

EXAMPLE 2.4: FORCE ON A PIPE BEND

Let us consider as an example a contracting section of pipe that is bent through $180°$, as shown in Fig. 2.8. If the pipe is short and smooth-walled

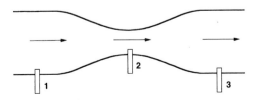

Fig. 2.7 Example 2.3: the Venturi tube, showing pressure tappings.

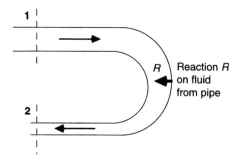

Fig. 2.8 Example 2.4: force on a bend.

there will be little loss of energy and we can apply Bernoulli's equation from inlet to outlet as follows:

$$\frac{P_1}{\rho}+\frac{v_1^2}{2}=\frac{P_2}{\rho}+\frac{v_2^2}{2} \tag{2.24}$$

The applied forces on the fluid within the pipe are

1. the forces on the end section, A_1P_1 and A_2P_2, which act to the right, and
2. the force R exerted by the inside surface of the pipe on the fluid. This force acts on the fluid to the left and is equal and opposite to the force exerted by the fluid on the pipe wall.

The sum of the forces, $A_1P_1 + A_2P_2 - R$, must equal the net creation of rightward momentum. The inlet momentum through section 1 is $wv_1 = A_1\rho v_1^2$; leftward momentum leaves section 2 at the rate $A_2\rho v_2^2$.

Thus the rate of creation of rightward momentum is $- A_1\rho v_1^2 - A_2\rho v_2^2$, and

$$R=\left(A_1P_1+A_1\rho v_1^2\right)+\left(A_2P_2+A_2\rho v_2^2\right) \tag{2.25}$$

Comparing this with equation (2.9) reveals that we have a difference in sign, and this results from the 180° bend in the tube. Indeed we can note that the impulse function F, defined as $(AP + A\rho v^2)$, is a vector and must be added accordingly:

$$R = F_1 + F_2 \tag{2.26}$$

There remains a small complication, however. In principle, the pressures in the equations of this section should be absolute pressures, as it is the absolute pressure times the area that gives rise to a force. We have however emphasized that R is the force on the inside surface of the pipe and there will be an additional force exerted by the surroundings on the outside surface of the pipe. This equals atmospheric pressure, P_a, times the projected area, which in this case is $A_1 + A_2$, and acts from right to left. Thus the total force on the pipe, due to the fluids inside and outside the pipe, is given by

$$R_T = \left(A_1(P_1 - P_a) + A_1 \rho v_1^2\right) + \left(A_2(P_2 - P_a) + A_2 \rho v_2^2\right) \qquad (2.27)$$

We see therefore that in order to obtain the **total** force on the system, we must use gauge and not absolute pressures. This is intuitively reasonable as, if the gauge pressure is zero throughout, there is clearly no force on the duct.

Let us consider a duct that contracts from a cross-sectional area A_1 of $4 \times 10^{-3}\,\text{m}^2$ to A_2 of $2 \times 10^{-3}\,\text{m}^2$ while being bent through an angle of $60°$, as shown in Fig. 2.9. Water discharges to atmosphere at section 2 with a velocity of $10\,\text{ms}^{-1}$.

From continuity, we can say that $v_1 = v_2 A_2/A_1 = 5\,\text{ms}^{-1}$. As the fluid discharges to atmosphere at section 2, the gauge pressure $P_2 = 0$, and from Bernoulli's equation

$$P_1 = P_2 + \frac{\rho}{2}\left(v_2^2 - v_1^2\right) = 37.5\,\text{kNm}^{-2}$$

The impulse function at section 1 is given by

$$F_1 = A_1\left(P_1 + \rho v_1^2\right) = 250\,\text{N}$$

and

$$F_2 = A_2\left(P_2 + \rho v_2^2\right) = 200\,\text{N}$$

Both these impulse functions act on the control surface, as shown in Fig. 2.9. The net force to the right, X, is given by $X = 250 - 200\cos60° = 150\,\text{N}$ and the net upward force $Y = 200\sin60° = 173\,\text{N}$. The resultant force $R = (150^2 + 173^2)^{0.5} = 229\,\text{N}$ and acts at an angle $\tan^{-1}(173/150) = 49°$ to the horizontal.

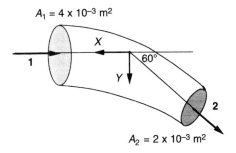

Fig. 2.9 Example 2.4: pipe bend through $60°$.

2.3 Laminar flows

2.3.1 Introduction

At low Reynolds numbers the flow is **laminar** and, as shown in Fig. 2.2, the assumption that the velocity is uniform across the duct is untenable. In particular, it is found that the velocity in contact with a stationary solid surface is zero. This is often called the **no-slip condition**. The critical Reynolds number below which laminar flow occurs depends on the geometry of the situation, but in a pipe of circular cross-section the critical Reynolds number is about 2200. Reynolds numbers below this critical value are commonly encountered in the more viscous liquids of the food industry.

In laminar flow the effects of **viscosity** are dominant. By definition the viscosity μ is the constant of proportionality between the shear stress τ and the velocity gradient dv/dy:

$$\tau = \mu \frac{dv}{dy} \tag{2.28}$$

This is most conveniently illustrated by considering two parallel planes a distance Y apart as in Fig. 2.10. The lower plate is held stationary and the upper plate is moved with velocity v. The velocity gradient is v/Y and hence the shear stress on the upper plate is $\mu v/Y$. Thus the force F required to maintain the motion is $A\mu v/Y$, where A is the area of the plate. Viscosity is the resistance of a fluid to distortion; fluids such as Golden Syrup have high viscosity in comparison to water. It takes its name from *viscum*, the Latin for mistletoe, because of the stickiness of the berries. If the viscosity μ is constant (that is, not a function of either τ or dv/dy), the fluid is said to be **Newtonian**. Non-Newtonian fluids will be discussed in Chapter 5.

The viscosity can be measured in a variety of commercially available viscometers, each type being appropriate for a particular range of viscosities. This too will be discussed in greater detail in Chapter 5. Viscos-

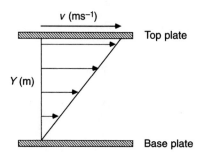

Fig. 2.10 Effect of viscosity: flow between parallel plates Y apart where the top plate moves at velocity v.

ity is a very important physical parameter, which controls the behaviour of laminar flows. Non-Newtonian fluids have more complex flow properties as a result of μ not being a constant. This section, however, only describes the behaviour of Newtonian fluids.

Viscosity is, however, a strong function of temperature, as anyone who has warmed syrup will know, and indeed engine-lubricating oils contain special additives in an attempt to limit this variation. In solutions, the viscosity is also a function of concentration. Thus when looking up tabulated values of viscosity, it is essential to ensure that the data are at the required temperature.

In many simple geometries, the velocity distribution and the associated pressure gradient can be obtained by a simple force balance, similar to that employed in the derivation of the momentum equation, and the definition of the viscosity. We shall illustrate the method by a single example.

2.3.2 Laminar flow in a tube of circular cross-section

We shall consider a fluid of viscosity μ flowing in a tube of radius R and length L under the influence of an overall pressure difference of magnitude ΔP. As the pressure gradient dP/dl is uniform along the tube it will equal $\Delta P/L$. We can find the shear stress τ at an arbitrary radius r from the centreline of the tube by considering a force balance on a cylindrical element of radius r and length δl as shown in Fig. 2.11. The difference between the forces on the two ends of the element, $\pi r^2 (dP/dl)\delta l$, must equal the force on the side of the element $2\pi r\tau\delta l$:

$$\pi r^2 \frac{dP}{dl}\delta l = 2\pi r\tau\delta l \tag{2.29}$$

where τ is the **shear stress**; that is, the shear force acting per unit area of the curved surface of the element. Equation (2.29) can be rewritten to give τ as

$$\tau = \frac{r}{2}\frac{dP}{dl} \tag{2.30}$$

By the definition of a Newtonian fluid, however, the shear stress can also be written as

$$\tau = \mu\frac{dv}{dr} \tag{2.31}$$

as dv/dr is the velocity gradient perpendicular to the surface on which τ acts. Combining equations (2.30) and (2.31) gives

$$\mu\frac{dv}{dr} = \frac{r}{2}\frac{dP}{dl} \tag{2.32}$$

and on integrating equation (2.32) with respect to r we have

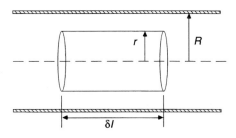

Fig. 2.11 Laminar flow in a tube of circular cross-section, radius R, showing section of radius r.

$$\mu v = \frac{r^2}{4}\frac{\mathrm{d}P}{\mathrm{d}l} + A \qquad (2.33)$$

where A is an arbitrary constant of integration. The constant A can be evaluated from the no-slip condition, that the velocity must be zero on the tube wall, i.e. that $v = 0$ on $r = R$. Hence

$$A = -\frac{R^2}{4}\frac{\mathrm{d}P}{\mathrm{d}l} \qquad (2.34)$$

and, substituting for A into equation (2.33),

$$\mu v = \frac{\left(r^2 - R^2\right)}{4}\frac{\mathrm{d}P}{\mathrm{d}l} \qquad (2.35)$$

The volumetric flowrate w_L can be found from the integral of the product of the velocity with the elementary area $2\pi r\,\mathrm{d}r$:

$$w_L = \int_0^R v 2\pi r\,\mathrm{d}r \qquad (2.36)$$

or

$$w_L = -\frac{\pi R^4}{8\mu}\frac{\mathrm{d}P}{\mathrm{d}l} \qquad (2.37)$$

The minus sign appearing, perhaps unexpectedly, in this equation is necessary as the pressure gradient $\mathrm{d}P/\mathrm{d}l$ is formally a negative quantity, because the fluid flows in the direction of decreasing pressure. Equation (2.37) can also be expressed in terms of the mean velocity v_m defined by

$$w_L = \pi R^2 v_m \qquad (2.38)$$

giving

$$v_m = -\frac{R^2}{8\mu}\frac{\mathrm{d}P}{\mathrm{d}l} \qquad (2.39)$$

Substituting this equation into equation (2.35) gives

$$v = 2v_m \left[1 - \left(\frac{r}{R} \right)^2 \right] \tag{2.40}$$

which is the equation quoted in section 2.1.3 and plotted in Fig. 2.2. Clearly the velocity profile is parabolic. Furthermore, by putting $r = 0$, it can be seen that the centreline velocity v_1 is twice the mean velocity v_m, as already noted in that section.

This type of analysis can be carried out in a wide range of simple geometries. For example, in a rectangular slot of width w and thickness b, where $b \ll w$, the result corresponding to equation (2.35) is

$$\mu v = \frac{\left(4y^2 - b^2 \right)}{8} \frac{dP}{dl} \tag{2.41}$$

where y is distance from the central plane, and equation (2.38) becomes

$$w_L = -\frac{b^3 w}{12\mu} \frac{dP}{dl} = bw v_m \tag{2.42}$$

The velocity profile is given by

$$v = 1.5 v_m \left[1 - \left(\frac{2y}{b} \right)^2 \right] = v_1 \left[1 - \left(\frac{2y}{b} \right)^2 \right] \tag{2.43}$$

Again, the profile is parabolic but, in this case, the mean velocity is two thirds of the centreline velocity.

Velocity profiles such as these are typical for all Newtonian fluids, including many food fluids. Thus when a food fluid flows down a pipe, different parts of the fluid will spend different lengths of time within the pipe. Thus, if cooking or sterilization is taking place, some parts of the fluid will be processed for longer times than others. This effect will give rise to uneven processing, and will be discussed further in Chapter 8 in the context of residence time distributions.

The equations derived above can be manipulated into a different form, which we shall find convenient in section 2.5. We can see from equation (2.29) that the magnitude of the shear stress on the wall, τ_w, is given by

$$\tau_w = -\frac{R}{2} \frac{dP}{dl} \tag{2.44}$$

and hence we can rewrite equation (2.39) in the form

$$\tau_w = \frac{16\mu v_m}{R} \tag{2.45}$$

Both sides of this equation can be divided by $\frac{1}{2}\rho v_m^2$ to give

$$\frac{\tau_w}{\frac{1}{2}\rho v_m^2} = 16 \frac{\mu}{\rho v_m (2R)} \tag{2.46}$$

This is traditionally written in the form

$$c_f = \frac{16}{Re} \tag{2.47}$$

where the friction factor c_f is defined by

$$c_f = \frac{\tau_w}{\frac{1}{2}\rho v_m^2} \tag{2.48}$$

and Re is the conventional Reynolds number. In this form we can make direct comparison with the corresponding results for turbulent flow, which will be presented in section 2.5. Correlations for the friction factor are very useful for predicting the pressure drop needed to pump a fluid along a pipe, and thus are important in the design of process plant.

EXAMPLE 2.5

Consider $0.6\,\mathrm{l\,s^{-1}}$ of a fluid of viscosity $0.015\,\mathrm{N\,s\,m^{-2}}$ flowing in a 50 mm diameter pipe: the mean velocity can thus be evaluated as $0.6 \times 10^{-3} \times 4/(\pi \times 0.05^2) = 0.306\,\mathrm{m\,s^{-1}}$. Assuming a density of about $1000\,\mathrm{kg\,m^{-3}}$, the Reynolds number will be $0.306 \times 0.05 \times 1000/0.015 = 1019$. This is well below the critical value of 2200 and laminar flow will therefore occur.

From equation (2.37) the pressure gradient is given by $-8 \times 0.015 \times 0.6 \times 10^{-3}/(\pi \times 0.025^4) = -58.7\,\mathrm{N\,m^{-3}}$. Thus if the pipe is 15 m long, the pressure drop will be $15 \times 58.7 = 881\,\mathrm{N\,m^{-2}}$. The centreline velocity will be twice the mean velocity, i.e. $0.612\,\mathrm{m\,s^{-1}}$, so that some fluid will spend only $15/0.612 = 24.5\,\mathrm{s}$ within the pipe compared with the mean residence time of twice this value, 49 s.

2.3.3   Flow through packed beds

In the food industry, it is often important to calculate the pressure drops through filters or membranes that consist of arrays of solid particles. These are both examples of flow through packed beds, a topic that was first studied in 1846 by Darcy, the gardening consultant for Dijon City Council, who was interested in the right sort of gravel to put round his fountains. Darcy's book (*Les Fontaines Publiques de la Ville de Dijon*, Paris, 1856) is generally regarded as the first serious study of fluid mechanics, and his conclusion, that the pressure gradient through a packed bed is directly proportional to the flowrate w_L, is commonly known as **Darcy's law**:

$$\frac{dP}{dl} \propto w_L \tag{2.49}$$

More detailed analysis by Carman and Kozeny, treated in texts such as Kay and Nedderman (1985), gives rise to the following result for beds composed of spherical particles:

$$\frac{\mathrm{d}P}{\mathrm{d}l} = \frac{180\mu v(1-\varepsilon)^2}{D^2\varepsilon^3} \tag{2.50}$$

where v is the superficial velocity, i.e. the volumetric flowrate per unit area of bed (w_L/A), D is the diameter of the particles and ε is the void fraction, i.e. the volumetric fraction of the bed occupied by the fluid. In the case of non-spherical particles or particles of mixed sizes an equivalent spherical diameter must be used and a shape factor has to be included. Details of these are given in Kay and Nedderman (1985).

The constant of proportionality between the superficial velocity and the pressure gradient is sometimes called the **permeability**. It is noteworthy that this is both inversely proportional to the square of the particle diameter and very sensitive to the void fraction. The permeability is proportional to $\varepsilon^3/(1-\varepsilon)^2$, i.e. roughly proportional to ε^5. Thus a small degree of compaction of the bed greatly decreases the permeability; for example, a 2% change in voidage causes a 10% change in the permeability.

The Carman–Kozeny equation (2.50) gives an excellent prediction of the pressure gradient provided the Reynolds number, here defined by

$$Re' = \frac{dv\rho}{\mu(1-\varepsilon)} \tag{2.51}$$

is less than about 10. At higher Reynolds numbers allowance must be made for inertial effects, and an extra term has to be inserted into equation (2.50), giving the result known as the **Ergun correlation**:

$$\frac{\mathrm{d}P}{\mathrm{d}l} = \frac{150\mu v(1-\varepsilon)^2}{d^2\varepsilon^3} + \frac{1.75\rho v^2(1-\varepsilon)}{d\varepsilon^3} \tag{2.52}$$

where ρ is the density of the fluid. This correlation is generally regarded as the best available. The discrepancy between the constant of 180 in the Carman–Kozeny equation and the 150 in the Ergun correlation is not easily explained away, and may be taken as an indication of the precision of these results. Again the extreme sensitivity of the pressure gradient to the void fraction should be noted.

EXAMPLE 2.6

We can calculate the pressure difference required to force water of viscosity $0.89 \times 10^{-3}\,\mathrm{N\,s\,m^{-2}}$ at $0.01\,\mathrm{m\,s^{-1}}$ through a filter cake of thickness 5 mm consisting of 20 μm spherical particles, packed to a voidage of 0.4.

First we must evaluate the Reynolds number, which in this case is

$$20 \times 10^{-6} \times 0.01 \times \frac{1000}{0.89 \times 10^{-3} \times (1-0.4)} = 0.375$$

which is well below the critical value of 10, enabling us to use the Carman–Kozeny equation. Thus from equation (2.50)

$$\frac{dP}{dl} = \frac{180 \times 0.89 \times 10^{-3} \times 0.01 \times (1-0.4)^2}{(20 \times 10^{-6})^2 \times 0.4^3} = 2.25 \times 10^7 \, \text{N m}^{-3}$$

The pressure drop ΔP is $2.25 \times 10^7 \times 0.005 = 1.13$ bar.

It is also instructive to consider gravity-driven flows, such as a fluid flowing vertically downwards through a filter. Here the fluid will be driven not only by any applied pressure gradient but also by its own weight. Thus we must modify the pressure gradient terms in equations (2.50) and (2.52) to $dP/dl + \rho g$.

EXAMPLE 2.7

Let us consider the flow of water through a sand filter consisting of a 50 mm thick layer of 400 μm spherical grains packed to a voidage of 0.4. If the depth of water above the bed is 15 cm, we can say that the pressure at the top of the bed will be $0.15 \times 1000 \times 9.81 = 1472 \, \text{N m}^{-2}$, and hence the pressure gradient will be $1472/0.05 = 29\,430 \, \text{N m}^{-3}$. Using the Ergun equation, (2.52), as we cannot be confident that the Reynolds number is below 10, we have

$$29\,430 + 1000 \times 9.81 = \frac{150 \times 0.89 \times 10^{-3} \times v \times (1-0.4)^2}{(400 \times 10^{-6})^2 \times 0.4^3}$$
$$+ \frac{1.75 \times 1000 \times v^2 \times (1-0.4)}{400 \times 10^{-6} \times 0.4^3}$$

or

$$39\,240 = 4\,693\,000 \, v + 41\,020\,000 \, v^2$$

from which we find that

$$v = 7.82 \times 10^{-3} \, \text{m s}^{-1}$$

The Reynolds number of the flow is

$$\frac{7.82 \times 10^{-3} \times 400 \times 10^{-6} \times 1000}{0.89 \times 10^{-3} \times (1-0.4)} = 5.86$$

showing that the use of the Ergun equation was unnecessarily complicated, and that it would have been sufficiently accurate to use the simpler Carman–Kozeny equation.

2.4   Dimensional analysis

2.4.1   Introduction

We noted in the previous sections that laminar flows in simple geometries can be analysed from first principles but that there is as yet no equally fundamental understanding of turbulent flow or of the processes of heat and mass transfer. Such topics must be investigated experimentally. The technique of dimensional analysis can be of the greatest help in minimizing the number of necessary experiments and in the determination of the most convenient and general presentation of the results. In particular, dimensional analysis permits us to deduce the behaviour of full-sized plant from tests on scale models.

2.4.2   Buckingham's theorem

The concept of dimensional analysis is based on the fact that the dimensions of all the terms in an equation must be the same. For example, distances are conventionally measured in miles and time in hours. Thus speed, which is calculated by dividing distance by time, must have the units of miles per hour. This principle of dimensional consistency is of the greatest value when considering scale-up and model tests, and consequently it is used widely throughout engineering science and is particularly useful in fluid mechanics. We should emphasize the difference between dimensional consistency, as discussed above, which is a physical requirement, and the use of consistent, preferably SI, units which is an arithmetical necessity.

First, we must decide what constitutes an independent dimension. This is a somewhat subjective matter but international convention recognizes seven independent dimensions of which **mass**, **length**, **time**, **temperature** and **quantity of material** are relevant to fluid mechanics and transfer processes. (The other two, electric current and luminous intensity, are of no interest in this context.) In the absence of heat and mass transfer, only mass, length and time are important and these will be denoted by M, L and T respectively. In the SI system, quantities with these dimensions are expressed with the units of kilograms, metres and seconds.

The need for dimensional consistency imposes as many constraints on the form of our equations as there are independent dimensions. This idea is formalized in Buckingham's theorem, which states that any relationship between M parameters, containing between them n independent dimensions, can be expressed in terms of $(M - n)$ dimensionless groups. This concept has similarities with the phase rule, which may be familiar from elementary chemistry.

We can illustrate the use of dimensional analysis by considering the force F exerted by a flowing stream on a sphere of diameter D. We can assume that the force on the sphere depends on the mean velocity of the fluid v_m

and the fluid properties, density ρ and viscosity μ as well as on its diameter. Thus

$$F = f\left(D, v_{\mathrm{m}}, \rho, \mu\right) \qquad (2.53)$$

The dimensions of these quantities are

$$
\begin{array}{ccccc}
F & D & v_{\mathrm{m}} & \rho & \mu \\[4pt]
\left(\dfrac{ML}{T^2}\right) & (L) & \left(\dfrac{L}{T}\right) & \left(\dfrac{M}{T^3}\right) & \left(\dfrac{M}{LT}\right)
\end{array}
$$

We see that three fundamental dimensions are involved: our five parameters can thus be expressed in terms of $(5 - 3) = 2$ dimensionless groups. There are many ways of obtaining these groups. Perhaps the most straightforward is to select two parameters of particular interest, F and μ say, and make these dimensionless by dividing by powers of the remaining parameters. Thus if we take $F/\rho^{\alpha}D^{\beta}v_{\mathrm{m}}^{\gamma}$, we can determine its dimensions as $(ML/T^2)(L^3/M)^{\alpha}(1/L)^{\beta}(T/L)^{\gamma}$. The whole group must be dimensionless and therefore we can equate the indices of each dimension to zero. Thus

$$\text{for } M \qquad 1 - \alpha = 0 \qquad\qquad\qquad (2.54)$$

$$\text{for } T \qquad -2 + \gamma = 0 \qquad\qquad\qquad (2.55)$$

$$\text{for } L \qquad 1 + 3\alpha - \beta - \gamma = 0 \qquad\qquad (2.56)$$

from which we find that $\alpha = 1$, $\gamma = 2$ and $\beta = 2$. Thus $F/\rho D^2 v_{\mathrm{m}}^2$ is dimensionless. This is a useful parameter, which is called the drag coefficient c_{D}. (Take care not to confuse the drag coefficient with the discharge coefficient defined in Example 2.1.)

Similarly $\mu/\rho D v_{\mathrm{m}}$ is dimensionless. However, this is the reciprocal of the familiar Reynolds number, which is traditionally used instead. Thus experimental data can be correlated in terms of c_{D} and Re. Confusingly, a constant of $8/\pi$ was inserted into the definition of the drag coefficient early in this century; it has been retained here to provide consistency with the classical results. Thus the drag coefficient and Reynolds numbers are usually defined by

$$c_{\mathrm{D}} = \frac{8F}{\pi \rho D^2 v_{\mathrm{m}}^2}$$

and

$$Re = \frac{v_{\mathrm{m}} D \rho}{\mu} \qquad (2.57)$$

These are clearly independent, as c_{D} is the only one to contain F and Re is the only one to contain μ.

We can therefore say that

$$c_D = f(Re) \qquad \text{only} \qquad (2.58)$$

This result is exact if equation (2.53) is a complete list of the relevant parameters. The compilation of such lists therefore requires some physical insight. The final result also demonstrates why it is important to select the dimensionless groups with care. As an alternative to the use of c_D and Re we could have used the groups $F/\rho D^2 v_m^2$ and $F\rho/\mu^2$. This is mathematically correct, but inconvenient if the objective is to predict the force, as F appears in both groups. However, the latter formulation is more convenient for the prediction of the velocity resulting from a specified force.

In the absence of any theoretical prediction of the drag on a sphere, a dimensionless formulation greatly simplifies experimental investigation and the resulting use of any data produced. Suppose we wanted to determine the dependence of the drag force on the other parameters (diameter, velocity, density and viscosity) experimentally. We would need to select about ten values of each and conduct a very large number of experiments. However, equation (2.58) shows that we need consider only one sphere and one fluid and conduct ten experiments at ten different velocities. It would, of course, be wise to perform one or two experiments with other fluids and another sphere just to confirm that our list of variables, equation (2.53), is complete. Such experiments have been performed many years ago and the set of equations

$$c_D = \frac{24}{Re}\left(1 + 0.15\, Re^{0.687}\right) \qquad Re < 1000$$
$$c_D = 0.44 \qquad 1000 < Re < 10^5$$
$$c_D = 0.1 \qquad Re < 10^5 \qquad (2.59)$$

has been found to be sufficiently accurate for most purposes. The experiments, however, show some inconsistent results for a range of Reynolds numbers close to 10^5, indicating that a parameter has been omitted from the list in equation (2.53). This turns out to be the surface roughness of the sphere, which makes a small difference to the values in the equations and a large difference in the critical Reynolds number for the sudden drop in c_D from 0.44 to 0.1. (This is why golf balls are dimpled. A well-struck golf ball will have a Reynolds number close to 10^5 and by roughening the surface the retarding force can be reduced by a factor of about 4, with obvious advantages.)

The Reynolds number is of particular interest in dimensional analysis as it controls the degree of turbulence and the flow pattern. It is usual to distinguish between **geometric similarity**, meaning of identical shape (that is, that ratios of lengths are the same) and **dynamic similarity** (ratios of forces are the same), which occurs at equal Reynolds numbers.

The same principles can be used to justify performing experiments on

scale models of any device of interest. We can illustrate this with the
following example.

EXAMPLE 2.8

Suppose we have designed a new type of a tubular air cooler of overall
length 8 m in which we intend to process $0.6\,m^3\,s^{-1}$ of air. Before building
it, let us make a $\frac{1}{10}$th scale model out of Perspex and use water to study the
flow pattern. At the same time we can measure the pressure drop and
hence predict the pressure drop that will occur in the full-size cooler.

The pressure drop ΔP will depend on the volumetric flowrate w_L, the
length L and the fluid properties μ and ρ:

$$\Delta P = f(w_L, L, \mu, \rho) \tag{2.60}$$

We have five parameters and three dimensions giving two independent
dimensionless groups. We cannot define a conventional Reynolds number
as we know neither the diameter nor the velocity, but $w_L \rho / \mu L$ is dimensionless (the flow coefficient) and serves the same purpose. The other group
must contain ΔP and, selecting ρ to eliminate the mass dimension, we find
that $\Delta P / \rho$ has dimensions $(M/LT^2)(L^3/M) = L^2/T^2$, which are the dimensions
of w_L^2/L^4.

Thus $\Delta P L^4 / \rho w_L^2$ is dimensionless (the pressure coefficient) and therefore

$$\frac{\Delta P L^4}{\rho w_L^2} = f\left(\frac{w_L \rho}{\mu L}\right) \tag{2.61}$$

is an acceptable (but not the only) way of correlating the results.

Suppose that tests on the model give the following results:

w_L (l s^{-1})	1.0	2.0	4.0	6.0	8.0
ΔP (bar)	0.031	0.088	0.250	0.460	0.707

The properties of the two fluids are

Air $\rho = 1.29\,kg\,m^{-3}$ $\mu = 1.71 \times 10^{-5}\,N\,s\,m^{-2}$
Water $\rho = 1000\,kg\,m^{-3}$ $\mu = 0.89 \times 10^{-3}\,N\,s\,m^{-2}$

From these values we can calculate

$$\frac{w_L \rho}{\mu L} = \frac{1000 w_L}{0.89 \times 10^{-3} \times 0.8} = 1404 \times 10^3 w_L$$

$$\frac{\Delta P L^4}{\rho w_L^2} = \frac{\Delta P \times 0.8^4}{1000 w_L^2} = 4.096 \times 10^{-4} \Delta P / w_L^2$$

giving the following values:

$\dfrac{w_L\rho}{\mu L}$	1404	2808	5618	8427	11236
$\dfrac{\Delta PL^4}{\rho w_L^2}$	1.270	0.901	0.640	0.532	0.452×10^6

These dimensionless results are plotted in Fig. 2.12. They apply generally to all coolers of this design irrespective of size and for all fluids, unlike the raw data above, which are specific for one cooler and one fluid.

The full-size cooler is geometrically similar to the model. It operates with a value of

$$\frac{w_L\rho}{\mu L} = \frac{1.29 \times 0.6}{1.71 \times 10^{-5} \times 8.0} = 5658$$

From the graph the value of $\Delta PL^4/\rho w_L^2$ corresponding to this value of $w_L\rho/\mu L$ is seen to be 0.638×10^6, so that the value of the pressure drop in the full-size cooler is given by

$$\Delta P = \frac{0.638 \times 10^6 \times 1.29 \times 0.6^2}{8.0^4} = 72.3 \, \text{Nm}^{-2}$$

The method we have used above was for demonstration purposes. However, it involved an unnecessary amount of arithmetic, as we have calculated several points on the graph but only used one value. We could have saved arithmetic by saying

$$\text{If}\left(\frac{w_L\rho}{\mu L}\right)_{FS} = \left(\frac{w_L\rho}{\mu L}\right)_M, \quad \text{then} \left(\frac{\Delta PL^4}{\rho w_L^2}\right)_{FS} = \left(\frac{\Delta PL^4}{\rho w_L^2}\right)_M$$

where the subscripts FS and M refer to the full-size and model respectively. Thus the 'equivalent flowrate' in the model, w_{LM}, is given by

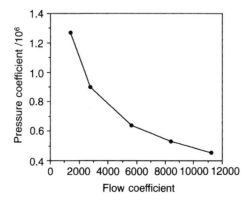

Fig. 2.12 Example 2.8: plot of dimensionless pressure coefficient versus flow coefficient.

$$W_{LM} = W_{LFS}\left(\frac{\rho_{FS}L_M\mu_M}{\rho_M L_{FS}\mu_{FS}}\right)$$

$$= 0.6 \times \frac{1.29}{1000} \times \frac{1}{10} \times \frac{0.89 \times 10^{-3}}{1.71 \times 10^{-5}} = 4.028 \times 10^{-3}\,\text{m}^3\,\text{s}^{-1}$$

This is the only flow through the model that gives us any information about the behaviour of the full-sized cooler when operating at $0.6\,\text{m}^3\text{s}^{-1}$, as it is necessary that we have dynamic similarity, i.e. equality of Reynolds numbers.

By interpolating from the original table we find that the 'equivalent pressure drop' in the model $\Delta P_M = 0.252$ bar. But, since we have equated our Reynolds numbers, the other group must remain unchanged, and therefore

$$\left(\frac{\Delta PL^4}{\rho W_L^2}\right)_{FS} = \left(\frac{\Delta PL^4}{\rho W_L^2}\right)_M$$

Hence the pressure drop in the full-sized cooler is given by

$$\Delta P_{FS} = \Delta P_M \left(\frac{L_M}{L_{FS}}\right)^4 \frac{\rho_{FS}}{\rho_M}\left(\frac{W_{LFS}}{W_{LM}}\right)^2$$

$$= 0.252 \times 10^5 \times \left(\frac{1}{10}\right)^4 \times \frac{1.29}{1000} \times \left(\frac{0.6}{4.028 \times 10^{-3}}\right)^2$$

$$= 72.3\,\text{Nm}^{-2} \text{ as before}$$

The same principles can be used for a great variety of problems. Not only can they be used for the interpretation of model tests, but many correlations are most conveniently expressed in dimensionless form. This is particularly so in the study of heat and mass transfer, as will be evident in later chapters. Indeed, it is generally accepted that all valid correlations must be capable of being expressed in dimensionless form. The appearance of any experimentally determined dimensional constant in a correlation is usually taken to be proof that some parameter of importance has been neglected. This principle can usefully be applied when studying published work. In some cases dimensionality may turn out to result from a parameter, such as the acceleration due to gravity, which cannot readily be varied. For example, it would be perfectly possible to correlate the velocity v of a falling mass with the distance h through which the mass has fallen, using the correlation $v = 3.13\sqrt{h}$. The constant 3.13 has the dimensions $L^{1/2}/T$ and therefore cannot be universal. Elementary mechanics tells us that $v = \sqrt{2gh}$. The constant 2 is dimensionless and universal. The first form of the correlation is valid only on Earth, whereas the dimensionally correct form would be valid on all planets.

EXAMPLE 2.9

Let us evaluate the terminal velocity of a sphere of diameter 5 mm and density 1020 kg m^{-3} falling through a liquid of density 1000 kg m^{-3} and viscosity 0.015 N s m^{-2} (a pea in a thickish soup!). At the terminal velocity the drag force F must equal the weight minus the Archimedean upthrust:

$$F = \frac{\pi}{6}D^3(\rho_s - \rho_f)g$$

and hence the drag coefficient is given by

$$C_D = \frac{4D(\rho_s - \rho_f)g}{3\rho_f v^2} \qquad (2.62)$$

Assuming that the Reynolds number is less than 1000, we can use the first part of the correlation (2.59):

$$C_D = \frac{24}{Re}(1 + 0.15Re^{0.687}) \qquad (2.63)$$

This pair of equations is inconvenient for solution as we do not yet know the velocity v. They are put in more convenient form by multiplying both sides of equation (2.63) by Re^2, giving

$$24Re(1 + 0.15Re^{0.687}) = C_D Re^2$$

$$= \frac{4D(\rho_s - \rho_f)g}{3\rho_f v^2}\left(\frac{\rho_f Dv}{\mu}\right)^2 = \frac{4D^3(\rho_s - \rho_f)\rho_f g}{3\mu^2}$$

$$= \frac{4 \times 0.005^3 \times (1020 - 1000) \times 1000 \times 9.81}{3 \times 0.015^2}$$

i.e.

$$24Re(1 + 0.15Re^{0.687}) = 145.33$$

which has solution $Re = 4.30$. Hence the terminal velocity is given by

$$4.30 \times \frac{0.015}{0.005 \times 1000} = 0.0129 \, m s^{-1}$$

This sort of settling velocity is found in the two-phase solid–liquid food mixtures studied in Chapter 8.

2.5 Turbulent flow

2.5.1 Introduction

The theory of turbulent flow is not yet sufficiently advanced for purely theoretical prediction to be possible and we must resort to correlations of experimental results, using the techniques of dimensional analysis, as outlined in section 2.4. However, for many aspects of turbulent pipe flow, the experiments have been carried out sufficiently often and with sufficient care that the resulting correlations may be considered to be more precise than is normally required in practical situations. The results can be used to predict pressure drops and flow velocities in realistic situations.

2.5.2   The friction factor c_f

A force balance on the full diameter D of an elementary length δl of horizontal pipe gives

$$\frac{\pi}{4} D^2 \delta P = \pi D \delta l \tau_w \qquad (2.64)$$

or

$$\tau_w = \frac{D}{4} \frac{dP}{dl} \qquad (2.65)$$

where τ_w is the wall shear stress, D is the pipe diameter and dP/dl is the pressure gradient. This result is seen to be equivalent to equation (2.44). Thus when correlating the frictional effects of a flow we can consider either τ_w or dP/dl. Traditionally the former is used, and we can say by inspection that the wall shear stress depends on the pipe diameter, the mean velocity v_m and the fluid properties ρ and μ. Thus

$$\tau_w = f(D, v_m, \rho, \mu) \qquad (2.66)$$

There five parameters contain between them three dimensions and, following the arguments of section 2.4.2, can be expressed in terms of two independent dimensionless groups. The two usually chosen are the Reynolds number Re defined by

$$Re = \frac{D v_m \rho}{\mu} \qquad (2.67)$$

and the friction factor c_f, which was introduced in section 2.3.2 and defined by equation (2.48):

$$c_f = \frac{\tau_w}{\frac{1}{2} \rho v_m^2} \qquad (2.68)$$

This is sometimes known as **Fanning's friction factor**. The appearance of the factor of $\frac{1}{2}$ in the definition of the friction factor is due to misconceptions in the past, but needs to be retained to maintain consistency with published correlations.

The experimentally determined dependence of the friction factor on the Reynolds number for a smooth-walled tube is shown in Fig. 2.13; logarith-

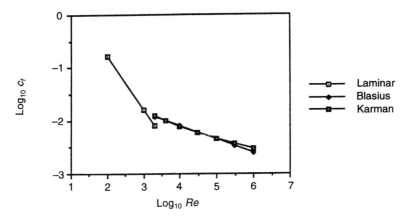

Fig. 2.13 Friction factor plotted against Reynolds number.

mic axes have been used in view of the wide range in the values of the Reynolds number. It is seen that there are two sections to the line, one for laminar flow at Reynolds numbers less than about 2000 and one for turbulent flow at greater Reynolds numbers. The effect of wall roughness is considered in section 2.5.4 below.

The theoretical prediction for laminar pipe flow, equation (2.37), can be rearranged to give

$$c_f = \frac{16}{Re} \qquad (2.69)$$

This equation is exact for a Newtonian fluid, being derived from the definition of viscosity and geometrical arguments only.

For turbulent flow in a smooth-walled pipe, the experimental results lie on a gentle curve. However, for the range of Reynolds numbers normally encountered, it is sufficiently accurate to draw a best-fit straight line that has the form

$$c_f = 0.079 \, Re^{-1/4} \qquad (2.70)$$

and which is shown in Fig. 2.13. This equation is known as the **Blasius correlation** and is accurate to ±5% over the range $3000 < Re < 10^5$. For greater values of the Reynolds number the Karman–Nikuradse formula

$$\sqrt{\frac{1}{c_f}} = 1.74 \, \ln\!\left(Re\sqrt{c_f}\right) - 0.40 \qquad (2.71)$$

is more accurate but this is clearly of much less convenient algebraic form than the Blasius expression.

It can be seen from Fig. 2.13 that in turbulent flow the friction factor normally lies in the narrow range $0.003 < c_f < 0.007$. Thus in the absence of more detailed information a rough guess of $c_f = 0.005$ is often sufficiently accurate for the prediction of pressure drops.

2.5.3   Fanning's friction formula

The flow in a pipe can be driven either by pressure difference or by change in elevation or by both. It is therefore more convenient to work in terms of loss of head as defined below. In a horizontal pipe the loss of head ΔH in a pipe of length L can be related to the pressure loss and pressure gradient by

$$\Delta H = \frac{\Delta P}{\rho g} = -\frac{1}{\rho g}\frac{dP}{dl}L \tag{2.72}$$

but if the pipe is inclined, allowance must be made for gravitational effects as in section 2.3.3. Thus it is appropriate to define the loss of head as

$$\Delta H = \frac{\Delta P}{\rho g} + \Delta h \tag{2.73}$$

where Δh is the decrease in elevation along the pipe: that is, the height of the pipe entry minus the height of the pipe exit. It is seen that, in this formulation, height and pressure are combined in exactly the same way as in Bernoulli's equation.

From equations (2.65), (2.68) and (2.73) we have

$$\Delta H = \frac{\Delta P}{\rho g} + \Delta h = \frac{4c_f v_m^2 L}{2gD} \tag{2.74}$$

This result is known as **Fanning's friction formula**.

As the velocity appears in this equation only as v_m^2, it seems that the head loss is independent of the sign of v_m. This is clearly incorrect as, if the flow were reversed, the sign of the head loss would be changed. Usually, however, the direction of the velocity is known and the sign of ΔH can be deduced by inspection.

We can illustrate the results of this section with a pair of examples.

EXAMPLE 2.10

Evaluate the pressure difference required to deliver $0.5 \, \text{ls}^{-1}$, i.e. $0.5 \times 10^{-3} \, \text{m}^3\text{s}^{-1}$ of water through $100 \, \text{m}$ of $25 \, \text{mm}$ diameter pipe to a tank $4 \, \text{m}$ above the supply tank. The density and viscosity of water may be taken to be $1000 \, \text{kg} \, \text{m}^{-3}$ and $0.89 \times 10^{-3} \, \text{N} \, \text{s} \, \text{m}^{-2}$.

The mean velocity is given by

$$v_m = \frac{4w_L}{\pi D^2} = \frac{4 \times 0.5 \times 10^{-3}}{\pi \times 0.025^2} = 1.019 \text{ m s}^{-1}$$

and the Reynolds number by

$$Re = \frac{v_m D \rho}{\mu} = \frac{1.019 \times 0.025 \times 1000}{0.89 \times 10^{-3}} = 28\,624$$

As this value lies in the range in which the Blasius expression holds we have

$$c_f = 0.079 Re^{-1/4} = 0.079 \times (28\,624)^{-1/4} = 0.00607$$

Thus from equation (2.74):

$$\Delta H = \frac{4 \times 0.00607 \times 1.019^2 \times 100}{2 \times 9.81 \times 0.025} = 5.14\,m$$

Recalling that we have an **increase** in elevation of 4 m so that $\Delta h = -4$, we have from equation (2.73)

$$\Delta P = (5.14 + 4) \times 1000 \times 9.81 = 0.897\,bar$$

The converse problem, of evaluating the flowrate from a known value of the pressure drop, results in marginally more difficult arithmetic, as illustrated below.

EXAMPLE 2.11

Find the flowrate of water through 230 m of 50 mm diameter pipe under the influence of a pressure drop of 0.6 bar.

The difficulty here is that we cannot as yet evaluate the friction factor. However, from the Blasius expression we can say

$$c_f = 0.079 \times \left(\frac{1000 \times 0.050 v_m}{0.89 \times 10^{-3}} \right)^{-1/4} = 0.00513\, v_m^{-1/4}$$

Thus, from Fanning's equation:

$$\frac{0.6 \times 10^5}{1000 \times 9.81} = \frac{4 \times 0.00513 v_m^{-1/4} v_m^2 \times 230}{2 \times 9.81 \times 0.05}$$

or

$$v_m^{7/4} = 1.271 \qquad \text{i.e.} \qquad v_m = 1.15\,ms^{-1}$$

The flowrate w_L is given by

$$w_L = \frac{\pi}{4} \times 0.05^2 \times 1.15 = 2.26\,ls^{-1}$$

It is important at this stage to check that the Reynolds number lies in the range for which the Blasius expression is valid.

From equation (2.67):

$$Re = \frac{0.05 \times 1.15 \times 1000}{0.89 \times 10^{-3}} = 6.5 \times 10^4$$

which is within the Blasius range, and therefore the calculation is appropriate.

2.5.4 Rough and non-circular ducts

The Blasius and Karman–Nikuradse formulae apply only for ducts with smooth walls. In reality, no wall is perfectly smooth, although many commercial pipes are sufficiently smooth for the Blasius expression to apply. This is a particular problem in the food industry, because of the frequent occurrence of fouling. Immediately after cleaning, a pipe will have a low value of the friction factor, but this will gradually increase during operation until the next cleaning phase occurs.

In general, the surface roughness can be characterized in terms of an experimentally determined quantity known as the **equivalent roughness size**, e. This is a measure of the average size of the irregularities on the tube wall, and the dependence of the friction factor on the roughness is given by the empirical Colebrook formula:

$$\frac{1}{\sqrt{c_f}} = 3.46 - 1.74 \ln\left(\frac{2e}{D} + \frac{9.33}{Re\sqrt{c_f}}\right) \tag{2.75}$$

Typical values of the roughness size for clean drawn tubing and commercial steel are 2×10^{-6} m and 5×10^{-5} m respectively, but it is very difficult to predict the effect of fouling on these values except by careful observation of similar situations.

As the Reynolds number increases, the last term in the Colebrook equation becomes progressively smaller, and the friction factor tends to an asymptote given by

$$\frac{1}{\sqrt{c_f}} = 3.46 - 1.74 \ln\left(\frac{2e}{D}\right) \tag{2.76}$$

Because of the awkward form of the Colebrook equation it is recommended that calculations are performed using either the Blasius expression or equation (2.76), and that the Colebrook equation (2.75) is then used to check that the assumptions are reasonable or to make minor adjustments to the friction factor.

For ducts of non-circular cross-section, the basic equations derived above can be used, at least in the turbulent flow regime, if the diameter D is replaced by the **hydraulic mean diameter** D_H defined by

$$D_H = \frac{4A}{P} \tag{2.77}$$

where A is the cross-sectional area of the duct and P is the wetted perimeter; that is, the length of the perimeter in contact with the flowing fluid. In this form the concept is applicable also to open channels, in which case the free top surface of the liquid is not included when evaluating the wetted perimeter. For a circular pipe, $A = \pi D^2/4$ and $P = \pi D$ and therefore from equation (2.77) we find that the hydraulic mean diameter is equal to the actual diameter. For a duct of square cross-section, the hydraulic mean diameter equals the length of the side.

Some authors use the **hydraulic mean radius** R_H defined as A/P. This is a confusing parameter! It is seen that the hydraulic mean radius is a **quarter** of the hydraulic mean diameter and, furthermore, for a circular pipe the hydraulic mean radius is not equal to the actual radius. The hydraulic mean radius should therefore be used with caution.

EXAMPLE 2.12

A pipe of length 100 m and diameter 150 mm has a height difference of 2 m between its ends. Evaluate the flow of water when it is running half full.

When half full the wetted perimeter P is $\pi D/2 = 0.2356$ m and the cross-sectional area A is $\pi D^2/8 = 0.00884$ m^2. The hydraulic mean diameter is $4A/P = 0.150$ m, i.e. the same as the diameter. The friction factor is therefore given by equation (2.70) as $0.079 \times (0.89 \times 10^{-3}/0.150 \times 1000 \times v_m)^{1/4} = 3.90 \times 10^{-3} v_m^{-1/4}$. Hence, from equation (2.74):

$$0 + 2.0 = \frac{4 \times 3.90 \times 10^{-3} \times v_m^{7/4} \times 100}{2 \times 9.81 \times 0.150}$$

i.e. $v_m = 2.14$ m s^{-1}. The volumetric flowrate is the product $Av_m = 0.00884 \times 2.14 = 0.0189$ m^3 s^{-1}.

These results can be contrasted with those for a semicircular pipe of the same dimensions. A will be unchanged but P will be $\pi D/2 + D = 0.3856$ m and hence $D_H = 4 \times 0.00884/0.3856 = 0.0917$ m. The friction factor will be

$$0.079 \times \left(\frac{0.89 \times 10^{-3}}{0.0917 \times 1000 \times v_m}\right)^{1/4} = 4.41 \times 10^{-3} \, v_m^{-1/4}$$

and hence the velocity is given by

$$0 + 2.0 = \frac{4 \times 4.41 \times 10^{-3} \times v_m^{7/4} \times 100}{2 \times 9.81 \times 0.0917}$$

i.e. $v_m = 1.50$ m s^{-1} and $w_L = 0.0133$ m^3 s^{-1}. The reduced flowrate results from the increased drag provided by the top surface of the semi-circular pipe.

2.5.5 *Pressure losses in bends and pipe fittings*

It is rare for pipework to be straight and free from fittings such as valves or sudden expansions and contractions. There will be pressure losses in all these items due to the formation of turbulent eddies. The example of an orifice plate has already been considered in Example 2.2, and many other situations can be analysed in a similar manner. Clearly, these losses must be taken into account when predicting the flow through the system.

As shown in Example 2.2, the pressure loss in a sudden pipe expansion or contraction is generally found to be proportional to the square of the flowrate. Although this result was derived for ideal flow, it applies equally well when the flow is turbulent: that is, at high Reynolds numbers. Thus for any given fitting we can express the head loss as some multiple of the velocity head, $v^2/2g$. Typical values for the number of velocity heads lost in various fittings are given in the first column of Table 2.1. In addition we must remember that as a fluid enters a pipe from a large reservoir it will gain kinetic energy and there will be a corresponding reduction in the head of $v^2/2g$. Thus people often refer to an entry loss of one velocity head. (Strictly this is not a loss, as in principle the head could be recovered by fitting a diffuser. More pedantic authors refer to this as the 'unrecovered kinetic energy at exit'.)

Taking an approximate value for the friction factor of 0.005, we can see from equation (2.73) that the head lost in a pipe of length L is given by

$$\Delta H = \frac{4 \times 0.005 \times v_{\mathrm{m}}^2 \times L}{2 \times g \times D} = \frac{0.02L}{D} \frac{v_{\mathrm{m}}^2}{2g}$$

Thus there is a loss of one velocity head in a pipe of length $50\,D$. Hence the list of velocity heads lost given in Table 2.1 can also be expressed in terms

Table 2.1

	Number of velocity heads lost	Equivalent pipe length
90° standard bend	0.75	$38\,D$
90° large radius bend	0.45	$23\,D$
90° square or mitre bend	1.3	$65\,D$
T-junction		
straight through	0.4	$20\,D$
to or from side branch	1.0	$50\,D$
Gate valve		
open	0.17	$9\,D$
$\frac{3}{4}$ open	0.9	$45\,D$
$\frac{1}{2}$ open	4.5	$225\,D$
$\frac{1}{4}$ open	24.0	$1200\,D$
Swing check valve	2.0	$100\,D$

of an equivalent length of pipe. The use of these two alternative formulations will be illustrated in the problem below.

EXAMPLE 2.13

A typical domestic water supply consists of 20 m of 1.0 cm diameter pipe containing eight right-angled bends and a $\frac{3}{4}$ open gate valve. The water is supplied from a tank 8.0 m above the discharge point. Find the discharge rate.

Method of equivalent pipe lengths

The equivalent pipe length can be evaluated as follows:

Actual	20 m
Bends 8 × 38 D = 8 × 38 × 0.01	3.04 m
Valve 45 D = 45 × 0.01	0.45 m
Entry loss 50 D = 50 × 0.01	0.50 m
Total	23.99 m

Using equations (2.73) and (2.70) we have

$$8.0 = 4 \times 0.079 \left(\frac{0.89 \times 10^{-3}}{1000 \times v_m \times 0.01} \right)^{1/4} \frac{v_m^2 \times 23.99}{2 \times 9.81 \times 0.01}$$

which on rearranging becomes

$$v_m^{7/4} = 2.132 \quad \text{or} \quad v_m = 1.541 \, \text{m s}^{-1}$$

Thus the volumetric flowrate is given by

$$w_L = \frac{\pi}{4} \times 0.01^2 \times 1.541 = 0.121 \, \text{l s}^{-1}$$

We can evaluate the Reynolds number at this flowrate and use the Blasius expression to find the friction factor. This turns out to be 0.0069, which differs from the value of 0.005 assumed in the evaluation of the equivalent pipe lengths given in Table 2.1. Thus this method is inconsistent and its accuracy suspect. It is, however, very simple and can be recommended whenever great accuracy is not required. A better estimate can be obtained from the use of the tabulation of velocity heads as illustrated below.

Method of velocity heads

From Table 2.1 we see that we have a loss of 8 × 0.75 velocity heads in the bends, 0.9 in the valve and 1 at inlet, giving a total of 7.9 in addition to the frictional loss in the pipe.

Thus the lost head can be expressed by

$$\Delta H = \frac{4c_f v_m^2 L}{2gD} + 7.9 \frac{v_m^2}{2g} \tag{2.78}$$

Putting in the values for this problem, we find that

$$8.0 = (8000c_f + 7.9) \frac{v_m^2}{2g} \tag{2.79}$$

Difficulties arise in the solution of this equation, as we cannot evaluate the friction factor until the velocity and hence the Reynolds number is known. The equation can be solved iteratively by

1. guessing a value for the friction factor;
2. substituting it into equation (2.79), evaluating the velocity and hence the Reynolds number; and
3. determining a better value for the friction factor.

This cycle can be repeated until convergence is achieved.

A value of 0.005 is always a good initial estimate for c_f. Thus

$$8.0 = (8000 \times 0.005 + 7.9) \frac{v_m^2}{2g}$$

from which we find that $v_m = 1.81 \text{ m s}^{-1}$. We can now re-evaluate the friction factor using equation (2.70):

$$c_f = 0.079 \times \left(\frac{1.81 \times 0.01 \times 1000}{0.89 \times 10^{-3}} \right)^{-1/4} = 0.00662$$

Inserting this value into equation (2.79) gives $v_m = 1.61 \text{ m s}^{-1}$, and reusing equation (2.70) gives $c_f = 0.00681$. This iteration can be repeated indefinitely and yields the following sequence of values for the velocity:

Iteration number	Velocity (m s^{-1})	Change in velocity (m s^{-1})
1	1.81	–
2	1.61	0.2
3	1.586	0.024
4	1.583	0.003

It can be seen that convergence is rapid, with each iteration making a change of about a tenth of the previous change. Thus an answer correct to about 1% can be obtained by the end of the third iteration, and further refinement is not warranted in view of the likely uncertainties in the data.

The value of 1.58 m s^{-1} differs only slightly from the previous estimate of

1.54 m s^{-1}. However, it is to be preferred as the concept of a lost velocity head has more generality than the concept of an equivalent pipe length.

2.5.6 The one-seventh power law

The velocity distribution in turbulent pipe flow is adequately described by the following empirical expression, which is known as the **one-seventh power law**:

$$v = v_1 \left(\frac{y}{R} \right)^{1/7} \tag{2.80}$$

where v is the velocity at a distance y from the wall, R is the pipe radius and v_1 is the centreline velocity. This expression is found to be appropriate over the same range of Reynolds numbers as the Blasius equation and indeed the indices in these expressions can be derived from each other.

The mean velocity v_m can be evaluated as follows:

$$\pi R^2 v_m = \int_0^R 2\pi r v \, dr = \int_0^R 2\pi (R - y) v_1 \left(\frac{y}{R} \right)^{1/7} dy \tag{2.81}$$

from which it follows that $v_m = \frac{49}{60} v_1$ or

$$v_1 = 1.22 v_m \tag{2.82}$$

The one-seventh power law has one major deficiency, in that it predicts an infinite velocity gradient at the wall. This can be seen by differentiating equation (2.80) to give

$$\frac{dv}{dy} = \frac{v_1}{7} R^{-1/7} y^{-6/7}$$

which gives $dv/dy = \infty$ when $y = 0$. This means that equation (2.80) cannot apply right up to the wall. However, it is found experimentally that turbulence is suppressed very close to a solid boundary and that a narrow laminar layer occurs between the wall and the turbulent core. This layer is known either as the viscous sublayer or the laminar sublayer and is of vital importance in the understanding of heat and mass transfer, as will become apparent in later chapters.

Within the laminar sublayer we can assume that the shear stress τ is given by

$$\tau = \mu \frac{dv}{dy} \tag{2.83}$$

provided the fluid is Newtonian. As the layer is thin and close to the wall we have that

$$v = \tau_w \frac{y}{\mu} \tag{2.84}$$

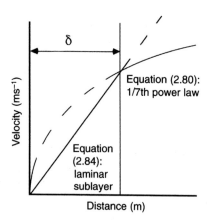

Fig. 2.14 The one-seventh power law, showing a laminar sublayer of thickness δ.

Equations (2.80) and (2.84) are sketched in Fig. 2.14 with the recommended profile being shown by the solid line. The evaluation of the thickness δ of the laminar sublayer is illustrated in the following example.

EXAMPLE 2.14

Find the laminar sublayer thickness for water flowing at a mean velocity of 1.5 m s⁻¹ in a 2.0 cm diameter tube. The density and viscosity of water may be taken as 1000 kg m⁻³ and 0.89 × 10⁻³ N s m⁻².

The Reynolds number is given by

$$Re = \frac{1.5 \times 0.02 \times 1000}{0.89 \times 10^{-3}} = 33\,700$$

This lies within the range for which the Blasius expression is applicable, and we can therefore evaluate the friction factor as

$$c_f = 0.079 \times (33\,700)^{-1/4} = 0.00583$$

Thus, from the definition of the friction factor, the wall shear stress is

$$\tau_w = \frac{1}{2} \times 1000 \times 1.5^2 \times 0.00583 = 6.56\,\text{N m}^{-2}$$

From equation (2.84) the velocity profile in the laminar sublayer is given by

$$v = \frac{\tau_w y}{\mu} = \frac{6.56}{0.89 \times 10^{-3}} y = 7370y \qquad (2.85)$$

The centreline velocity of the water in the tube is given by equation (2.82):

$$v_1 = 1.22 \times 1.5 = 1.83\,\mathrm{m\,s^{-1}}$$

and thus from the one-seventh power law, equation (2.80), the velocity profile in the turbulent core is given by

$$v = 1.83\left(\frac{y}{0.01}\right)^{1/7} = 3.53y^{1/7} \qquad (2.86)$$

Equations (2.85) and (2.86) intersect at the edge of the laminar sublayer. The velocity predicted at that point must be the same for both equations. Hence the laminar sublayer thickness δ is given by eliminating v from these two equations:

$$3.53\ \delta^{1/7} = 7370\ \delta$$

from which we find that $\delta = 0.134\,\mathrm{mm}$.

It is noteworthy that the thickness of the laminar sublayer is of the order of 0.1 mm, a hundredth of the tube diameter. Thus the one-seventh power law is applicable for all but a very small fraction of the cross-section of the tube. It might therefore be thought that this parameter can be neglected. However, despite its very small thickness, the laminar sublayer plays a dominant role in heat and mass transfer, as will be discussed in Chapters 3 and 4. This is because it provides a zone across which heat and mass must be transferred by conduction or diffusion, both of which are molecular processes and therefore slow. Thus it provides a barrier between the wall and the effectively well-mixed turbulent core.

Conclusions

This chapter has introduced some of the basic ideas of fluid mechanics in order to help you understand how fluids move when they are pumped around or interact with solid particles (such as in a spray drier). Like the first chapter, the emphasis here has been to establish some essential principles and to show how these can be used. As noted in the introduction, many fluids – particularly liquids – in the food industry are viscous and non-Newtonian. Despite this, analysis based on ideal (non-viscous) and Newtonian (i.e. constant viscosity) fluids can be extremely useful, and this chapter is confined to such situations. You should understand the differences between an ideal and a real fluid, and appreciate how ideal fluids can often serve as a reasonable first basis for understanding the relations between flow and pressure, as well as explaining the principles of some common flow measurement techniques.

You should also understand: the differences between laminar and turbulent flows; how, for Newtonian fluids, the Reynolds number provides a basis for discriminating between them; the profound implications of the flow regimes for velocity profiles and for flow/pressure drop relationships. You should also understand the importance of dimensional analysis in handling complex problems and how, with proper scaling, results can be extrapolated. Two typical operations are used as the basis for most of the presentation here. The first is the ubiquitous operation of pumping through pipes, where our emphasis is on ways of calculating the pressure (or head) requirements for a particular flow. The second covers some processes where the fluid either interacts with particles or flows through beds or porous filters.

Once again, this chapter can only scratch the surface of a huge field. Chapters 3 and 4, which deal with the processes of heat and mass transfer, will be found to rely on some of the principles and ideas developed here. Chapter 5 extends the discussion to more realistic fluid materials, in particular ones where the Newtonian assumption is not valid. Some ideas for further reading are listed below.

Further reading

There are many basic texts on engineering fluid mechanics which descibe the material in this chapter in greater detail. A selection is listed below, although any good technical bookshop or library will contain many more.

Coulson, J.M. and Richardson, J.F. (1977) *Chemical Engineering*, Volume 1, Pergamon, London.
Kay, J.M. and Nedderman, R.M. (1985) *Fluid Mechanics and Transport Processes*, Cambridge University Press, Cambridge.
Tritton, D.J. (1988) *Physical Fluid Dynamics*, 2nd edn, Chapman & Hall, London.

3 Introduction to heat transfer

A.N. HAYHURST

Introduction

The importance of heat transfer in food processing is obvious; the changes in food safety and palatability on heating are so marked that many food processes are built around heat transfer. The physical principles which underlie these processes are introduced here. Two modes of heat transfer are discussed: thermal conduction through a stationary medium, and thermal convection through a moving fluid. In the latter case, mixing of hot and cold fluids is the main mechanism of heat transfer, which is usually more rapid than thermal conduction.

Heat transfer operations are usually carried out within some type of specifically designed heat exchanger, such as shell-and-tube or plate exchangers. These units must be designed using equations which predict the heat transfer rate. Some of these equations will use the dimensionless form introduced in Chapter 2; they aim to predict the heat transfer coefficient which relates the heat flux in a given situation to the temperature difference. Various equations are given here to illustrate simple models for heat transfer and to allow simple design calculations to be made. The rate of heat transfer can be related to the power input to the system and thus to the pressure drop through it; models will be developed to take account of these factors.

It is very rare that a single heat transfer process governs the heating of a food material: usually heating or cooling occurs as a result of a combination of processes. For example, in canning, steam condensing on the outside of the can gives rapid heat transfer; but the heat must then be conducted slowly into the food. The slowest process will control the overall heat transfer rate, and identification of this process can simplify the design of process plant. For example, the slowest process in the cooling of solids is usually that of conduction of heat within the solid, so there is no point in enhancing heat transfer between the outside of the solids and its surroundings, beyond the point where it is no longer critical. This key point is often missed in industrial practice. This chapter develops two ways of analysing the problem: first, equations for calculating the overall combined effect of sequential heat

Chemical Engineering for the Food Industry. Edited by P.J. Fryer, D.L. Pyle and C.D. Rielly. Published in 1997 by Blackie A & P, an imprint of Chapman & Hall, London. ISBN 0 412 49500 7

transfer resistances are developed, and secondly, a dimensionless group which shows the relative significance of internal and external heat transfer is derived. These principles are developed further in Chapter 9.

3.1 Heat conduction

3.1.1 Fourier's law

The importance of heat transfer to food processing requires no emphasis when both heating and chilling are such common operations. In addition, freezing and sterilization are operations involving heat transfer. Initially we shall consider the transfer of heat solely by conduction. Inevitably, heat conduction occurs from some hot region of space to some colder neighbouring part. The physical law governing heat conduction within a solid or a stationary fluid is most easily expressed by considering a long, thin metal rod, as depicted in Fig. 3.1. In this one-dimensional situation, position is characterized by the distance x from the left-hand end of the rod. Suppose we begin with the left-hand end relatively hot, so that temperature varies along the rod as shown in Fig. 3.1. This is for an initial time, $t = 0$. If the rod is left for an infinite time ($t = \infty$), a uniform temperature profile (shown by the broken line) will be reached. In general, the rate at which heat flows past any plane along the rod is found to be proportional to the local temperature gradient (dT/dx). This leads to **Fourier's law**:

$$q = -\lambda \frac{dT}{dx} \qquad (3.1)$$

where q is the rate at which heat flows through unit area per unit time; its units are $Jm^{-2}s^{-1}$ or Wm^{-2} (i.e. those of a heat flux); dT/dx is the local 'driving force' for heat transfer (units Km^{-1}); and λ is a constant of proportionality, called the **thermal conductivity**, with units $Wm^{-1}K^{-1}$.

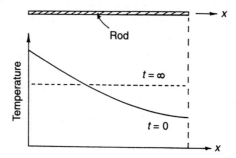

Fig. 3.1 Initial and final temperature in a long heat-conducting rod.

Table 3.1 Values of thermal conductivity, λ, at 20 °C

Substance	λ $(\mathrm{W\,m^{-1}K^{-1}})$	Substance	λ $(\mathrm{W\,m^{-1}K^{-1}})$
Silver	41	Mercury	8.8
Copper	386	Water	0.60
Aluminium	200	Ethanol	0.18
Iron	73	Olive oil	0.17
Stainless steel	~42	Benzene	0.15
Ice	2.0	Toluene	0.15
Glass (window)	0.8	Hexane	0.12
Brick (masonry)	~0.7	CCl_2F_2	0.07
Wood	~0.3	CO_2	0.015
Concrete (dry)	0.13	H_2	0.18
Charcoal	0.05	O_2	0.026
Asbestos	0.11	N_2	0.025
Cork	0.045	Air	0.025
Carbohydrate	0.58	NH_3	0.024
Apple (75% water)	0.51	H_2O vapour	0.023
Chicken meat	0.49	Banana (75% water)	0.48
Muscle	0.41	Human skin	0.37
Protein	0.20	Fat	0.18

Figure 3.1 shows that dT/dx is negative and yet heat flows in a 'positive' direction; this is why the minus sign is included in equation (3.1). This can be compared with the Hagen–Poiseuille equation (2.37) relating volumetric flowrate to pressure gradient for laminar flow; again the minus sign appears. Table 3.1 lists values of λ for various substances at room temperature and pressure. It is seen that λ varies immensely for solids, but not much for liquids, except for liquid metals and water, which are somewhat anomalous. As for gases, λ for H_2 and He is large, because these have small molecular masses and sizes. Thus a larger heavy molecule like CO_2 has a smaller λ than air. The kinetic theory of gases provides a good theoretical basis for predicting λ for a pure gas and also mixtures of gases. Also, λ for a gas is independent of pressure, but increases with temperature. The value of λ for N_2 at 100 °C is $0.031\,\mathrm{W\,m^{-1}K^{-1}}$, only slightly larger than that listed above. Thus if heat is being conducted from 100 to 20 °C in N_2, it is sufficiently accurate to use a mean λ of $(0.025 + 0.031)/2 = 0.028\,\mathrm{W\,m^{-1}K^{-1}}$. Some foods, such as potato, have λ close to that of their major constituents (in this case water and carbohydrate). Otherwise, linear rules exist for predicting λ for heterogeneous mixtures, with the contribution from each component being proportional to its volume fraction, as well as its value of λ. For solids, liquids and gases the thermal conductivity increases with temperature. This is often not very significant for pure substances experiencing small changes in temperature. However, because (for example) starch solution gels at

around 60°C, the associated change in its thermal conductivity can be appreciable.

3.1.2 Steady-state heat conduction

Most thermal processes in the food industry are non-steady-state ones (because temperature changes with time), with, for example, the need to freeze or sterilize a food. Unsteady-state processes are very complex mathematically; before dealing with them, we shall consider the simpler case of constant temperatures, which do not vary with time. We now consider the conduction of heat through an infinitely wide slab of material, which has two parallel faces a distance L apart, as shown in Fig. 3.2. This geometry is of relevance in both the thawing of meats and the heating of packet foods. Suppose that the upper face is held at a fixed temperature T_1, whereas the cooler, lower face is always at T_2, with $T_1 > T_2$. The temperature within the material will eventually reach a **steady** distribution, which does not change with time; this is shown in Fig. 3.3, where x is now the distance from the upper face. Heat flows from the hot face to the cold one at a rate given by equation (3.1). Thus the heat flux is

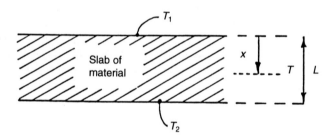

Fig. 3.2 A large slab of material with two parallel faces, distance L apart and at temperatures T_1 and T_2, with $T_1 > T_2$.

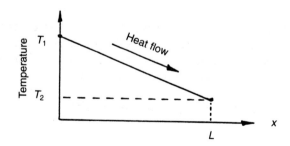

Fig. 3.3 Steady-state variation of temperature within the material of Fig. 3.2.

$$q = -\lambda \frac{\mathrm{d}T}{\mathrm{d}x} = \frac{\lambda(T_1 - T_2)}{L}$$

In this situation q does not vary with x; otherwise heat would be accumulating or being lost somewhere, which is not possible here in the steady state. Because q is not a function of x, equation (3.1) requires that $\mathrm{d}T/\mathrm{d}x$ is independent of x, i.e. q is a constant, so that temperature must vary linearly with x from T_1 at the top face to T_2 at the lower side. It is now convenient to introduce two new parameters. The first is a **heat transfer coefficient** h defined by

$$q = h(T_1 - T_2) \tag{3.2}$$

Equation (3.2) asserts that in this situation the heat flux q is proportional to the applied temperature difference, or overall driving force, $(T_1 - T_2)$, for heat transfer. Hence h is simply a constant of proportionality and has units of $W\,m^{-2}\,K^{-1}$. Comparison of the two preceding equations gives

$$h = \frac{\lambda}{L} \tag{3.3}$$

The heat transfer coefficient turns out to be a very convenient way of expressing measured heat fluxes as a function of an applied temperature difference.

The second new parameter is a dimensionless group, which in general is equal to hd/λ, where d is a characteristic dimension for the particular problem. Here one can only take $d = L$, so that this group, called the **Nusselt number**, is given by

$$Nu = \frac{hL}{\lambda}$$

Use of equation (3.3) yields $Nu = 1$ for this general problem.

EXAMPLE 3.1

A room in a house has one external wall, 6m × 3m. The temperature in the room is 20 °C; outside it is –5 °C. Calculate the rate of energy loss through this external wall, given that it is 0.3m thick and made of brick (without a cavity) with a thermal conductivity of 0.7 W m⁻¹ K⁻¹.

$$\text{Rate of heat loss} = \lambda \times \text{Area} \times \frac{\Delta T}{\text{thickness}}$$

$$= 0.7 \times 6 \times 3 \times \frac{25}{0.3} = 1.05\,\mathrm{kW}$$

A similar analysis will now be carried out for the radial flow of heat in a very long pipe with thick walls. The pipe is shown in Fig. 3.4. The inside wall is held at a constant temperature T_1 (for example, by passing a mixture of steam and boiling water through the pipe), while the outer wall is held at a lower, but constant temperature T_2. Heat thus flows radially outwards. Figure 3.4 shows an imaginary surface of radius r, with $r_1 < r < r_2$. The rate at which heat flows past this surface is $Q = 2\pi r q L$ for length L of the pipe or of the imaginary surface. Again, Q cannot be a function of r in the steady state, so substitution into equation (3.1) leads to

$$q = \frac{Q}{2\pi r L} = -\lambda \frac{dT}{dr}$$

or

$$\frac{Q}{2\pi L} \int_{r_1}^{r_2} \frac{dr}{r} = -\lambda \int_{T_1}^{T_2} dT$$

That is,

$$\frac{Q}{2\pi L} \ln\left(\frac{r_2}{r_1}\right) = \lambda(T_1 - T_2) \tag{3.4}$$

This enables Q to be calculated. Alternatively, the variation of T with r within the pipe's walls could have been calculated, using in addition

$$\frac{Q}{2\pi L} \ln\left(\frac{r}{r_1}\right) = \lambda(T_1 - T)$$

The above definition of $Q = 2\pi r q L$ and equation (3.4) lead to

$$\frac{Q}{2\pi L} = rq = \frac{\lambda(T_1 - T_2)}{\ln\left(\dfrac{r_2}{r_1}\right)} = \text{a constant}$$

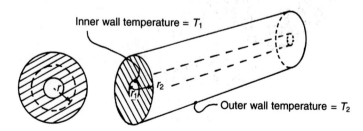

Fig. 3.4 Long pipe with thick walls and length L, and the inside wall maintained hotter than the outside wall. Inner and outer radii are r_1 and r_2.

so that the product qr is a constant. This makes it now impossible to define a unique heat transfer coefficient, $h = q/\Delta T$, where $\Delta T = T_1 - T_2$ and is the applied temperature difference (the driving force) leading to heat transfer. In fact, because qr is constant, we have to specify r in order to obtain a value for h. Two possibilities arise. If we choose $r = r_1$, then h referred to this inner surface will be

$$h_1 = \frac{\lambda}{r_1 \ln\left(\dfrac{r_2}{r_1}\right)}$$

Alternatively, if we choose $r = r_2$, then the heat transfer coefficient with respect to the outer surface of the pipe would be

$$h_2 = \frac{\lambda}{r_2 \ln\left(\dfrac{r_2}{r_1}\right)}$$

As for the Nusselt number, we have:

at $r = r_1$; $Nu = \dfrac{h_1 r_1}{\lambda} = \dfrac{1}{\ln\left(r_2/r_1\right)}$

at $r = r_2$; $Nu = \dfrac{h_2 r_2}{\lambda} = \dfrac{1}{\ln\left(r_2/r_1\right)}$

So although h depends on whether $r = r_1$ or r_2, the corresponding Nu does not. Herein lies a major importance of the Nusselt number.

EXAMPLE 3.2

In a nuclear reactor, the fuel elements may be considered to consist of long cylindrical rods of uranium oxide of diameter 8mm surrounded by a

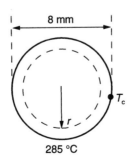

8 mm

T_c

285 °C

very thin layer of aluminium cladding. The elements are cooled by boiling water at 285°C with a heat transfer coefficient of 35 kW m²K⁻¹. If heat is generated uniformly throughout the uranium oxide at a rate of 760 MW m⁻³, find the temperature of the cladding and the maximum temperature in the uranium oxide. The thermal conductivity of uranium oxide may be taken to be 2.3 W m⁻¹K⁻¹.

Consider unit length of rod.
Rate of heat transfer from cylinder to water

$$= \pi \times 8 \times 10^{-3} \times 35 \times 10^3 (T_c - 285)$$

$$= \frac{\pi}{4} (8 \times 10^{-3})^2 \times 760 \times 10^6$$

$$= 38\,202\,W$$

$$T_c - 285 = 43.4 \Rightarrow T_c = 328.4\,°C$$

Heat flux across imaginary cylinder of radius r (see diagram)

$$= \frac{\pi r^2 \times 760 \times 10^6}{2 \pi r}$$

$$= 380 \times 10^6 r = -\lambda \frac{dT}{dr}$$

Therefore

$$\frac{380 \times 10^6}{2.3} \int_{4 \times 10^3}^{0} r \, dr = -\int_{328.4}^{T_{max}} dT$$

$$\frac{380 \times 10^6}{2.3} \times \frac{(4 \times 10^{-3})^2}{2} = T_{max} - 328.4$$

$$1321.7 = T_{max} - 328.4$$

$$T_{max} = 1650.1\,°C$$

As a final example of steady-state heat conduction, consider a hollow sphere with thick walls; a cross-section is shown in Fig. 3.5. Again the inner and outer radii are r_1 and r_2, where the temperatures are held at T_1 and T_2, respectively. Assume $T_1 > T_2$, so that heat flows radially outwards past any imaginary sphere of radius r, where $r_1 < r < r_2$. The total rate at which heat passes this surface of radius r is

$$Q = 4\pi r^2 q$$

where q is the heat flux (in W m⁻²) at r. In the steady state Q is independent of r, or else, for example, there might be a local accumulation of heat. In this case equation (3.1) becomes

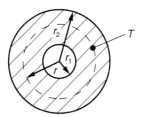

Fig. 3.5 Cross-section of a spherical shell with thick walls. The inner surface is held at a constant temperature T_1, while the outer surface is maintained at T_2.

$$q = \frac{Q}{4\pi r^2} = -\lambda \frac{dT}{dr} \tag{3.5}$$

or

$$\frac{Q}{4\pi} \int_{r_1}^{r_2} \frac{dr}{r^2} = -\lambda \int_{T_1}^{T_2} dT$$

or

$$\frac{Q}{4\pi} \left(\frac{1}{r_1} - \frac{1}{r_2} \right) = \lambda (T_1 - T_2) \tag{3.6}$$

Equation (3.5) shows that q is proportional to $1/r^2$, which again creates problems when defining h. Thus

$$h = \frac{q}{\Delta T} = \frac{Q/(4\pi r^2)}{T_1 - T_2} \tag{3.7}$$

so that h is a function of r and once again there is not one unique h for this problem. The most interesting case is for $r_2 \to \infty$, corresponding to heat conduction from a sphere of radius r_1 into an infinite stagnant medium. In this case equation (3.6) gives

$$\frac{Q}{4\pi r_1} = \lambda (T_1 - T_2)$$

for $T = T_2$ at $r_2 = \infty$. We can thus obtain h referred to $r = r_1$ from equation (3.7) as

$$h_1 = \frac{Q/(4\pi r_1^2)}{T_1 - T_2} = \frac{\lambda}{r_1}$$

When defining a Nusselt number it is traditional to use the diameter of the sphere as the characteristic dimension. In this case

$$Nu = \frac{h(2r_1)}{\lambda} = 2 \qquad\qquad (3.8)$$

EXAMPLE 3.3

Estimate the heat transfer coefficient h *for a sphere of diameter* d $= 25\,mm$ *surrounded by stagnant air, using* $\lambda = 0.025\,W\,m^{-1}\,K^{-1}$.

Here $Nu = 2 = \dfrac{hd}{\lambda}$

Therefore

$$h = \frac{2\lambda}{d} = \frac{2 \times 0.025}{25 \times 10^{-3}} = 2.0\,W\,m^{-2}\,K^{-1}$$

EXAMPLE 3.4

Estimate h *for a sphere of diameter* d $= 1\,mm$ *in stagnant air.*

Because $h \propto 1/d$, from equation (3.8):

$$h = 2.0 \times 25/1 = 50\,W\,m^{-2}\,K^{-1}$$

Note that, because $h \propto 1/d$, h becomes large for small spheres.

3.1.3   Problems of thawing and freezing foods

The problems are best illustrated by considering water (e.g. on a pond) freezing, with the air above the ice inevitably at a temperature below the melting point of ice. The situation is depicted in Fig. 3.6, where the interface between the ice and water is at T_{mp}, the melting point of ice (0°C). If A is the area of the pond's surface, the heat conducted through the ice to the air is $A\rho h_{fi} dx$ when the thickness of the ice increases by an amount dx. Here ρ is the density of ice and h_{fi} is its latent heat of fusion. The situation is similar to that shown in Fig. 3.3, and once again dT/dx is constant between the upper and lower surfaces of the ice. Substitution into Equation (3.1) yields

$$q = -\frac{A\rho h_{fi} dx}{A dt} = -\lambda \frac{(T_{mp} - T_A)}{x}$$

or

$$\frac{dx}{dt} = \frac{\lambda(T_{mp} - T_a)}{\rho h_{fi} x}$$

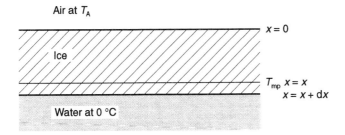

Fig. 3.6 Ice forming on a pond. At a time t the thickness of the ice is x, but at a later time $(t + dt)$ the thickness has grown to $x + dx$.

If $x = x_0$ at $t = 0$, then after a time t the thickness grows to

$$x^2 = x_0^2 + \frac{2\lambda\left(T_{mp} - T_A\right)}{\rho h_{fi}} \cdot t$$

which is obtained by integrating the previous equation. It is worthwhile stressing that the above treatment has assumed: (a) only the removal of latent heat is significant in this problem; (b) all the physical properties (λ, ρ, h_{fi}) of ice can be taken not to vary with temperature; (c) the freezing front is at a constant temperature; and (d) the system is in effect in a steady state. It is worthwhile inserting the following numerical values: $T_A = -10°C$, $\rho = 920\,kg\,m^{-3}$, $\lambda = 2.0\,W\,m^{-1}\,K^{-1}$, $x_0 = 0$ and $h_{fi} = 334\,kJ\,kg^{-1}$. In this case the first 10 mm of ice takes 768 s (12.8 min) to form, the second 10 mm a further 38.4 min, and so on.

As shown below, this approach can simply be applied to foods.

EXAMPLE 3.5

It is intended to freeze a hamburger (of thickness 0.012 m), which is 60wt% water, using air at –40 °C on both sides. Estimate the freezing time using the above approach. Will it be an over- or underestimate?

Data

Latent heat of fusion of water: $334\,kJ\,kg^{-1}$
Thermal conductivity of burger: $0.18\,W\,m^{-1}\,K^{-1}$
Density of burger: $870\,kg\,m^{-3}$

Since the burger has two sides, it is only necessary for the freezing front from each side to move 0.006 m into the food.

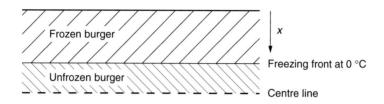

$$q = -\lambda \frac{40}{x} = -h_{fi} \times 0.6\rho \frac{dx}{dt}$$

$$\frac{40\lambda}{0.6h_{fi}\rho} = x \frac{dx}{dt} \quad \text{or} \quad x^2 = \frac{80\lambda t}{0.6h_{fi}\rho}$$

The freezing time is $\dfrac{0.6 \times 334 \times 10^3 \times 870 \times (0.012/2)^2}{80 \times 0.18}$

or 436 s. This is an underestimate because heat transfer through the air has been ignored. This is dealt with below in section 3.3.4. There are other errors, such as the sensible heat (i.e. that associated with a change of temperature, in contrast with latent heats, which are transferred without a body changing temperature) being ignored. Thus a greater amount of heat than that calculated above must be conducted through the burger to reduce its temperature from above zero to almost –40 °C. A more general version of the above treatment is given in section 3.3.4.

3.1.4 Unsteady-state heat conduction

Previous problems have involved temperatures that are constant with time, but vary in space. If unsteady-state processes (those that vary with time) are considered, time derivatives must be taken into account, as well as spatial ones. Consider the long thin metal rod of Fig. 3.1 with a temperature profile that changes with time. The rod is shown in Fig. 3.7. The heat flux from left to right at position x is q $(= -\lambda dT/dx)$. Let the heat flux in the same, positive, direction at $x + dx$ be $q + dq$. The increment between x and $x + dx$ has a volume $A dx$ and mass $A\rho dx$, where A is the constant cross-sectional area and ρ is density. The rate at which the heat content, or enthalpy, of this increment of length decreases is

$$-A\rho\,dx c_p \frac{\partial T}{\partial t} = A\,dq$$

Here c_p is the heat capacity of the rod per unit mass, so c_p has units $J kg^{-1} K^{-1}$. Note that q is the heat flux away from the origin, so that if dq is

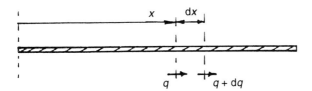

Fig. 3.7 A long thin rod of cross-sectional area A, where the temperature varies both with position x and with time.

positive, the increment cools. Thus the signs in the above equation are correct and

$$-\rho\,c_P\left(\frac{\partial T}{\partial t}\right)dx = dq = d\left(-\lambda\,\frac{\partial T}{\partial x}\right)$$

Here, as the temperature is a function both of distance and time, the notation for partial differentiation is needed and leads to:

$$\frac{\partial T}{\partial t} = \frac{1}{\rho c_P}\frac{\partial}{\partial x}\left(\lambda\,\frac{\partial T}{\partial x}\right)$$

If λ is independent of temperature, this becomes

$$\frac{\partial T}{\partial t} = \frac{\lambda}{\rho c_P}\frac{\partial^2 T}{\partial x^2} = \alpha\,\frac{\partial^2 T}{\partial x^2} \tag{3.9}$$

Here α $(= \lambda/\rho c_P)$ is called the **thermal diffusivity** of the rod. Its units are $m^2 s^{-1}$, which also are those of kinematic viscosity and the diffusion coefficient.

EXAMPLE 3.6

Estimate the thermal diffusivity for air and water, respectively, both at 20 °C, given $\rho = 1.29\,kg\,m^{-3}$ for air and $c_P = 1005\,J\,kg^{-1}\,K^{-1}$ for air and $c_P = 4.187\,J\,kg^{-1}\,K^{-1}$ for water. Use the values of λ in Table 3.1.

For air:

$$\alpha = \frac{\lambda}{\rho c_P} = \frac{0.025}{1.29 \times 1005} = 1.9 \times 10^{-5}\,m^2\,s^{-1}$$

For water:

$$\alpha = \frac{0.60}{10^3 \times 4.187 \times 10^3} = 1.4 \times 10^{-7}\,m^2\,s^{-1}$$

The difference between the two values of α should be noted.

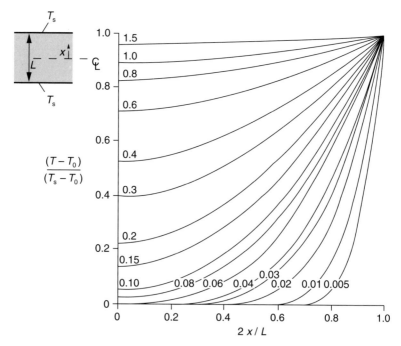

Fig. 3.8 Temperature distributions at various times within a slab of initial temperature T_0 and surface temperatures of T_s. The numbers on the curves correspond to the values of $4\alpha t/L^2$.

Equation (3.9) presents difficulties as far as obtaining simple analytical solutions is concerned; in fact they only exist for a few problems. In general, solutions can be obtained for equation (3.9), provided the boundary conditions are specified, using computerized techniques. We shall just present graphical solutions to a restricted number of problems. Consider first the slab in Fig. 3.2. Suppose the entire material initially has a uniform temperature T_0, but at time $t = 0$ the two faces are suddenly raised to a temperature T_s, which is then maintained at all subsequent times. Figure 3.8 is a plot of $(T - T_0)/(T_s - T_0)$ against $2x/L$ for various values of $4\alpha t/L^2$. It is clear from Fig. 3.8 that when $4\alpha t/L^2 = 2.0$, the material is uniformly heated. This corresponds to a heating time of $L^2/2\alpha$ for the slab. Similar plots are given in Fig. 3.9 for a solid sphere which is initially at uniform temperature T_0. From a time $t = 0$ the surface of the sphere is held at a temperature T_s so that heat flows radially inwards. The curves in Fig. 3.9 are again of the fractional temperature rise $(T - T_0)/(T_s - T_0)$ against dimensionless radius r/r_s, where r_s is the sphere's radius, for increasing values of $\alpha t/r_s^2$. Figure 3.9 shows that at a time when $\alpha t/r_s^2 = 0.5$, the sphere is close to being at a uniform temperature T_s. Thus $r_s^2/2\alpha$ is a characteristic heating time, proportional to $1/\alpha$. Something more accurate is presented in the following example.

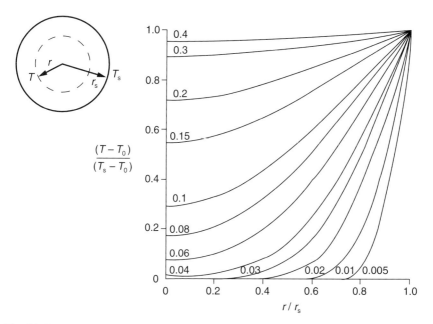

Fig. 3.9 Temperature profiles at various times t in a solid sphere of radius r_s, with initial temperature T_0 and constant surface temperature T_s. The numbers on the curves are the values of $\alpha t/r_s^2$, where $\alpha = \lambda/\rho c_P$ is the thermal diffusivity of the solid. The graph thus gives information on the temperature T at a distance r from the centre of symmetry.

EXAMPLE 3.7

A potato has the following properties:

$$\lambda = 0.50\,W\,m^{-1}\,K^{-1}$$
$$\rho = 1100\,kg\,m^{-3}$$
$$c_P = 3.5\,kJ\,kg^{-1}\,K^{-1}$$

It may be considered to be boiled when its centre reaches 85 °C, when immersed in water boiling at 100 °C. Estimate the time taken to boil a potato (initially at 20 °C) of radius 25 mm. Assume the potato is spherical.

When the centre has reached 85 °C:

$$\frac{T - T_0}{T_s - T_0} = \frac{85 - 20}{100 - 20} = 0.8125$$

From Fig. 3.9 the ratio $(T - T_0)/(T_s - T_0) = 0.8125$ at $r = 0$ when $\alpha t/r_s^2 = 0.24$. Thus the boiling time is

$$t = \frac{0.24\,r_s^2}{\alpha} = 0.24 \times \left(25 \times 10^{-3}\right)^2 \times \frac{1100 \times 3.5 \times 10^3}{0.50}$$

$$= 1155\,s = 19.3\,min$$

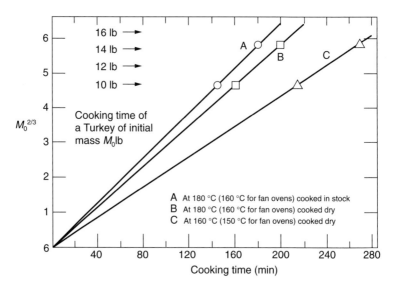

Fig. 3.10 Plots of $M_0^{2/3}$ (where M_0 is the initial mass of a turkey) against the cooking time determined experimentally. Conditions for cooking schemes A, B and C are given on the graph.

Charts such as Figs 3.8 and 3.9 are useful in calculating the cooking or freezing times of foods with simple geometries. The complex shapes of real foods are often difficult to approximate; computer simulations are thus necessary to predict their process times.

The above discussion can be taken a stage further. Consider the roasting of a turkey. It turns out that the optimal cooking time is the minimum time required to heat the centre of the bird to 70°C. This gives a reasonably tender piece of meat with an exterior that is slightly overcooked, i.e. browned. If a turkey is assumed to be spherical, it will have an initial mass equal to $M_0 = 4\pi r_{\mathrm{m}}^3 \rho/3$ for an initial density ρ and mean radius r_{m}. As a result $r_{\mathrm{m}} = (3M_0/4\pi\rho)^{1/3}$. The above discussion indicates that $\alpha t_{\mathrm{r}}/r_{\mathrm{m}}^2$ will be a constant, if t_{r} is the time for the temperature (at the centre of the turkey) to reach 70°C with a fixed oven temperature. Thus a graph of r_{m}^2 against roasting time t_{r} should be a straight-line plot through the origin. This is seen to be the case in Fig. 3.10, which is actually a plot of $M_0^{2/3}$ (proportional to r_{m}^2) against cooking time. In each of the three cooking situations a straight-line plot through the origin is obtained. Such charts are obviously useful for predicting cooking times.

3.2 Heat transfer in flowing systems

Conduction of heat is slower than convective heat transfer, where heat is mainly transferred by the movement of a fluid. Convective processes cannot

be modelled analytically in the way conduction can; it is accordingly necessary to construct more empirical models and also to devise correlations to
predict heat transfer rates. First we investigate the result of dimensional
analysis. This approach will be seen to identify some relevant parameters,
which in fact are dimensionless groups. Afterwards in sections 3.2.2 and
3.2.3 two oversimple models (the film model and the Reynolds analogy) are
described, because they bring out the relevant dimensionless groups, but
without being quantitatively precise.

3.2.1 Dimensional analysis

Here we consider one fluid flowing, so that the transfer of heat will be by
convection, as well as by conduction. Nevertheless, it is possible to use the
heat transfer coefficient, defined by $q = h\Delta T$ in equation (3.2). We begin by
considering the situation in Fig. 3.11. Here a cold fluid is passed through a
thin-walled pipe whose walls are maintained uniformly hot: for example, by
having steam condense on the exterior surface. Heat thus flows from the
pipe to the fluid inside it. It is possible to define a local heat transfer
coefficient $h = q/\Delta T$ for a point along the system. Here q is the local heat flux
and $\Delta T = (T_w - T)$ is the difference between the wall and fluid temperatures
at the particular point. This parameter h is likely to depend on the following
seven quantities:

d = pipe's internal diameter (m)
v = mean velocity of the fluid in the pipe (m s^{-1})
λ = thermal conductivity of the fluid (W m^{-1}K^{-1})
ρ = density of the fluid (kg m^{-3})
c_P = specific heat capacity of the fluid (J kg^{-1}K^{-1})
μ = viscosity of the fluid (N s m^{-2})
T = temperature of the fluid (K)

It has been assumed that the pipe's length does not matter. Four of the
above (λ, ρ, c_P and μ) are physical properties of the fluid being heated.
Dimensional analysis, as discussed in Chapter 2, leads to

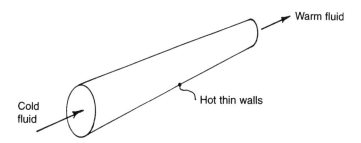

Warm fluid

Cold
fluid

Hot thin walls

Fig. 3.11 A fluid being heated by passing it through a pipe whose walls are maintained hot.

$$Nu = f\left(Re,\ Pr\right) \tag{3.10}$$

where

$$Nu = \frac{hd}{\lambda}$$

$$Re = \frac{\rho v d}{\mu}$$

$$Pr = \frac{\mu c_P}{\lambda}$$

The three dimensionless groups are the **Nusselt, Reynolds** and **Prandtl numbers**. They incorporate h and the above seven variables. The Nusselt number gives h, the Reynolds number characterizes the nature of the fluid flow (laminar or turbulent), and the Prandtl number is determined entirely by the physical properties of the fluid being heated.

As a digression it is seen that

$$Pr = \frac{\mu}{\rho} \cdot \frac{\rho c_P}{\lambda} = \frac{v}{\alpha}$$

where $v = \mu/\rho$ is the kinematic viscosity of the fluid. Both v and α have dimensions of $m^2 s^{-1}$. It turns out that Pr for all gases is close to unity. However, for liquids Pr varies considerably, as seen from Table 3.2, where the effects of μ and λ are clear. Note that food materials with high viscosities, such as soups, will tend to have Pr greater than that of water.

It is common to introduce another dimensionless group, the **Stanton number**. This is given by

$$St = \frac{h}{\rho v c_P} = \frac{hd}{\lambda} \cdot \frac{\lambda}{\mu c_P} \frac{\mu}{\rho v d} = \frac{Nu}{Pr.Re}$$

Thus equation (3.10) could be re-written as

$$St = f\left(Re,\ Pr\right) \tag{3.11}$$

Table 3.2 Values of Prandtl number for various liquids

Liquid	Pr	Comment
Mercury	0.0027	μ is low, λ high
Water	6	
Kerosene	127	
Glycerine	17000	μ is high, λ low
Liquid polymers	$>10^4$	

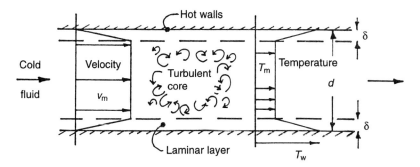

Fig. 3.12 The film model of turbulent flow through a pipe. The fluid has two regions: a turbulent core and a laminar layer adjacent to the walls. The velocity and temperature profiles across the pipe are as shown, v_m and T_m being their mean values in the middle of the fluid.

No new information is obtained by introducing St, only algebraic convenience. The dimensionless group St crops up quite naturally in a variety of situations and so is sometimes used as an alternative to the Nusselt number.

3.2.2 Film model

We now consider various theories of heat transfer to the fluid in Fig. 3.11 when it is in turbulent flow: that is, $Re > 4000$. It should be stressed that any model, such as the film model, oversimplifies a situation in order that some progress can be made in the analysis of a difficult problem. Thus sections 3.2.2 and 3.2.3 must not be taken too literally; they are intended only as simplified pictures of a complex situation. The **film model** is depicted in Fig. 3.12. The assumption is a crude one and is that two regions exist in the flowing fluid: a laminar region next to the walls, and a turbulent well-mixed core for the fluid. The temperature and velocity profiles in a radial direction within the fluid are also shown in Fig. 3.12. In this model all transfer of momentum and heat occurs across a single layer of thickness δ, where $\delta \ll d$, the internal diameter of the pipe. The velocity gradient at the wall is v_m/δ, so that the shear stress in the fluid adjacent to the wall, assuming a Newtonian fluid, is

$$\tau_w = \frac{\mu v_m}{\delta}$$

From Fig. 3.11 the heat flux from the wall to the liquid is

$$q = \frac{\lambda(T_w - T_m)}{\delta}$$

so that the heat transfer coefficient is

$$h = \frac{q}{T_w - T_m} = \frac{\lambda}{\delta} = \frac{\lambda \tau_w}{\mu v_m}$$

One can now derive the Nusselt number:

$$Nu = \frac{hd}{\lambda} = \frac{\tau_w d}{\mu v_m} = \frac{1}{2} \frac{\tau_w}{\left(\frac{1}{2} \rho v_m^2\right)} \cdot \frac{\rho v_m d}{\mu}$$

Remembering the friction factor c_f to be defined by $\tau_w = c_f(\rho v_m^2/2)$, this gives

$$Nu = \frac{c_f Re}{2} \qquad (3.12)$$

The friction factor is normally a function of Reynolds number only. In fact, for $4000 < Re < 10^5$ (turbulent flow within a pipe) the Blasius relation

$$c_f = 0.079 Re^{-1/4} \qquad (3.13)$$

holds, so that equation (3.12) becomes

$$Nu = 0.040 Re^{3/4} \qquad (3.14)$$

This is a particular from of equation (3.10), and is interesting in that it predicts that Nu is independent of Pr. The very simple assumptions in the film model should be noted, especially of there being heat transfer by simple conduction across a boundary layer or film. The picture in Fig. 3.12 of high temperatures in the fluid adjacent to the wall is a useful one: for example, in the study of fouling (see sections 3.3.3 and 8.3).

Equation (3.14) enables us to estimate Nu. If $4000 < Re < 10^5$, then from equation (3.13) $0.01 > c_f > 0.0044$ and $20 < Nu < 220$. The above model gives $h = \lambda/\delta$, so that $Nu = hd/\lambda = d/\delta$. Thus the Nusselt number is the ratio of the two distances shown in Fig. 3.11. Thus, according to this model, heat is conducted across a thin layer which has thickness roughly equal to 1/10th to 1/100th of the pipe's radius. If $Nu = 200$ and the fluid is water flowing through a pipe 30 mm internal diameter, then $h = 200 \lambda/d = 200 \times 0.6/30 \times 10^{-3} = 4000 \, W \, m^{-2} K^{-1}$. Alternatively,

$$Nu = \frac{h}{\lambda/d}$$

is the ratio of two heat transfer coefficients: the actual h for the transfer of heat (mainly by convection) from the walls of the pipe to the fluid; and λ/d, the heat transfer coefficient (see equation (3.3)) for conduction across a film of constant thickness d. Finally, equation (3.12) can be recast to yield

$$St \, Pr = \frac{c_f}{2} \qquad (3.15)$$

Also, it should be mentioned that the film model provides a way of visual-izing heat transfer situations in a simple way. Thus it is common to think of there being a film, across which there is a linear temperature profile. Of couse, this is not strictly true, but it helps to think about problems generally.

3.2.3 Reynolds analogy

An alternative approach to the film model is the **Reynolds analogy**, which takes a quite different, but simple, view as to what is important in a turbulent fluid flowing close to a containing wall. Here the path of a tiny fluid element is as shown in Fig. 3.13. The eddy stays in the bulk of the fluid and occasionally transfers very rapidly to the wall, where it remains for a period before suddenly transferring back to the body of the moving fluid. Let m be the mass of eddies arriving at unit area of the wall per unit time. Because there is no net mass transfer, m is also the mass of fluid returning to the bulk from unit area of the wall per unit time. On moving from the bulk to the wall the eddies bring a momentum in the x direction equal to mv_m (v_m = mean bulk velocity of the fluid) and also a heat or enthalpy of mc_pT_m (T_m = mean temperature of fluid of heat capacity c_p). The eddies returning to the bulk do so with the properties of the fluid adjacent to the wall. They thus bring x-wise momentum equal to mv_w, where v_w is the fluid velocity at the wall. We shall take $v_w = 0$. In addition, the eddies arriving in the bulk fluid from the wall have heat mc_pT_w, where T_w is the wall's temperature. Thus

Net momentum flux to the wall $= mv_m = \tau_w$
Net heat flux from the wall $= mc_p(T_w - T_m) = q$

and

$$\frac{\tau_w}{v_m} = \frac{q}{c_P\left(T_w - T_m\right)}$$

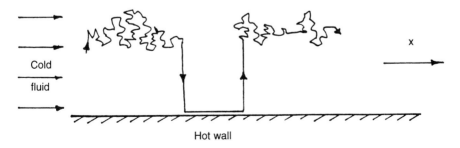

Fig. 3.13 Assumed typical path of a fluid element inside a pipe or over a general surface, which is hot enough to be transferring heat to the fluid.

But

$$h = \frac{q}{\left(T_w - T_m\right)}$$

so

$$\frac{\tau_w}{v_m} = \frac{h}{c_P}$$

and

$$\frac{\tau_w}{\rho v_m^2} = \frac{h}{\rho c_P v_m}$$

or

$$St = \frac{c_f}{2} \tag{3.16}$$

Equation (3.16) is the prediction of this model for turbulent flow and should be compared with equation (3.15) from the film model. Of course, when $Pr = 1$ for a gas, there is no difference between equations (3.15) and (3.16). However, for a typical liquid with $Pr =$ up to 10, the difference is important. In fact, h predicted by the Reynolds analogy is up to ten times larger than that given by the film model. For viscous food fluids, the Reynolds analogy and also the film model may predict h poorly, because the flow is probably not turbulent. Nevertheless, note that so far we have examined two over-simplified models of heat transfer in a turbulent fluid. The film model assumes that heat conduction in the fluid adjacent to the wall is the controlling factor. In the other model, the Reynolds analogy, the random motion of eddies is all important. We now ask the question: which model is nearer the truth?

3.2.4   The j-factor analogy

By way of a recap, we have had so far that

$$St = f\left(Re, Pr\right) \tag{3.11}$$

from dimensional analysis. The film model gave

$$St\, Pr = \frac{c_f}{2} \tag{3.15}$$

whereas the Reynolds analogy resulted in

$$St = \frac{c_f}{2} \tag{3.16}$$

These last two equations are of the general form $St\,Pr^n = c_f/2$, where n is either unity or zero. The j-factor analogy puts the truth somewhere between equations (3.15) and (3.16), so that

$$St\,Pr^{2/3} = \frac{c_f}{2} \qquad (3.17)$$

Thus the Prandtl number now appears raised to the intermediate power of 2/3. This result of what is called the j-factor analogy derives partly from theoretical treatment: for example, of heat transfer from a plane surface into a region of laminar flow. However, as seen below, it does give an acceptable description of experimental measurements within their considerable experimental errors. Thus we have a simple result in equation (3.17), which derives from both theory and experiment. This is a common situation, whereby a simple result has been arrived at from a mixture of theory and experiment. This approach has also borne fruit in analysis of mass transfer, as noted in Chapter 4.

3.2.5 Experimental measurements

Measurements have been made of heat transfer rates to a turbulent fluid flowing in pipes. For smooth, straight, clean circular pipes the result of Dittus–Boelter (Kay and Nedderman, 1985) is

$$Nu = 0.023\,Re^{0.8}\,Pr^{0.4} \qquad (3.18)$$

It has to be stressed that the reproducibility and precision of the measurements are not good; there is an uncertainty of 30% in the magnitude of Nu predicted by equation (3.18), which holds for $Re > 5000$. Equation (3.17) for the j-factor analogy can be recast as

$$Nu = 0.040\,Re^{3/4}\,Pr^{1/3}$$

and predictions of Nu from these two equations give values of Nu in very satisfactory agreement. The difference between $Pr^{0.4}$ and $Pr^{1/3}$ is of no consequence for liquids of $Pr < 10$, because $10^{0.4}/10^{1/3} = 1.17$ and 17% is well within experimental accuracy. Thus in practice one would either use an experimental correlation like equation (3.18), if one is available or use the j-factor analogy. The film model and Reynolds analogy are only of historical interest. The values of Nu for turbulent flow are much higher than those for **laminar** flow in a pipe, for which the semi-theoretical result

$$Nu = 1.86\big(Re.\,Pr.\,d/L\big)^{1/3}\big(\mu/\mu_w\big)^{0.14} \qquad (3.19)$$

of Sieder and Tate (Kay and Nedderman, 1985) holds. Here d/L is the ratio of internal diameter to length for the pipe; the term arises because the steady state is established slowly for laminar flow. Indeed the fluid must flow quite a distance (equal to around 25 internal diameters of the pipe) before a parabolic velocity profile is established. The final term in equation (3.19), μ/μ_w, is the ratio of the viscosity on the centreline of the fluid to that at the walls. The difference arises because the fluid might well be hotter at the walls, so that $\mu > \mu_w$. Generally speaking Nu and h are some ten times larger for turbulent than for laminar flow. For this reason laminar flow is avoided in heat transfer devices whenever possible. However, it was noted above that some liquid foods, such as soups, are very viscous fluids, so that they are unlikely to be in turbulent flow. In these cases, laminar flow is unavoidable. Moreover, not only are food fluids viscous, they can be sensitive to shear.

EXAMPLE 3.8

Air at 40 °C flows with a mean velocity of 15 m s⁻¹ inside a smooth tube of internal diameter 2.4 cm. Calculate the Reynolds number for the flow and confirm that the flow is turbulent. Calculate the heat transfer coefficient using Blasius's law ($c_f = 0.079 Re^{-0.25}$) and:

(a) Reynolds analogy ($St = \tfrac{1}{2}c_f$)
(b) the film model ($St Pr = \tfrac{1}{2}c_f$)
(c) the j-factor correlation ($St Pr^{2/3} = \tfrac{1}{2}c_f$)
(d) the Dittus–Boelter correlation ($Nu = 0.023 Re^{0.8} Pr^{0.4}$)

Data for air at 40 °C

$$\rho = 1.13 \, \text{kg m}^{-3}$$
$$\mu = 1.90 \times 10^{-5} \, \text{N s m}^{-2}$$
$$c_p = 1006 \, \text{J kg}^{-1}\text{K}^{-1}$$
$$\lambda = 0.027 \, \text{W m}^{-1}\text{K}^{-1}$$

$$Pr = \frac{\mu c_p}{\lambda} = \frac{1.90 \times 10^{-5} \times 1006}{0.027} = 0.708$$

$$Re = \frac{15 \times 1.13 \times 2.4 \times 10^{-2}}{1.9 \times 10^{-5}} = 21\,410.5$$

(N.B. $Re > 2000$, so it is turbulent.)

$$c_f = 0.079 \, Re^{-1/4} = 6.531 \times 10^{-3}$$

15 m s⁻¹

2.4 x 10⁻² m

(a) Reynolds analogy

$$St = c_f/2 = \frac{h}{\rho v c_P}$$

Therefore

$$h = \frac{6.531 \times 10^{-3}}{2} \times 1.13 \times 15 \times 1006$$
$$= 55.7 \text{ W m}^{-2} \text{ K}^{-1}$$

(b) Film model

$$St \, Pr = \frac{1}{2} c_f$$

Therefore

$$h = \frac{55.7}{0.708}$$
$$= 78.7 \text{ W m}^{-2} \text{ K}^{-1}$$

(c) j-factor

$$St \, Pr^{2/3} = \frac{1}{2} c_f$$

Therefore

$$h = \frac{55.7}{(0.708)^{2/3}}$$
$$= 70.1 \text{ W m}^{-2} \text{ K}^{-1}$$

(d) Dittus–Boelter

$$Nu = 0.023 \, Re^{0.8} \, Pr^{0.4} = 58.4$$

Therefore

$$h = 58.4 \times \frac{\lambda}{d} = 58.4 \times \frac{0.027}{2.4 \times 10^{-2}}$$
$$= 65.7 \text{ W m}^{-2} \text{ K}^{-1}$$

EXAMPLE 3.9

Using the data for air in Example 3.8, derive the Nusselt number for laminar flow inside a pipe with Re = 400, d/L = 10⁻² *and* μ/μ_w = 1.

Equation (3.19) gives

$$Nu = 1.86(Re.\ Pr.\ d/L)^{1/3}$$

Therefore

$$Nu = 1.86\left(400 \times 0.708 \times 10^{-2}\right)^{1/3} = 1.3$$

Note that Nu is much lower for laminar flow than for turbulent flows. Of course, Pr for a liquid can be larger than for a gas, which also affects Nu.

3.2.6 Other geometries

The above discussion related primarily to flow inside a circular pipe. However, pressure drops and hence c_f have been measured for flow in rough pipes, around bends, in coiled or non-circular pipes, and so on. If c_f is known from measuring the pressure drop in one of these situations, then St and h can be predicted by using the j-factor analogy, equation (3.17). This is a particularly useful feature for internal flows. As for a fluid flowing over the exterior of an object, such as a sphere or a cylinder, remember that the above theories made an analogy between the transfer of heat and momentum. Normally one measures a drag force when a fluid flows over an object and in fact the drag force has two components: form drag and skin friction drag. It is the latter skin frictional drag that is related to heat transfer and so has to be isolated. Some useful correlations are as follows:

1. For flow over a flat plate:

$$Nu = 0.66\,Re^{1/2}\,Pr^{1/3} \qquad \text{for } Re < 10^5$$
$$Nu = 0.036\,Re^{0.8}\,Pr^{1/3} \qquad \text{for } Re > 10^5$$

2. For turbulent flow across the outside of a cylinder:

$$Nu = 0.38\,Re^{0.57}\,Pr^{1/3}$$

3. For flow over a sphere:

$$Nu = 2.0 + 0.7\,Re^{1/2}\,Pr^{1/3}$$

This last result clearly contains two terms added together. The first term is equation (3.8) for heat conduction with $Re = 0$ (no flow), whereas the second term is due to convection with turbulence. The correlation, for a

solid sphere with fluid flowing over its surface, is most useful for predicting heat transfer rates in typical foods containing two phases of a solid
and a liquid.
4. For flow in a plate heat exchanger: these exchangers have complex
geometries, but are often made from stacks of flat plates, with alternately
hot and cold fluids in between the plates and their heat transfer correlations are not generally published. Equations such as

$$Nu = 0.068\, Re^{0.7}\, Pr^{0.4}$$

can be used, but only with caution, and for turbulent flow. Nevertheless,
an equation of the type $Nu = l\, Re^m\, Pr^n$ is of the right form for a plate heat
exchanger, with the constants l, m and n depending on the particular
geometry.

3.3 Heat exchange: more practical aspects

3.3.1 Overall heat transfer coefficients

Consider the situation depicted in Fig. 3.14, which is a modification of Fig.
3.11. Cold liquid flows inside the thin-walled tube, whose walls are heated
by hot air blown over the external surface. Thus heat flows first from the hot
air to the pipe, followed by heat conduction through the pipe's wall and
then finally there is heat transfer to the liquid flowing inside the tube. So far
we have developed expressions to predict h for the transfer of heat from the
hot air to the tube and also from the tube to the colder liquid flowing
internally. Figure 3.15 shows the rough shape of the plot of temperature
against radial distance from the axis of the system. Of course, Fig. 3.15
refers to one distance along the length of the tube. There the temperatures
of the bulk of the liquid, of the incident air and the wall are T_L, T_A and T_W,
respectively. At this axial distance, one can write the local heat flux (per
unit area of wall) as

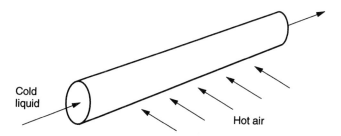

Fig. 3.14 A long thin-walled tube inside which flows a liquid and over which flows much
hotter air.

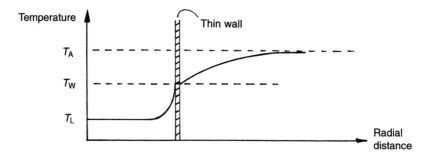

Fig. 3.15 Radial temperature profile at some arbitrary point along the tube in Fig. 3.14.

$$q = h_A\left(T_A - T_W\right) = h_L\left(T_W - T_L\right) \qquad (3.20)$$

Here h_A and h_L are called the air-side and liquid-side heat transfer coefficients, respectively. In addition, an overall heat transfer coefficient, U, can be defined using

$$q = U\left(T_A - T_L\right)$$

Thus U gives q in terms of the overall temperature difference between the incident air and the liquid at this axial distance. Clearly T_L and T_W both increase with distance along the pipe. Equation (3.20) gives

$$T_A - T_W = \frac{q}{h_A}$$

and

$$T_W - T_L = \frac{q}{h_L}$$

which on addition, to eliminate the unknown T_W, yield

$$T_A - T_L = q\left(\frac{1}{h_A} + \frac{1}{h_L}\right) \equiv \frac{q}{U}$$

Hence

$$\frac{1}{U} = \frac{1}{h_A} + \frac{1}{h_L} \qquad (3.21)$$

so that heat transfer coefficients in this case add by their reciprocals. If $h_L \gg h_A$ then $U \approx h_A$ and heat transfer is air-side-controlled, so $T_L \approx T_W$. Alternatively, if $h_A \gg h_L$ then $U \approx h_L$; that is, heat transfer is liquid-side-controlled, with $T_A \approx T_W$.

EXAMPLE 3.10

*An oil-cooler consists of 100 thin-walled tubes each of 15mm internal di-
ameter operated in parallel. The oil flows through the shell side of the heat
exchanger (that is, around the outside of the tubes) and the water flows
inside the tubes. The shell-side heat transfer coefficient is 1.2kWm⁻²K⁻¹,*
whereas that on the water side is given by Nu = 0.023Re⁰·⁸Pr⁰·⁴. *Find the
water-side heat transfer coefficient and hence the overall heat transfer
coefficient when the flowrate of water is (a) 10kgs⁻¹, (b) 20kgs⁻¹.*

Data for water

$$\mu = 1 \times 10^{-3}\,\mathrm{N\,s\,m^{-2}}$$
$$\lambda = 0.61\,\mathrm{W\,m^{-1}\,K^{-1}}$$
$$c_p = 4190\,\mathrm{J\,kg^{-1}\,K^{-1}}$$

(a) Flowrate 10 kg s⁻¹

Water-side: $Nu = 0.023\,Re^{0.8}\,Pr^{0.4}$

$$10\ \mathrm{kg\ s^{-1}} = \frac{\pi d^2}{4} \times 100 \times v\rho \Rightarrow v = \frac{40}{\pi(15\times10^{-3})^2 \times 10^3} = 0.566\ \mathrm{m\ s^{-1}}$$

$$Re = \frac{\rho v d}{\mu} = 10^3 \times \frac{0.566 \times 15 \times 10^{-3}}{10^{-3}} = 8488$$

$$Pr = \frac{\mu c_p}{\lambda} = \frac{10^{-3} \times 4190}{0.61} = 6.87$$

$$Nu = 0.023(8488)^{0.8} \times 6.87^{0.4} = 69.1 = \frac{h_w d}{\lambda}$$

Therefore

$$h_w = \frac{69.1 \times 0.61}{15 \times 10^{-3}} = 2810\ \mathrm{W\ m^{-2}\ K^{-1}}$$

$$\frac{1}{U} = \frac{1}{2810} + \frac{1}{1200} \Rightarrow U = 841\,\mathrm{W\ m^{-2}\ K^{-1}}$$

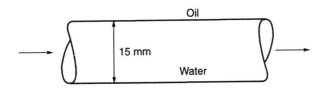

(b) Flowrate $20\,\text{kg}\,\text{s}^{-1}$

$$Nu = 69.1 \times 2^{0.8} = 120.3$$

$$h_W = \frac{120.3 \times 0.61}{15 \times 10^{-3}} = 4893\ \text{W m}^{-2}\ \text{K}^{-1}$$

$$\frac{1}{U} = \frac{1}{4893} + \frac{1}{1200} \Rightarrow U = 964\ \text{W m}^{-2}\ \text{K}^{-1}$$

3.3.2 Cylindrical pipe with thick wall

Suppose the wall in Figs 3.14 and 3.15 is thick enough for the temperature difference between its inner and outer surfaces to be significant. As in Fig. 3.4 the inner and outer radii of the walls are r_1 and r_2, where the temperatures are T_1 and T_2, respectively. Equation (3.4), after adjustment for heat flowing radially inwards (Q is negative), rather than outwards, gives

$$T_2 - T_1 = \frac{Q}{2\pi\lambda L} \cdot \ln\left(\frac{r_2}{r_1}\right)$$

where Q is the overall rate at which heat is transferred in a pipe of length L. But from above

$$T_A - T_2 = \frac{Q}{2\pi r_2 h_A L}$$

$$T_1 - T_L = \frac{Q}{2\pi r_1 h_L L}$$

Addition of the above three equations yields

$$T_A - T_L = \frac{Q}{2\pi L}\left[\frac{1}{r_1 h_L} + \frac{1}{r_2 h_A} + \frac{\ln(r_2/r_1)}{\lambda}\right]$$

As for an overall heat transfer coefficient, again there is a choice, because one has either

$$Q = 2\pi r_1 U_1\left(T_A - T_B\right)L$$

or

$$Q = 2\pi r_2 U_2\left(T_A - T_B\right)L$$

depending on whether the inner or outer radius is used as the reference surface. Thus

$$\frac{1}{r_1 U_1} = \frac{1}{r_2 U_2} = \frac{1}{r_1 h_L} + \frac{1}{r_2 h_A} + \frac{\ln(r_2/r_1)}{\lambda} \qquad (3.22)$$

Here U_1 is the overall heat transfer coefficient with respect to the inside surface of the pipe, and U_2 is referred to the outer surface. Equation (3.22) could be used for a thin-walled tube of radius r_1, but with lagging from r_1 to r_2.

EXAMPLE 3.11

Water flows at 2kgs^{-1} along a circular pipe of 50mm internal diameter, which is lagged with a 10mm thickness of ceramic fibre insulation (λ = 0.2Wm^{-2}K^{-1}). The heat transfer coefficient at the outer surface is 50Wm^{-2}K^{-1}. Using the Dittus–Boelter correlation (Nu = 0.023Re$^{0.8}$Pr$^{0.4}$) for the inner surface, calculate the overall heat transfer coefficient: (a) based on the outer surface area; (b) based on the inner surface area.

Data for water

$$\mu = 1 \times 10^{-3}\,\mathrm{N\,s\,m^{-2}}$$
$$\lambda = 0.61\,\mathrm{W\,m^{-1}\,K^{-1}}$$
$$c_p = 4190\,\mathrm{J\,kg^{-1}\,K^{-1}}$$

(a)   Outer surface area

$$Q = \frac{2\pi\lambda L(T_2 - T_1)}{\ln(r_2/r_1)} \tag{1}$$

$$2\,\mathrm{kg\,s^{-1}} = \frac{\pi d_1^2}{4}v\rho \text{ for } d_1 = 2r_1$$

$$\Rightarrow v = \frac{2 \times 4}{\pi(50 \times 10^{-3})^2 \times 1000} = 1.019\,\mathrm{m\,s^{-1}}$$

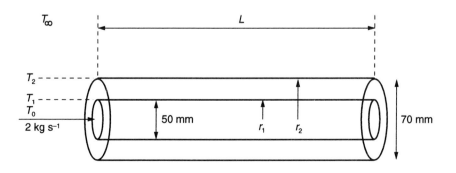

$$Pr = \frac{\mu c_P}{\lambda} = \frac{10^{-3} \times 4190}{0.61} = 6.869$$

$$Re = \frac{d_1 v \rho}{\mu} = \frac{50 \times 10^{-3} \times 1.019 \times 1000}{10^{-3}} = 5.095 \times 10^4$$

$$Nu = 0.023 \times \left(5.095 \times 10^4\right)^{0.8} \times 6.869^{0.4} = 289.9 = \frac{h_w d_1}{\lambda}$$

$$h_w = \frac{\lambda Nu}{d_1} = \frac{289.9 \times 0.61}{50 \times 10^{-3}} = 3536$$

$$Q = \pi d_2 L U_2 \left(T_\infty - T_0\right) \Rightarrow T_\infty - T_0 = \frac{Q}{\pi d_2 L U_2}$$

$$Q = 50 \, \pi d_2 L \left(T_\infty - T_2\right) \Rightarrow T_\infty - T_2 = \frac{Q}{50 \pi d_2 L} \tag{2}$$

$$(1) \Rightarrow T_2 - T_1 = \frac{Q \ln(d_2/d_1)}{2\pi \lambda L} \tag{3}$$

$$Q = \pi d_1 L \times 3536 \left(T_1 - T_0\right) \Rightarrow T_1 - T_0 = \frac{Q}{3536 \pi d_1 L} \tag{4}$$

Add (2) + (3) + (4):

$$\left(T_\infty - T_0\right) = Q \left[\frac{1}{50 \pi d_2 L} + \frac{\ln(d_2/d_1)}{2\pi \lambda L} + \frac{1}{3536 \pi d_1 L}\right]$$

Therefore

$$\frac{1}{\pi d_2 L U_2} = \frac{1}{50 \pi d_2 L} + \frac{\ln(d_2/d_1)}{2\pi \lambda L} + \frac{1}{3536 \pi d_1 L}$$

$$\frac{1}{d_2 U_2} = \left\{\frac{1}{50 \times 70 \times 10^{-3}} + \frac{\ln(7/5)}{2 \times 0.2} + \frac{1}{3536 \times 50 \times 10^{-3}}\right\}$$

$$= \frac{1}{3.5} + 0.8412 + \frac{1}{176.8} = 1.1326$$

Therefore

$$U_2 = \frac{1}{70 \times 10^{-3} \times 1.1326} = 12.6 \ \text{W m}^{-2} \ \text{K}^{-1}$$

(b)   Inner surface area

Write:

$$Q = \pi d_1 L U_1 (T_\infty - T_0)$$

So

$$d_1 U_1 = d_2 U_2$$

Therefore

$$U_1 = \frac{d_2 U_2}{d_1} = \frac{7}{5} \times 12.6 = 17.7 \text{ W m}^{-2} \text{ K}^{-1}$$

3.3.3 Fouling

The deposition of solids in heat exchangers can be a severe problem in food processing (see section 9.3). Even the effect of thin layers on heat transfer can be considerable. Consider the thin-walled tube of Fig. 3.14, for which equations (3.20) and (3.21) apply. Suppose there is a very thin layer of grease applied to the inner or outer surface of the tube. If the thickness of the grease is $\delta = 0.01$ mm $= 10\,\mu$m, equation (3.3) gives the heat transfer coefficient for conduction through the grease as λ/δ. Thus equation (3.21) becomes

$$\frac{1}{U} = \frac{1}{h_A} + \frac{1}{h_L} + \frac{\delta}{\lambda}$$

Typical values are $h_A = 50$ W m^{-2}K^{-1} and $h_L = 3600$ W m^{-2}K^{-1}, indicating that for clean surfaces the resistance to heat transfer is almost all on the gas side. This would give $U \approx h_A$ and $T_W \approx T_L$. Grease has a typical value of $\lambda = 0.1$ W m^{-1}K^{-1}, so that now

$$\frac{1}{U} = \frac{1}{50} + \frac{1}{3600} + \frac{10^{-5}}{0.1}$$

This gives $U = 49.07$ W m^{-2}K^{-1} with the grease, but $U = 49.32$ W m^{-2}K^{-1} with totally clean surfaces. The change in U in this case is not dramatic, because $U \approx h_A$. Nevertheless, the resistance to heat transfer across this very thin layer of grease is comparable to that on the liquid side and is consequently important. In general, fouling arises by corrosion and also the deposition of algae; in food preparation, surfaces also scale by solid deposits from proteins, sugars and fats undergoing heterogeneous reactions. The thicknesses of these surface deposits are normally much in excess of the $10\,\mu$m assumed here. For numerical examples with fouling, see Examples 3.14 and 3.15 below, where $\delta/\lambda = F$ is called the fouling factor.

3.3.4 Freezing times

Having dealt with resistances to heat transfer in series, it is now possible to take Example 3.5 and calculate more realistically the time to freeze an

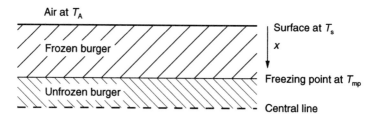

Fig. 3.16 Freezing of a beef burger: schematic diagram.

object, but now including h, the heat transfer coefficient between the cold air and the exterior surface of the burger. The situation is shown in Fig. 3.16.
    Again, the same assumptions will be made:

1. The heat being transferred is mainly the latent heat associated with freezing, so that sensible heats (i.e. those associated with merely temperature changes and equal to $\int c_p dT$) are negligible.
2. Heat transfer is one-dimensional in the burger and is through a frozen layer of thickness x from a freezing front at T_{mp} to the surface temperature T_s.
3. All physical properties are constant.

    Considering unit area of the burger's outer surface, the rates of heat arrival and loss are equal. Therefore

$$q = h\left(T_s - T_A\right) = \frac{\lambda}{x}\left(T_{mp} - T_s\right)$$

Thus

$$T_s - T_A = \frac{q}{h}$$

$$T_{mp} - T_s = \frac{q}{\left(\lambda/x\right)}$$

Addition of the last two equations eliminates T_s and yields

$$T_{mp} - T_A = \Delta T = q\left\{\frac{1}{h} + \frac{x}{\lambda}\right\}$$

where ΔT is the temperature difference, as defined above.
    But the heat flux q is related to the rate of freezing; so

$$q = \theta_w h_{fi} \rho_s \frac{dx}{dt}$$

where θ_w is the fraction of water (by mass) in the burger of density ρ_s. Also

$$\frac{dx}{dt}\left(\frac{1}{h}+\frac{x}{\lambda}\right)=\frac{\Delta T}{\theta_w h_{fi}\rho_s}$$

Integration with the boundary condition that $x = 0$ for $t = 0$ gives

$$\frac{x}{h}+\frac{x^2}{2\lambda}=\frac{\Delta Tt}{\theta_w h_{fi}\rho_s}$$

Thus the freezing time can be estimated. Likewise the treatment can be modified to deduce the time to thaw an object.

3.3.5 Unsteady-state heat transfer revisited

Consider a particle (such as a potato), when it is rapidly immersed into a hotter fluid such as boiling water. The situation is shown in Fig. 3.17. The water is kept boiling at a temperature T_w which exceeds T_0, the initial temperature of the potato. In this situation it is usual to define a dimensionless group, the **Biot number**, where

$$Bi = \frac{\text{internal resistance to heat conduction inside potato}}{\text{surface resistance to heat transfer from}}$$

$$\text{the boiling water to the potato}$$

$$= \frac{V/A}{\lambda}\bigg/\frac{1}{h}=\frac{Vh}{A\lambda}$$

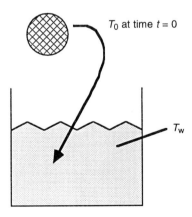

T_0 at time $t = 0$

T_w

Fig. 3.17 A potato, initially at temperature T_0, being immersed in boiling water at temperature T_w.

where

$$\frac{V}{A} = \frac{\text{volume of potato}}{\text{surface area of potato}} = L = \text{a characteristic length}$$

and h is the heat transfer coefficient from the boiling liquid to the surface of the potato. If the potato is spherical, then

$$L = \frac{V}{A} = \frac{\pi d^3/6}{\pi d^2} = \frac{d}{6}$$

where d is the diameter. Thus the Biot number becomes

$$Bi = \frac{hL}{\lambda} = \frac{hd}{6\lambda}$$

It can now be seen that if Bi is large ($Bi > 40$), then the dominant resistance to the transfer of heat from the boiling water to the colder potato

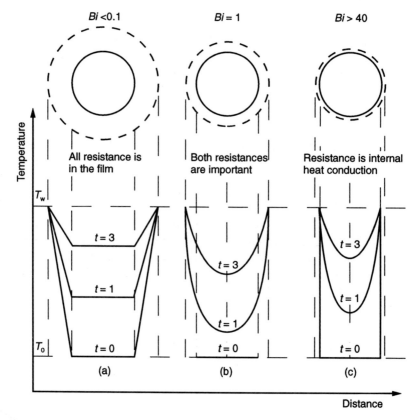

Fig. 3.18 Plots of temperature along a line through the centre of the potato (see text for description) for increasing times ($t = 0, 1, 3$ arbitrary units), as well as for the cases of small, intermediate and large Biot numbers. The film around the potato is also shown.

is internal: that is, associated with heat conduction from the surface of the potato towards its colder centre. This is shown in Fig. 3.18, which is a plot of temperature versus distance through the centre of symmetry for increasing times. Thus part (c) of Fig. 3.18 shows a thin external film, and the surface temperature of the potato is always the temperature of the boiling water. This situation, of $Bi \gg 1$, has already been described in Fig. 3.9. It is worth noting that alternative definitions of Bi exist, so that care must be exercised to ascertain the precise definition. Thus Bi is often written as $Bi = hd/2\lambda$, so that the characteristic length is taken here to be $d/2$: that is, the radius, rather than $d/6$ as used above. Care always has to be taken to ascertain this characteristic distance; thus elsewhere in other chapters $d/2$ is used occasionally instead of $d/6$. This lack of consistency is common in the literature and must be accepted as a fact of life.

EXAMPLE 3.12

Consider the potato in Example 3.7, but with a diameter of 20mm. Evaluate Bi *when immersed in vigorously boiling water, such that the transfer of heat from the water to the potato is governed by* Nu = 250. *Given also that the thermal conductivity of water is 0.6 W m^{-1} K^{-1}, derive and comment on the value of the Biot number.*

$$Bi = \frac{dh}{6\lambda} = \frac{Nu.\lambda_w}{6\lambda} = \frac{250 \times 0.6}{6 \times 0.5} = 50$$

As *Bi* is the ratio of the resistances to internal and external heat transfer, the conclusion is that there is in effect no temperature gradient in the liquid adjacent to the potato. However, there are temperature gradients in the potato.

The other extreme of small Biot number is described in part (a) of Fig. 3.18. Here, at a given time, the potato has the same internal temperature, independent of position within it; also, the external film is thick. This situation of Bi approaching zero is easy to analyse mathematically. The total rate of heat transfer is

$$hA(T_w - T) = V\rho c_P \frac{dT}{dt}$$

where T is the temperature of the potato. Thus, using $L = V/A = d/6$:

$$\frac{dT}{dt} = \frac{hA}{V\rho c_P}(T_w - T) = \frac{h}{L\rho c_P}(T_w - T)$$

which leads to

$$\frac{T_w - T}{T_w - T_o} = \exp\left(-\frac{ht}{L\rho c_P}\right)$$

Finally, for the intermediate case, $Bi \approx 1$, one has the time-dependent heat conduction equation (3.9), but modified for this three-dimensional situation, where position can be defined as a radius r. Also, an extra equation couples the heat fluxes at the surface of the potato:

$$hA\left(T_w - T_s\right) = \lambda A\left(\frac{\partial T}{\partial r}\right)_{surface}$$

Here T_s is the surface temperature of the potato. In this general case, the solution gives temperature as a function of r and t and is usually expressed on charts.

3.3.6 Concentric tube heat exchanger

This simplest heat exchanger for the transfer of heat from one flowing fluid to another is shown in Fig. 3.19. It is useful to analyse this simple idealization. Hot fluid flows from left to right within the central tube of diameter d. The flowrate is $W\,kg\,s^{-1}$ and its specific heat capacity is $C_P\,J\,kg^{-1}\,K^{-1}$. Initially its temperature is T_1, which falls to T_2, but becomes T at a distance x (see Fig. 3.19) along the system. Its temperature is taken to be $T + \delta T$ at a distance $x + \delta x$. As for the outer concentric tube, cold fluid flows within it from right to left, so that this fluid is heated to a temperature θ_1 from θ_2. This fluid in the outer shell has flowrate $w\,kg\,s^{-1}$ and heat capacity $c_p\,J\,kg^{-1}\,K^{-1}$; its temperatures at x and $x + \delta x$ are θ and $\theta + \delta\theta$, respectively. The whole system is lagged. The theory below can be made to cover the case of co-current flow of the two fluids simply by reversing the sign of w. Consider the increment of length δx in Fig. 3.19; the overall heat transfer coefficient is U. Thus within this increment of length δx the rate of heat transfer from the inner to the outer fluid is

$$\pi d\,\delta x\,U\left(T - \theta\right)$$

This is the rate at which heat is lost by the inner fluid, i.e. $-WC_p\delta T$, or alternatively it equals the rate with which heat is gained by the outer fluid, i.e. $-wc_p\delta\theta$. Hence

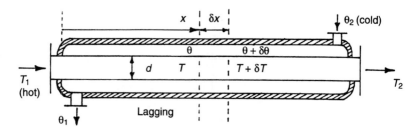

Fig. 3.19 A lagged heat exchanger with a concentric tube and outer shell for counter-current flow of two fluids.

$$\frac{\mathrm{d}T}{\mathrm{d}x} = -\frac{\pi Ud}{WC_P}\left(T - \theta\right)$$

$$\frac{\mathrm{d}\theta}{\mathrm{d}x} = -\frac{\pi Ud}{wc_P}\left(T - \theta\right)$$

Now introduce $\Delta T = T - \theta$, which is the local temperature difference: that is, the local driving force leading to the transfer of heat. Subtraction of the second from the first equation above gives

$$\frac{\mathrm{d}(\Delta T)}{\mathrm{d}x} = -\pi Ud\left(\frac{1}{WC_P} - \frac{1}{wc_P}\right)\Delta T$$

$$-\int_{\Delta T_1}^{\Delta T_2} \frac{\mathrm{d}(\Delta T)}{\Delta T} = \pi Ud\left(\frac{1}{WC_P} - \frac{1}{wc_P}\right)\int_0^L \mathrm{d}x$$

where L is the overall length of the heat exchanger and ΔT_1 and ΔT_2 are the differences in temperature of the two fluids at the left- and right-hand ends, respectively. Thus

$$\Delta T_1 = T_1 - \theta_1 \quad \text{at} \quad x = 0$$
$$\Delta T_2 = T_2 - \theta_2 \quad \text{at} \quad x = L$$

and the above leads to

$$\ln\left(\frac{\Delta T_1}{\Delta T_2}\right) = \pi UdL\left(\frac{1}{WC_P} - \frac{1}{wc_P}\right)$$

$$= AU\left(\frac{1}{WC_P} - \frac{1}{wc_P}\right)$$

(3.23)

where $A = L\pi d$ is the total surface area available for heat transfer. Once the above heat exchanger is operating in the steady state, the overall rate with which heat is transferred from the inner to the outer fluid is

$$Q = WC_P\left(T_1 - T_2\right) = wc_P\left(\theta_1 - \theta_2\right)$$

Hence

$$\Delta T_1 - \Delta T_2 = T_1 - \theta_1 - T_2 + \theta_2$$

$$= Q\left(\frac{1}{WC_P} - \frac{1}{wc_P}\right)$$

(3.24)

Equations (3.23) and (3.24) give

$$\ln\left(\frac{\Delta T_1}{\Delta T_2}\right) = \frac{AU(\Delta T_1 - \Delta T_2)}{Q}$$

or

$$Q = \frac{AU\left(\Delta T_1 - \Delta T_2\right)}{\ln\left(\dfrac{\Delta T_1}{\Delta T_2}\right)} \qquad (3.25)$$

Equation (3.25) is of the form Q = area for heat transfer × heat transfer coefficient × mean temperature difference between the two fluids. This latter quantity is seen from equation (3.25) to be the logarithmic mean (ΔT_{1m}) of the ΔT at the two ends of the heat exchanger. Equation (3.25) is thus

$$Q = AU\Delta T_{1m} \qquad (3.26)$$

with

$$\Delta T_{1m} = \frac{\Delta T_1 - \Delta T_2}{\ln\left(\Delta T_1 / \Delta T_2\right)}$$

Equation (3.26) is a general result applicable to both co- and counter-current flows. This is because the result is independent of the sign of w. Also, an identical result is obtained for the case shown in Fig. 3.10, when the wall temperature was maintained constant: for example, by having steam condense on the outer surface. A special case arises in the above theory when $WC_P = wc_P$. Here $T_1 - T_2 = \theta_1 - \theta_2$, so that $\Delta T_1 = \Delta T_2$. Here the logarithmic mean of ΔT_1 and ΔT_2 is ΔT_1, so that $Q = UA\Delta T_1$. A useful result is that the logarithmic mean of ΔT_1 and ΔT_2 in general lies between their arithmetic and geometric means.

EXAMPLE 3.13

Air flows at 0.002 kg s⁻¹ through a 15 mm diameter tube of length 1.2 m. The tube's wall is maintained at 100 °C and the air's inlet temperature is 25 °C. Using the Dittus–Boelter correlation ($Nu = 0.023 Re^{0.8} Pr^{0.4}$), calculate the heat transfer coefficient and the temperature of the air leaving the tube. Why are these values unaffected by the thermal expansion of the air?

Data for air (assume constant)

$$c_P = 1005 \, \text{J kg}^{-1}\text{K}^{-1}$$
$$\mu = 1.8 \times 10^{-5} \, \text{Pa s}$$
$$Pr = 0.74$$

$$\text{Total mass flow rate} = w = \frac{\pi d^2 v \rho}{4}$$

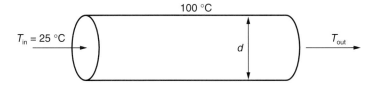

Therefore

$$Re = \frac{\rho vd}{\mu} = \frac{4w}{\pi d^2} \cdot \frac{d}{\mu} = \frac{4w}{\pi D\mu}$$

Hence Re is proportional to w only and so is not affected by any thermal expansion of the fluid. Thus

$$Re = \frac{4 \times 0.002}{\pi \times 15 \times 10^{-3} \times 1.8 \times 10^{-5}} = 9431$$

$$Nu = 0.023 Re^{0.8} Pr^{0.4} = 0.023 \times 9431^{0.8} \times 0.74^{0.4} = 30.8$$

Therefore

$$h = \frac{Nu.\lambda}{d} = \frac{Nu}{d} \frac{\mu c_P}{Pr} = \frac{30.8 \times 1.8 \times 10^{-5} \times 1005}{15 \times 10^{-3} \times 0.74} = 50.3 \text{ W m}^{-2}\text{ K}^{-1}$$

$$w(T_{out} - T_{in})c_P = \pi dLh \left| \frac{(100 - 25) - (100 - T_{out})}{\ln\dfrac{100 - 25}{100 - T_{out}}} \right|$$

After cancelling, this gives:

$$\ln\left(\frac{100 - 25}{100 - T_{out}}\right) = \frac{\pi dL}{wc_P} \cdot \frac{Nu\,\lambda}{d}$$

Therefore T_{out} is independent of pressure and so is unaffected by thermal expansion. Now because

$$\lambda = \mu c_P / Pr$$

$$\ln\left(\frac{100 - 25}{100 - T_{out}}\right) = \frac{\pi \times 1.2 \times 30.8 \times 1.8 \times 10^{-5}}{0.002 \times 0.74} = 1.414$$

Therefore

$$\frac{75}{100 - T_{out}} = 4.112$$

$$T_{out} = 81.76\,°C = 81.8\,°C$$

EXAMPLE 3.14

Water flows at 60 °C with a mass flowrate of 10 kg s⁻¹ along a thin-walled circular pipe of 50 mm internal diameter, which is surrounded by air at 20 °C. The heat transfer coefficient at the outer surface is 200 W m⁻² K⁻¹, whereas at the inner surface, heat transfer is determined by the Dittus–Boelter correlation (Nu = 0.023Re⁰·⁸Pr⁰·⁴).

(a) Assuming that the tube wall is sufficiently thin for conduction to be neglected, calculate the overall heat transfer coefficient and hence the heat flux from the water.
(b) During use, a thin scale is deposited on the inner tube wall. If the fouling factor for the deposit is 0.001 m² K W⁻¹, calculate the percentage reduction in the heat flux.

Data for water

$$\mu = 1.5 \times 10^{-3}\,\text{Pa s}$$
$$c_P = 4187\,\text{J kg}^{-1}\text{K}^{-1}$$
$$\lambda = 0.6\,\text{W m}^{-1}\text{K}^{-1}$$

(a) $10\,\text{kg s}^{-1} = \dfrac{\pi d^2}{4}\,v\rho$

Therefore

$$v = \frac{4 \times 10}{\pi \times \left(5 \times 10^{-2}\right)^2 \times 1000} = 5.093\,\text{m s}^{-1}$$

$$Re = \frac{\rho v d}{\mu} = \frac{1000 \times 5.093 \times 50 \times 10^{-3}}{1.5 \times 10^{-3}} = 169765$$

$$Pr = \frac{\mu c_P}{\lambda} = \frac{1.5 \times 10^{-3} \times 4187}{0.6} = 10.47$$

$$Nu = 0.023 \times 169765^{0.8} \times 10.47^{0.4} = 898.6 = \frac{hd}{\lambda}$$

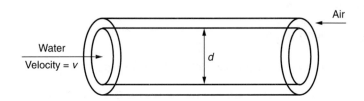

$$h = \frac{898.6 \times 0.6}{50 \times 10^{-3}} = 10784 \, W \, m^{-2} \, K^{-1}$$

$$\frac{1}{U} = \frac{1}{h_{outer}} + \frac{1}{h_{inner}} = \frac{1}{200} + \frac{1}{10784}$$

$$U = 196.4 \, W \, m^{-2} \, K^{-1}$$

Therefore

$$q = U(60 - 20) = 7.854 \, kW \, m^{-2}$$

(b) Percentage reduction due to fouling

$$\frac{1}{U} = \frac{1}{h_{outer}} + \frac{1}{h_{inner}} + F$$

where F is the fouling factor

$$\frac{1}{U} = \frac{1}{200} + \frac{1}{10784} + 10^{-3} \Rightarrow U = 164.1 \, W \, m^{-2} \, K^{-1}$$
$$q = 40 \times 164.1 = 6.565 \, kW \, m^{-2}$$

Percentage reduction in the heat flux, q

$$= 16.41\%$$

EXAMPLE 3.15

A corrosive drink flows at 0.4 kg s⁻¹ and 100 °C into a counter-current heat exchanger, where it loses heat to a flow of cooling water. The water flows at 0.3 kg s⁻¹ and enters the exchanger at 20 °C. When newly installed, the heat exchanger has an overall heat transfer coefficient of 300 W m⁻² K⁻¹ and the drink is cooled to 50 °C. Calculate the outlet water temperature and hence the surface area of the heat exchanger.

Corrosion occurs during operation, such that the overall heat transfer coefficient decreases to 200 W m⁻² K⁻¹. If the flowrates and inlet temperatures are unaltered, calculate the outlet temperature of the drink.
Specific heat capacity (c_P) data:
Water: $c_P = 4180 \, J \, kg^{-1} \, K^{-1}$
Drink: $C_P = 3900 \, J \, kg^{-1} \, K^{-1}$

Overall heat transfer rate $= Q = WC_P(T_1 - T_2) = wc_P(\theta_1 - \theta_2)$

$$Q = 0.4 \times 3900 \times (100 - 50) = 78 \, kW = 0.3 \times 4180(\theta_1 - 20)$$

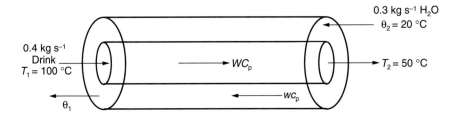

Therefore

$$\theta_1 = 82.2\,°C$$

$$\Delta T_1 = 100 - 82.2 = 17.8\,°C; \quad \Delta T_2 = 50 - 20 = 30\,°C$$

$$\Delta T_{lm} = \frac{30 - 17.8}{\ln\left(\dfrac{30}{17.8}\right)} = 23.4\,°C$$

$$Q = Ah\Delta T_{lm}$$

Therefore

$$A = \frac{78 \times 10^3}{300 \times 23.4} = 11.1\,\text{m}^2$$

After corrosion:

$$wc_p(\theta_1 - 20) = WC_p(100 - T_2) = Q$$

$$0.3 \times 4180(\theta_1 - 20) = 0.4 \times 3900(100 - T_2)$$

$$\theta_1 - 20 = 1.244(100 - T_2)$$

$$\theta_1 = 144.4 - 1.244\,T_2$$

$$WC_p(100 - T_2) = wc_p(\theta_1 - 20) = Q$$

$$100 - T_2 = \frac{Q}{WC_p}; \quad \theta_1 - 20 = \frac{Q}{wc_p}$$

$$(100 - T_2) - (\theta_1 - 20) = \Delta T_1 - \Delta T_2$$

$$= \left(\frac{1}{0.4 \times 3900} - \frac{1}{0.3 \times 4180}\right)\frac{UA(\Delta T_1 - \Delta T_2)}{\ln\left(\dfrac{\Delta T_1}{\Delta T_2}\right)}$$

Therefore after cancelling $(\Delta T_1 - \Delta T_2)$

$$\ln\left(\frac{\Delta T_1}{\Delta T_2}\right) = \left(\frac{1}{0.4 \times 3900} - \frac{1}{0.3 \times 4180}\right)200 \times 11.1 = -0.3472$$

Therefore

$$\frac{\Delta T_1}{\Delta T_2} = 0.7066 = \frac{100 - \theta_1}{T_2 - 20} = \frac{-44.4 + 1.244\, T_2}{T_2 - 20}$$

$$0.7066\, T_2 - 20 \times 0.7066 = -44.4 + 1.244\, T_2$$

$$T_2 = 56.3\,^\circ\text{C}$$

3.3.7 Equipment for heat transfer

Section 9.2 examines more fully the types of heat transfer equipment used in the food industry. In practice heat exchangers are more complicated than that shown in Fig. 3.19. A typical but possibly simple one used in the chemical industry is shown in Fig. 3.20. This achieves a large increase in the area for heat transfer, which is the major difficulty with the heat exchanger in Fig. 3.19. The fluid on the shell side of Fig. 3.20 has a flow affected by baffles. These support the long tubes and also generate turbulence on the shell side. Alternatively, the two fluids can be separated by plates, rather than flowing through tubes; plate heat exchangers are widely used in pasteurization and sterilization plants. Figure 3.21 shows one of the more complex heat exchangers used in the food industry. This is a scraped-surface heat exchanger and is a modification of that in Fig. 3.19. There is an outer concentric tube with one fluid flowing inside it. The inner region, through which the other fluid flows from end to end, has a rotating shaft (500–700 rpm) with blades attached. Thus the surface of the inner pipe shown in Fig. 3.21 is maintained free of deposits. A heat exchanger such as that in Fig. 3.21 can handle fluids containing solid particles up to 25 mm in size. Although the physical operation of these exchangers is complex, the principles on which they operate are the same as those which govern the simpler systems, such as that shown in Fig. 3.19.

Also, complicated heat exchangers can be analysed in a manner analogous to that for the concentric tube heat exchanger shown in Fig. 3.19. Thus the overall rate of heat transfer can be expressed in general as

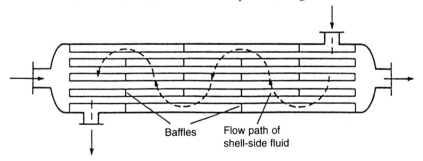

Baffles   Flow path of
           shell-side fluid

Fig. 3.20 A single-pass shell and tube heat exchanger.

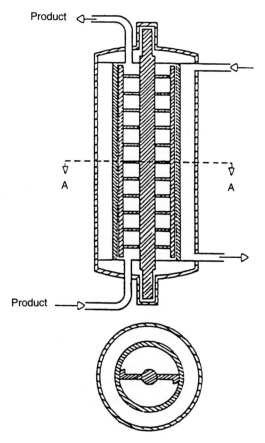

Fig. 3.21 Schematic diagram of a scraped-surface heat exchanger, together with a plan view of the cross-section A–A.

$$Q = AUY\Delta T_{\text{lm}}$$

where Y is a correction factor introduced into equation (3.26). Values of Y are tabulated (for example, in Kay and Nedderman, 1985) for various configurations, such as multipass heat exchangers.

As a final comment, it should be stressed that the chemical industry usually insists (for economic reasons) that a local driving force for heat transfer (ΔT) between two fluids should be at least 10 °C. In the food industry it is rarely possible to have ΔT as large as this, otherwise several problems arise, such as fouling from one of the fluids undergoing chemical change. The fact that $\Delta T < 10$ °C can accordingly result in heat exchangers being relatively large and expensive. In addition, the use of $\Delta T < 10$ °C has consequences when networks of heat exchangers are employed. These matters are discussed further in Chapter 9.

Conclusions

The two mechanisms of heat transfer which are most relevant to the thermal operations in the food industry are conduction and convection. Heat is transferred through the walls of a container or vessel and within solid foods or stagnant fluids by conduction. You should understand the basic laws of conduction, how to define the Nusselt number and why it provides a convenient dimensionless group to describe the process. You should also understand how the basic laws of conduction can be applied both to steady (i.e. time-invariant) and unsteady state processes, which are typical of many food process operations such as canning, freezing, baking, etc.

You should also understand how the process of convection operates in the transfer of heat in flowing systems. Under these conditions heat transfer will depend on the Reynolds number(s) of the moving phase(s) and their physical properties, as measured by a new dimensionless group, the Prandtl number. You should understand how the heat transfer coefficient is defined and some of the approaches to its prediction when heat transfer occurs between a flowing gas or liquid and a solid surface.

In practice, for example in heat transfer across the walls in a heat exchanger or between a hot gas and a biscuit, various heat transfer processes operate in series. You should understand how the processes of convection and conduction can be combined to give an overall heat transfer coefficient. The equations given here to calculate heat transfer coefficients again only apply to particular situations, but the principle of combining the various steps is general. The more complex case of radiative heat transfer is not dealt with here, although many of the key concepts remain valid; radiation can be combined with other processes as described here. The classical problem of the transient heating of a solid by convection from a surrounding fluid was also analysed, and from this you should appreciate the significance of the Biot number which can be used as a measure of the relative importance of the external (convective) and internal (conductive) processes. The idea of a limiting resistance, corresponding to the slowest or rate-controlling process, is a very important one which will also be used in the next chapter.

Some of the basic principles of heat exchanger operation and design were also introduced and, as a result, you should know how to calculate the heat transfer area for a given operation. This particular discussion is taken further in Chapter 9, and is also illustrated by a realistic example in the disk accompanying this book.

Further reading

As with fluid mechanics, all libraries contain many texts on introductory heat transfer. Amongst these are:

Carslaw, H.S. and Jaeger, J.C. (1986) *Conduction of Heat in Solids*, Clarendon Press, Oxford.
Coulson, J.M., Richardson, J.F., Backhurst, J.R. and Harker, J.H. (1977) *Chemical Engineering: Vol 1*, Pergamon, Oxford.
Hallström, B., Skjöldebrand, C. and Trägårdh, C. (1988) *Heat Transfer and Food Products*, Elsevier, London.
Kay, J.M. and Nedderman, R.M. (1985) *Fluid Mechanics and Transfer Processes*, Cambridge University Press, Cambridge.
Levenspiel, O. (1984) *Engineering Flow and Heat Exchange*, Plenum, New York.
McAdams, W.H. (1954) *Heat Transmission*, McGraw-Hill, New York.

4 Mass transfer in food and bioprocesses

D.L. PYLE, K. NIRANJAN and J. VARLEY

Introduction

As well as the movement of heat, many processing operations involve mass transfer; this can be the extraction of a product, such as apple juice from apples, or the supply of a material such as the oxygen required by a bacterial fermentation. The principles of mass transfer are similar to those of heat transfer; however, the process is more complicated. This is for a number of reasons, not least because the range of species which may be transferred is much larger. The concept of equilibrium is also more difficult in mass transfer than in heat transfer; whilst for two bodies to be in thermal equilibrium they have to be the same temperature, two phases may be in equilibrium in mass transfer terms even if the concentration of the species transferring is different in both. Before the processes of mass transfer can be described, therefore, it is necessary to discuss the idea of equilibrium between phases, expressed by such ideas as the partition coefficient or the equilibrium constant.

The previous chapter has shown that heat transfer in static (conduction) and in moving systems (convection) can be very different. The same applies to mass transfer. In a static system, such as the movement of moisture through to the surface of a solid, the governing process is diffusion; when the fluid is moving, the data are best expressed using mass transfer coefficients. This chapter introduces the concepts of mass transfer with reference to a number of specific examples, such as the problem of getting enough air into a fermentation to ensure that the bacteria will grow at the optimal rate.

One of the key ideas of process engineering, that the rate of a process which occurs in several steps is controlled by the rate of the slowest step, was introduced in the previous chapter. Since mass transfer is usually a slower process than heat transfer, this idea is even more important. In studying any process, it is vital to identify the limiting condition; in drying, for example, the rate of internal diffusion within a solid will usually be much slower than the rate of mass transfer from the surface to the surrounding air. This limits the possibility of enhancing mass transfer by increasing the air velocity over a body, and thus the mass transfer coefficient. In addition,

Chemical Engineering for the Food Industry. Edited by P.J. Fryer, D.L. Pyle and C.D. Rielly. Published in 1997 by Blackie A & P, an imprint of Chapman & Hall, London. ISBN 0 412 49500 7

many 'reaction' processes are in practice controlled by the rate of supply of reactants or the rate of removal of products from the reaction zone. The ideas developed in this chapter are thus directly useful in the design of processes and equipment.

Mass transfer is concerned with the net movement of molecules in response to a driving force. Operations depending on mass transfer are of great importance in the food industry in, most obviously, recovery and extraction processes, such as oil extraction from seeds, sugar from cane and beet, or the extraction of flavours and colours. However, there are many other operations where mass transfer plays a key role such as aeration, drying (where mass and heat transfer are intimately linked), and in biological processes with immobilized cells or enzymes. In most of these processes fast transfer is a requirement; in others, such as in the use of packaging, it is important to eliminate transfer as far as possible.

In many situations of importance there are significant analogies and interrelationships between the transfer of mass and the transfer of heat and momentum. In particular we shall see many connections between the material in this chapter and that in Chapter 3 of this book on heat transfer processes.

4.1   Why does transfer occur?

Just as a ball rolls downhill when released or heat is transferred when temperatures are not uniform, so mass transfer also occurs when a system is not at equilibrium. If an oilseed is immersed in a solvent in which the oil is very soluble, oil will tend to move into solution in the solvent. If a packaging material is at all permeable gases on either side will tend – however slowly – to equilibrate. In other situations solvents move across semipermeable membranes under osmotic driving forces. Bulk flows will also transport molecules from one region to another. As we shall see, there are many mechanisms for transfer, and we must take care in defining the equilibrium conditions and the frame of reference for transfer. Order can be imposed on the study of mass transfer, however, by recognizing that in many situations the component flux (that is, the flowrate/unit area) is proportional to:

- the driving force, that is, the distance from equilibrium, and
- the reciprocal of the resistance to movement (which depends on the solute and the medium, such as the packaging film).

4.2   Mechanisms

In the real world molecules are never at rest; even in an otherwise totally stationary medium their random motion gives rise to **diffusion**. Diffusion is usually a rather slow process, and not surprisingly it is slower with large molecules and as the surrounding medium becomes more viscous or solid. If we waited for diffusion to mix the contents of a cake mix we would wait for an awfully long time. This process is analogous to that of conduction in heat transfer.

Fortunately for life on earth, mass transfer also occurs by **convection**: that is, by bulk motion. Sometimes this arises naturally when there is a low-density region (perhaps because it is hotter) underneath one of higher density; in other situations convection is imposed, as in a mixing device (see Chapter 10 for a more detailed discussion), or as a result of mixing and movement due to turbulent eddies in the fluid.

Before discussing these mechanisms in a little more detail we first consider what we mean by equilibrium.

4.3   Equilibrium

4.3.1   The equilibrium state

In an environment at rest in which there is only one physical phase, such as the liquid contents of a bottle of lemonade, and in the absence of any imposed potential gradients or driving forces, the equilibrium state is one of uniform concentration. Local variations in concentration will, even when the bottle isn't shaken, tend to disappear. If there is an imposed potential – if the bottle is swung in a high-speed centrifuge for example, or there is an imposed electrical field – the equilibrium state is no longer necessarily uniform.

In the simplest cases of transfer within a single phase, therefore, the driving force to restore equilibrium will usually be simply related to the local concentration gradients.

However, most realistic situations involve two or more distinct phases in contact. The lemonade bottle initially contains a (small) gas phase and this phase and its components are also in equilibrium with the liquid. Thus the carbon dioxide in the gas is equilibrated with the dissolved species. Indeed, all the species in the recipe will be in equilibrium across the two phases; at equilibrium their chemical potentials are equal and, it is important to note, this no longer implies that the concentrations and relative proportions of the species in the two phases are the same. Indeed we capitalize on this fact in extraction processes such as solvent extraction.

A convenient way of handling equilibrium processes is to define a **partition** or **equilibrium coefficient**. This relates the equilibrium concentrations (usually in molar units) of a given species or solute in the two phases:

$$K = \frac{x}{y} \tag{4.1}$$

where x, y are the mole fractions in phases 1, 2.

It will be seen that K is a measure of the enrichment of the species, as a value other than 1 implies that the concentration in one phase is greater than that in the other.

In the context of separation processes, where the differential extraction of different species is sought, the **selectivity** is important. This is defined as the ratio of the enrichments of two species. With two solutes A and B for example, with concentrations x_A, etc. the selectivity is

$$S_{A/B} = \frac{\left[x_A / y_A \right]}{\left[x_B / y_B \right]} = K_A / K_B \qquad (4.2)$$

Thus, for example, a K-value of 100 implies a 100-fold higher concentration of the particular species in one phase over the other; an S-value of 1 implies no differential enrichment of one species over the other.

While the K-values can be handled as if they were purely empirical constants, they can be related to more fundamental thermodynamic measures, as at equilibrium the chemical potentials of the various species in the different phases are equal. We shall look at some examples of the use of partition coefficients in subsequent sections.

4.3.2   The equilibrium stage

If the contact or processing time is sufficiently long for mass transfer to occur, or agitation sufficiently rapid, the system will approach **equilibrium**. The idea of an operation that has essentially reached equilibrium is an important one, and is particularly useful in analysing separation processes such as distillation, solvent extraction and evaporators. In Chapter 3, on heat transfer, we saw some ways of estimating whether transfer was fast or slow in relation to the processing time – that is, whether equilibrium is approached or not – and we shall develop similar ideas in relation to mass transfer in section 4.5. We shall be concerned there to estimate (roughly) a characteristic time (really a relaxation time or time constant) for mass transfer. Equilibrium will be approached if the characteristic time for mass transfer is short in comparison to the processing time. However, if mass transfer is relatively slow – that is, has a long characteristic time compared with other processes – equilibrium will not be approached and the process is likely to be controlled by the rate of transfer. First, let us see how the idea of an equilibrium stage can be developed and used.

Consider first a single equilibrium stage, such as a solid/liquid or liquid/liquid contactor. The stage either operates batchwise (with quantities F and S of feed and solvent) or continuously with feed rate F and pure solvent feed S. The concentrations of the species of interest are also indicated in Fig. 4.1.

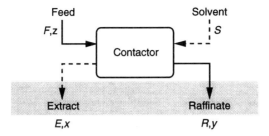

Fig. 4.1 The equilibrium stage.

If we assume that the feed and solvent phases are immiscible and mutually insoluble then

$$F = R$$

and

$$S = E$$

(These relationships are strictly true only when the extent of mass transfer is small or the concentrations are defined on a solute-free basis.)

A mass balance on solute at steady state gives

$$Fz = Ex + Ry \qquad (4.3)$$

Now the equilibrium assumption implies that the phases **leaving** the stage have equilibrated, so that equation (4.1) applies to streams E and R and

$$x = Ky$$

and from these two

$$y = \frac{z}{1 + EK/F} \qquad (4.4)$$

and

$$x = \frac{Kz}{1 + EK/F} \qquad (4.5)$$

Lower values of y (that is, more complete extraction) can be achieved by high solvent/feed ratios and a high K-value. For a given partition coefficient, more complete extraction can be achieved by using higher solvent/feed ('treat') ratios; unfortunately this will also give lower concentrations of the solute in the extract phase, so there is a trade-off between efficient recovery and concentration.

EXAMPLE 4.1

An aqueous stream contains 10 wt% (on a solute-free basis) of a component that can be recovered by solvent extraction. The partition coefficient $K = 2$, and it is proposed to use a solvent/feed ratio of 2 in a single-stage extraction. Calculate the recovery and concentrations of the component in the extract and waste streams.

As $z = 0.1$, substitution for K and E/F into equations (4.4) and (4.5) gives $y = 0.02$ and $x = 0.04$. 80% of the solute is recovered, but it is more dilute in the extract than in the feed. Doubling K or E/F would lead to an improved recovery, as $y = 0.0111$. If this was achieved by doubling E/F, the extract concentration x would be 0.0222 (which is lower than in the first calculation); if K was doubled, $x = 0.0444$. In practice, of course, it is usually easier to change E/F than the partition coefficient.

4.3.3   Multistage processes

In practice, with a single stage it is difficult in general to achieve high extractions; an obvious extension to circumvent this is to add further stages to recover more solute (Fig. 4.2). In the first scheme, (a), the extract stream from stage 2 will presumably be rather dilute; alternatively it can itself be used as the solvent feed to stage 1, as shown in Fig. 4.2(b). In practice, this is commonly done; many stagewise extraction processes have similar, or more complicated, structures.

The equilibrium stages need not necessarily be identified with separate pieces of equipment: a distillation or solvent extraction column with a set of plates inside is essentially a multistage countercurrent process. Surprisingly, perhaps, multistage equilibrium systems, for which the steady-state mathematical models are simply sets of algebraic equations, can often also be used as fair mathematical models for column-based separations, such as chromatographs, where the 'stage' is identified with a defined length of column.

EXAMPLE 4.2

Consider the two-stage process shown in Fig. 4.2(b), where in view of the equilibrium assumption $x_1 = Ky_1$ and $x_2 = Ky_2$ (assuming that the K-values are the same in the two stages). We assume the same values of z, E/F and K as in Example 4.1. Calculate the unknown concentrations and the extraction yield.

For the two-stage unit we can set up a mass balance over each unit, giving

$$Fz - Fy_1 = Ex_1 - Ex_2$$

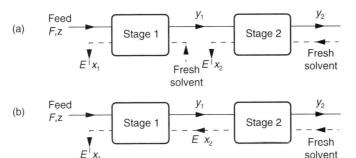

Fig. 4.2 Two multistage flowsheets.

and

$$Fy_1 - Fy_2 = Ex_2$$

where because of the assumption that equilibrium is achieved in both stages

$$x_1 = Ky_1$$

and

$$x_2 = Ky_2$$

There are thus four linear equations for the four unknowns. Solving by repeated substitution gives

$$y_1 = 0.0238 \qquad y_2 = 0.00476$$
$$x_1 = 0.0476 \qquad x_2 = 0.00952$$

95% of the solute is now recovered, as a result of the addition of the extra stage. Further stages would give increased recovery.

For a single-component system an n-stage process would be described by n material balance equations and n equilibrium relationships. The method illustrated above for a single species and constant K-values can be readily extended to multicomponent systems, ones where the K-values are not constant, and ones where the feed enters at an intermediate stage. There are many numerical and graphical techniques (of which the most famous is probably the McCabe Thiele method (e.g. King, 1984; Coulson and Richardson, Vol 2, 1977) for the solution of these problems.

4.4 Diffusion

As noted above, theories of mass transfer must account for two phenomena: diffusion and convection. We first consider **molecular diffusion**: that is, transfer in the absence of convection. The earliest classical experiment on diffusional exchange was carried out on the transfer between two reservoirs connected by a tube, the reservoirs initially having different concentrations of the component. These experiments showed clearly that the rate of mass transfer between the reservoirs was proportional to the cross-sectional area of the tube and to the concentration difference. In fact the result holds only for equimolar counterdiffusion (that is, where the flow of molecules in one direction is exactly balanced by a compensating flow of another species in the opposite direction); strictly, the finding is true for the flow relative to the net velocity. This result was subsequently embodied in **Fick's law**, which states that the flux j (that is, the flowrate per unit area, or the species velocity) is directly proportional to the local concentration gradient. Thus, as diffusion occurs down the gradient:

$$j = -\mathcal{D}\frac{dc}{dz} \qquad (4.6)$$

The constant of proportionality $\mathcal{D}$ is the **molecular diffusion coefficent**, which depends on the molecule and its environment. Note that in this equation the flux is measured in units such as $mol\,m^{-2}s^{-1}$, and the diffusion coefficient will be in m^2s^{-1}. Fick's law has Fourier's law (equation (3.1)) as its analogue in heat conduction, and we can draw on this in finding the solution to many common problems.

Typical orders of magnitude of the diffusion coefficient are as follows

Gases 10^{-5}
Liquids 10^{-9}
Solids 10^{-12}–10^{-14}

4.4.1   The effective diffusion coefficient

While the diffusion coefficient of, say, sucrose in water is around $4.5 \times 10^{-10}\,m^2s^{-1}$ (in fact its value depends on the concentration), its measured value in extraction from beet would be smaller than this, even if the cell walls were well and truly disrupted. This is one example of the way in which the **effective diffusion coefficient** might differ from the molecular co-efficient; in a porous medium the measured coefficient will be significantly smaller than the molecular diffusion coefficient because of tortuosity effects (the more tortuous the region the more devious the route between two points) and because of the hindering effects of the surface of the pores on the molecule's random oscillations. There are many situations in food and biotechnology processing where the effective diffusion coefficient is the key parameter. Situations where movement is governed by Fick's law include processes such as oil extraction from seeds, the movement of salt in cheese, and the movement of solutes in immobilized pellets in biological reactors.

4.4.2   Transport across a film: 1

Let us see how Fick's law can be used to describe the steady diffusional flow across a film of defined thickness L; the concentration of the species is kept constant on either side of the film as shown in Fig. 4.3.

If the flow is steady (that is, doesn't vary with time), then the flux at any distance z into the film must be constant. Thus from equation (4.6) we can write

$$j = \text{constant with distance} = a = -\mathcal{D}\frac{dc}{dz}$$

and the concentration must therefore vary linearly with z across the film.

The form of the linear variation can be seen intuitively or more formally by integrating the flux equation; using the two boundary conditions, this gives

$$c = c_1 - \frac{\left(c_1 - c_2\right)z}{L} \tag{4.7}$$

Note that the concentration profile is independent of the diffusion coefficient: but a moment's thought will surely show that this is as it ought to be. The flux, however, does depend on $\mathcal{D}$ as it is given by the differential of equation (4.7):

$$j = \frac{\mathcal{D}}{L}\left(c_1 - c_2\right) \tag{4.8}$$

The value of $\mathcal{D}$ to use is its value in the film. This result is precisely analogous to the steady-state heat conduction problem in section 3.1.1; equation (4.8) is mathematically identical to equation (3.2) for the heat flux:

$$q = h\left(T_1 - T_2\right)$$

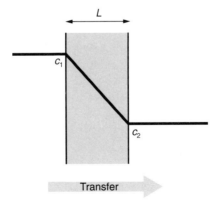

Fig. 4.3 Mass transfer across a film.

and, by analogy with Chapter 3, we can define a mass transfer coefficient $k = \mathcal{D}/L$ and write

$$j = k(c_1 - c_2) \tag{4.9}$$

Note that the mass transfer coefficient has the dimensions of velocity: $m\,s^{-1}$.

We can also introduce another important dimensionless group, analogous to the Nusselt number in heat transfer, which we define as $kd/\mathcal{D}$, where d is a characteristic dimension (here the film thickness, L). In this problem the dimensionless group, called the **Sherwood number**, Sh, is therefore

$$Sh = \frac{kL}{\mathcal{D}}$$

and from equation (4.9) we see that $Sh = 1$ for this problem (just as $Nu = 1$ for the corresponding heat conduction problem). (Note, the requirement that j is constant with distance leads to $dj/dz = 0$ and thus to $\mathcal{D}d^2c/dz^2 = 0$, which is known as **Fick's second law**.)

You might also consider how in a realistic situation the concentrations c_1 and c_2 could be maintained constant.

4.4.3 Steady diffusion from a sphere

Another result of theoretical and practical importance, which can also be deduced by using the analogy with heat conduction, is that for steady diffusion into or out of a sphere in an infinite stagnant medium. (This might, for example, describe the supply of a nutrient to a microorganism, or the slow leaching of sugar from a spherical piece of beet.)

Following the treatment of conductive heat transfer through a thick-walled hollow sphere (section 3.1.2), the total rate of mass transfer past any radius r (Fig. 4.4) is

$$J = 4\pi r^2 j \tag{4.10}$$

where Fick's law is:

$$j = -\mathcal{D}\frac{dc}{dr} \tag{4.6}$$

Now, as J must be independent of r for there to be no accumulation of mass (that is, steady state) then (cf. equation (3.5)):

$$j = \frac{J}{4\pi r^2} = -\mathcal{D}\frac{dc}{dr} \tag{4.11}$$

which can be integrated as in Chapter 3 to give an equation for the total rate of mass transfer between the spherical surfaces at r_1 and r_2:

$$J = \frac{4\pi\mathcal{D}(c_1 - c_2)}{(1/r_1 - 1/r_2)} \tag{4.12}$$

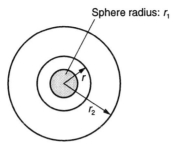

Sphere radius: r_1

Fig. 4.4 Transfer from a sphere.

For the particular case of mass transfer from a sphere of radius r_1 into an infinite environment, i.e. $r_2 \to \infty$, we obtain

$$\frac{J}{4\pi r_1} = \mathcal{D}(c_1 - c_2)$$

or

$$\frac{J}{4\pi r_1^2} = \frac{\mathcal{D}(c_1 - c_2)}{r_1}$$

That is,

$$j = k(c_1 - c_2) \tag{4.13}$$

where k ($= \mathcal{D}/r_1$) is the **mass transfer coefficient**, and c_1, c_2 are the concentrations at the sphere boundary and infinity respectively. (Of course, the same expression holds for transfer in the reverse direction.) In defining the Sherwood number for this situation it is, as with the Nusselt number, usual to use the sphere diameter ($= 2r_1$) as the characteristic length dimension, so that in this case

$$Sh = \frac{kD}{\mathcal{D}} = 2 \tag{4.14}$$

EXAMPLE 4.3

Calculate the maximum rate of uptake of glucose to a spherical bacterium of diameter (a) 1 μm (= 10^{-6} m) and (b) 100 μm (which is unrealistically large in practice) in a stagnant medium containing 100 kg m^{-3} glucose. Take the molecular diffusion coefficient of glucose in aqueous solution to be 6 × 10^{-10} m^2 s^{-1}.

In this situation we have $Sh = 2$ so that the mass transfer coefficient is

$$k = 1.2\ 10^{-3}\,\mathrm{m\,s^{-1}},\ D = 1\,\mu m$$
$$k = 1.2\ 10^{-5}\,\mathrm{m\,s^{-1}},\ D = 100\,\mu m$$

Now the rate of mass transfer of glucose is

$$J = \pi D^2 k (100 - c)$$

where c is the glucose concentration at the bacterium surface; the maximum transfer rate to the organism will occur when the glucose is instantaneously consumed so that $c = 0$, and is

$$J = \pi D^2 k 100$$
$$= 1.2\pi 10^{-13}\,\mathrm{kg\,s^{-1}},\ D = 1\,\mu m$$
$$= 1.2\pi 10^{-11}\,\mathrm{kg\,s^{-1}},\ D = 100\,\mu m$$

Note how the mass transfer coefficient varies with D^{-1}, and the absolute rate of transfer varies directly with diameter. (You may like to carry this calculation a little further so as to estimate the maximum doubling time for the bacterium, assuming a yield coefficient of 1. Because the mass of the organism is proportional to D^3, and the rate of nutrient uptake varies with D the growth rate falls dramatically with increasing diameter. We can conclude that while a small bacterium can happily achieve reasonable growth rates when nutrient is supplied by molecular diffusion only, the same would not be true of an elephant (Haldane, 1985).

4.4.4   Transport across a film: 2

The example in section 4.4.2 is not one that is easily realized in practice. As a more realistic example, consider what happens when the transported species is soluble in the film, as a gas might be in plastic packaging; specifically, let us assume that the solubility of the species in the packaging film, c_{film}, is related to its composition in the gas adjacent to the film, c_{gas}, (with which it is in equilibrium) by

$$c_{film} = K c_{gas} \tag{4.15}$$

where the partition coefficient $K \ll 1$; see Fig. 4.5.

Consider now the steady transport of the component across the packaging film from the interior, where its concentration is c_1, to the outside environment, where it can be assumed that its concentration is effectively zero. Then the previous result (equation (4.8)) leads to

$$j = \frac{D}{L} K c_1 \tag{4.16}$$

The mass transfer coefficient k written in terms of the overall driving force $(= c_1)$ is KD/L.

Thus we arrive at the result that the rates of diffusional loss across the film, or transfer into the packaged material (as the boundary conditions and

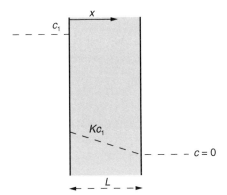

Fig. 4.5 Mass transfer across a film: 2.

direction of movement can readily be reversed), are proportional to the effective diffusion coefficent of the species in the film and to its solubility in the film, while being inversely proportional to the film thickness.

4.5 Transient behaviour

The steady-state assumption gives considerable insight into transfer, but it is extremely restrictive. If oxygen, say, was diffusing across the packaging film the concentration in the pack would change with time, implying that one of the boundary conditions was not constant. So, too, the extraction of sugar from beet or coffee components from the bean imply a depletion of the extracted component with time. Many processes are time-varying.

We can make some progress towards understanding this situation by extending the simple one-dimensional film model above. Because the local concentration changes with time we can no longer assume constant flux. Instead, consider a material balance on the diffusing species across a very thin element dz of the film (Fig. 4.6).

Flux across plane z – flux across plane $z + dz$ = accumulation in dz. That is:

$$-\mathcal{D}\frac{\partial c}{\partial z}\bigg|_z + \mathcal{D}\frac{\partial c}{\partial z}\bigg|_{z+dz} = \frac{\partial c}{\partial t} \times dz$$

Using

$$c(z + dz) = c(z) + \frac{dc}{dz} \times dz + \dots$$

leads to

$$\mathcal{D}\frac{\partial^2 c}{\partial z^2} = \frac{\partial c}{\partial t} \tag{4.17}$$

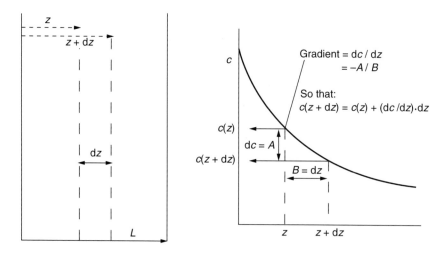

Fig. 4.6 Concentration profile for mass balance.

which is precisely analogous to the equation for unsteady one-dimensional heat transfer, equation (3.9); $\mathcal{D}$ in equation (4.17) corresponds to the thermal diffusivity α in the heat transfer equation. Thus many of the results obtained for transient heat transfer can readily be adapted to the corresponding mass transfer problem. For example, the results presented in Fig. 3.7 for the variation in the temperature distribution within a slab can be translated directly to the analogous mass transfer problem of a slab with initial uniform concentration c_0 immersed in a well-stirred environment such that thereafter the surface concentration is maintained at c_s, by substituting c_0 and c_s for T_0 and T_s respectively. Instead of being $4\alpha t/l^2$ the dimensionless parameter (compare equations (3.9) and (4.17)) is now $4\mathcal{D}t/l^2$. As before, when $4\mathcal{D}t/l^2 = 2$ (that is, an immersion time $t = l^2/2\mathcal{D}$), the concentration profile is uniform: transfer is essentially complete. In other words, significant mass transfer occurs while the processing time $\ll l^2/2\mathcal{D}$, so that the key concentrations will be changing during this transient period. However, for processing times $> l^2/2\mathcal{D}$ one can fairly assume that the system has come to equilibrium and that transfer is essentially complete.

For example, for a sugar beet cassette slice 1 cm thick, the time for complete transfer of the sugar will be of order 2.5×10^5 s – that is, 70 h – assuming an effective diffusivity in the beet of 2×10^{-10} m^{2}s^{-1}.

In the same way, Fig. 3.8 can be transformed to show the transient concentration profiles inside a sphere of radius r_s that is exchanging mass with a well-mixed external environment held at some concentration c_s. To do this we replace T_0 by the initial concentration in the sphere, c_0, and T_s by c_s; the characteristic dimensionless group is now Dt/r_s^2, and the characteristic time for complete transfer is $r_s^2/2\mathcal{D}$.

These characteristic times ($= l^2/2\mathcal{D}$) for a plate of thickness l and a sphere of radius l respectively) give a fair measure of the time to reach equilibrium – the **transient period** – and are very useful indicators. For example, if a process lasts longer than the characteristic time, it can be considered to act as an equilibrium stage (see above). A transfer process will be to all intents and purposes steady over a time interval that is small in comparison with the characteristic time. For example, gas diffusion across a packaging film is so slow that over a period of an hour or so the change in concentration on either side of the film will be so small that the flux is given by equation (4.16) rather than the solution to equation (4.17).

4.6   Flowing systems

4.6.1   Bulk convection and diffusion

As noted in the introduction to this chapter, few situations involving mass transfer are stagnant. Just as we stir the cup of tea to speed up the rate of dissolution and transfer, so many industrial processes involve fluids in motion, which *inter alia* enhance the rate of transfer: the liquid surrounding the cassettes of sugar beet or the coffee bean from which species are being extracted (by diffusion!) is invariably moving. From the discussion in Chapter 3 of convective heat transfer we would expect analogous behaviour in the moving fluid insofar as mass transfer is concerned. And it is true that we can often usefully visualize mass transfer as occurring through the movement of packets of fluid. Although there are important limits to the quantitative analogies that we can draw between the transfer of heat and mass, perhaps the single most useful point is that we can deal with both processes in terms of a transfer coefficient.

4.6.2   Flowing systems: film theory

As noted above, many real situations involve the coupled effects of convective motion – that is, where molecules are swept along by a moving fluid – and diffusion. Turbulence and complex geometries make many of these situations rather difficult to analyse from first principles; however, it is possible to handle many complex problems in ways analogous to those used to deal with convective heat transfer. In particular, the simplest model for mass transfer is built around the film theory as developed in Chapter 2. In this theory it is assumed that all the resistance to mass transfer lies within a (more or less) thin boundary layer in the region between the bulk flow and its boundary: that is, it is assumed that all the concentration changes occur over this region. This is analogous to the assumption made in the treatment of heat transfer in Chapter 2 that transfer across the film was by pure conduction. As with heat transfer we expect the film thickness L to vary with the operating conditions. The film model thus assumes a concentration profile (for transfer from the bulk to the solid boundary) of the form shown in Fig. 4.7.

The concentration profile is given by the theory developed earlier for transfer across a film (section 4.4.2):

$$c = c_1 - \frac{\left(c_1 - c_2\right)z}{L} \tag{4.7}$$

and the flux is given by

$$j = \frac{\mathcal{D}}{L}\left(c_1 - c_2\right) \tag{4.8}$$

which, as we saw, can be written

$$j = k\left(c_1 - c_2\right) \tag{4.9}$$

where k $(= \mathcal{D}/L)$ is the **mass transfer coefficient**.

We would expect the film thickness to depend on a variety of factors including the bulk flow velocity (or more likely the Reynolds number) and the physical properties of the fluid and the transported species. Typical calculated values for the film thickness in transfer to or from a bulk fluid to a sphere or gas bubble are around 10^{-4} m for a gas and 10^{-5} m for a liquid.

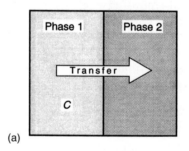

(a)

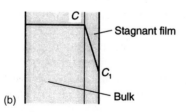

(b)

Fig. 4.7 The film theory. The interfacial region in each fluid phase (e.g. phase 1) is treated as a hypothetical stagnant film. Mass transfer occurs across this film by diffusion; there is no resistance to mass transfer in the remaining bulk region, so the concentration there is constant, as shown schematically in (b).

Values of the mass transfer coefficient k range very widely: from 10^{-2} to $1\,m\,s^{-1}$ in gases and from 10^{-5} to $10^{-3}\,m\,s^{-1}$ in liquids. The transfer coefficient in a porous medium could be up to a factor of ten smaller still (cf. the discussion earlier about effective and molecular diffusion coefficients). The stagnant diffusion situation sets a lower bound on the coefficient.

It is important to realize that the film theory depends on a drastically simplified picture, and that there are more realistic and complicated theories and models available. According to the film theory (equations (4.8) and (4.9)) the mass transfer coefficient should be proportional to the diffusion coefficient; because of the range and magnitude of the diffusion coefficients encountered in practice it is not easy to test this theory, but the evidence available suggests that it is not true and that it is more likely that k varies with $D^{2/3}$, as predicted by other more realistic models.

4.6.3 Dimensionless groups

In a typical situation we might expect the mass transfer coefficient k for forced convection in a given fluid to depend on the following five quantities (cf. section 3.2.1):

L = a characteristic length dimension, e.g. a pipe or sphere diameter (m)
v_m = a characteristic mean velocity $(m\,s^{-1})$
$\mathcal{D}$ = the molecular diffusivity $(m^2\,s^{-1})$
ρ = the density of the bulk fluid $(kg\,m^{-3})$
μ = fluid viscosity $(N\,s\,m^{-2})$

In addition, in processes driven by natural convection or density differences we should also include:

g = gravitational acceleration $(m\,s^{-2})$
$\Delta\rho$ = the density difference between the phases $(kg\,m^{-3})$

Note that five independent quantities are needed to describe forced convection. Dimensionless analysis of the convective transfer situation leads to

$$Sh = f(Re, Sc)$$

where Sh is the Sherwood number = $kL/\mathcal{D}$; Re is the Reynold number = $\rho v l/\mu$; Sc is the Schmidt number = $\mu/\rho\mathcal{D} = v/\mathcal{D}$.

We have already met the Sherwood number and commented on its similarity to the Nusselt number. The **Schmidt number** (cf. the Prandtl number) involves the ratio of the kinematic viscosity to the diffusivity of mass. Like the Prandtl number its value is around unity for most gases, but higher and more variable (typically 10^2–10^3) for liquids. (For example, $Sc \approx$ 560 and 2250 for dissolved oxygen and sucrose in water respectively.)

When a flow is developing – as in laminar flow along a pipe – the mass transfer coefficient might also depend on a second length dimension such as the distance along the pipe, x. In this case, the correlation will also include a dependence on x/L.

The treatment of natural convection adds an additional dimensionless group, the **Grashof number**:

$$Gr = \frac{\rho \Delta \rho g L^3}{\mu^2}$$

4.6.4 Some results and correlations

Not surprisingly, many of the correlations developed for the simpler situations in mass transfer bear a striking resemblence to those for heat transfer.

Flow in circular pipes. Application of the film model (section 3.2.2) to mass transfer between a flowing fluid and a pipe wall leads directly, for turbulent flow, to

$$Sh = 0.04 Re^{3/4} \tag{4.18}$$

The j-factor method (section 3.2.4), also for turbulent flows, assumes that the factors j_D and j_H for mass and heat transfer are equal and, in particular, equal to $c_f/2$, where c_f is the friction factor. Thus, while j_H is defined by equation (3.17) (= $St\ Pr^{2/3}$), here, for dilute systems, the analogous mass transfer equivalent, j_D, is given by

$$j_D = \left(\frac{k}{v_m}\right) Sc^{2/3}$$

(where k/v_m is a modified Stanton number). Thus

$$j_D = \left(\frac{k}{v_m}\right) Sc^{2/3} = \frac{c_f}{2} \tag{4.19}$$

Setting $j_D = j_H$ and using the Dittus–Boelter equation for heat transfer (see section 3.2.5) gives its equivalent for mass transfer:

$$Sh = 0.023 Re^{0.8} Sc^{0.33} \tag{4.20}$$

The same observations about the reliability and accuracy of these correlations can be made as were noted in the earlier chapter on heat transfer.

For laminar flow in a circular pipe a typical correlation has the form

$$Sh = 1.67 \left[\left(\frac{d}{x}\right) Re Sc\right]^{1/3} \tag{4.21}$$

which, for large $x/d \rightarrow kx/\mathcal{D} = 3.65$. The term in x/d allows for the development of the flow field along the pipe towards the fully developed parabolic velocity profile (see Chapter 2). This is very similar to equation (3.19).

Note that in laminar flow the mass transfer coefficient increases with $Re^{1/3}$, while in turbulent flow the dependence is much stronger, the mass transfer coefficient varying with $Re^{0.8}$. The equation corresponding to (4.21) for laminar flow over a flat plate is

$$\frac{kx}{\mathcal{D}} = 0.332 \left(\frac{xv\rho}{\mu} \right)^{0.5} \left(\frac{\mu}{\rho\mathcal{D}} \right)^{0.333} \tag{4.22}$$

In equations (4.21) and (4.22) the mass transfer coefficient is an average over the pipe length x; it should be used in conjunction with a logarithmic mean driving force.

Spheres, pellets and bubbles. Many situations of industrial importance involve transfer to or from solid, liquid or gaseous entities with a surrounding phase. Often, we can approximate these 'objects' by regular geometrical shapes such as spheres or cylinders (the assumption will be a fair one for peas, but less good for potatoes, which should not be seen as a modeller's argument for identical food products).

We must distinguish between transfer inside and outside the object. For example, the extraction of coffee from ground beans in a packed bed involves at least two distinct mass transfer steps: first, transport of the extracted solutes through the bean to the surface; second, transport away from the bean and into the bulk, moving fluid. Usually, these processes will be dominated by different mechanisms and will occur at very different rates (Fig. 4.8). Movement within a porous or semiporous body, as in many solid/liquid extractions, or in adsorption processes, is normally dominated by (slow) diffusion; transfer away from the solid into the bulk liquid will

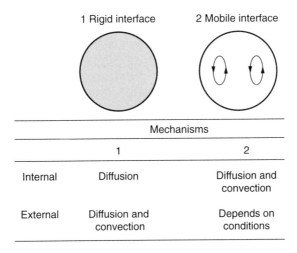

	1 Rigid interface	2 Mobile interface
	Mechanisms	
	1	2
Internal	Diffusion	Diffusion and convection
External	Diffusion and convection	Depends on conditions

Fig. 4.8 Mass transfer from a sphere.

typically involve convective transfer. If the 'object' is a gas bubble or liquid droplet, internal transfer will involve convection, if the contents are in motion. Proteins or surfactants adsorbed on the fluid/fluid interface may add an additional barrier to transfer.

The transfer rate will also depend on the relative proximity of other objects, as these can seriously modify the flow and concentration fields. In other words, the rate of mass transfer from a single bubble of diameter d will not be the same as that from the same-sized bubble rising in a swarm; transfer from a sphere in an infinite fluid is different from transfer from the same sphere in a packed bed.

A few examples of some typical correlations for transfer from solid, liquid and gaseous spheres are given below. In these correlations the characteristic length is the appropriate sphere diameter d.

External transfer coefficient

Rigid interface
Single particles:

$$\text{Low } Re, \qquad Sh = 2 \text{ as } Re \to 0 \qquad (4.14)$$

$$\text{More generally,} \quad Sh = 2 + bRe^{0.5}Sc^{0.33} \qquad (4.23)$$

For larger particles at low Re:

$$k = 0.3\left(g\Delta\rho\mathcal{D}^2/\nu\rho\right)^{1/3} \qquad (4.24)$$

Packed bed of particles:

$$j_D = 1.17\, Re^{-0.415} \qquad (4.25)$$

where Re is defined in terms of the particle diameter (or the diameter of the equivalent sphere) and the superficial velocity in the bed.

Mobile interface

$$k = 0.4\left[1+\left(\frac{\rho_i}{\rho}\right)^{0.5}\right]^{-0.5}\left(\frac{g^2\Delta\rho^2\mathcal{D}^3}{\nu\rho^2}\right)^{1/6} \qquad (4.26)$$

Internal transfer coefficient

Rigid sphere. Transfer is governed by the unsteady mass transfer equation (4.17). An approximate solution to the problem gives for short transfer times, i.e. early in the transfer process:

$$Sh = 10 \qquad (4.27)$$

Mobile interface. Equation (4.26) also holds for this case. In this equation ρ and v are properties of the external phase; the value of $\mathcal{D}$ depends on the phase considered: that is, when calculating the external coefficient, $\mathcal{D}$ should correspond to diffusion of the solute in the external phase. When the internal coefficient is being computed, the appropriate value of $\mathcal{D}$ is that for the solute in the internal phase.

EXAMPLE 4.4

50 kg of sugar crystals have been left in the bottom of a cylindrical vessel, and it is decided to dissolve them by recirculating a large volume (5 m³) of water through the bed of crystals. The superficial velocity of the liquid through the bed is 0.5 ms⁻¹. Assume that the crystals have an initial uniform equivalent diameter of 1 mm. The rate of mass transfer per unit area of crystal surface can be assumed to be given by

$$k_L(660 - c)$$

where c is the instantaneous concentration of sugar in solution and k_L is the liquid-side transfer coefficient.
    How long will it take to dissolve the crystals?
    Assume:

$$\rho(crystals) = 1200\,kg\,m^{-3}$$
$$\rho = 1000\,kg\,m^{-3}$$
$$\mu = 1\,mNs\,m^{-2}$$
$$\mathcal{D} = 5 \times 10^{-10}\,m^2\,s^{-1}$$

Hence Re = 500 and Sc = 2000, based on the initial crystal size.
    From equations (4.19) and (4.25),

$$j_D = kSc^{2/3}/v_m = 1.17Re^{-0.415} = 0.089$$

and

$$k = 0.00028\,m\,s^{-1}$$

Now consider a single crystal, diameter D_c; then at any moment

$$\frac{1200\,d}{dt}(\pi D_c^3/6) = -k_L\pi D_c^2(660 - c)$$

Now the sugar solution is always very dilute, so we can assume $c \ll 660$, and thus

$$\frac{d(D_c)}{dt} = -3.3k_L$$

Integrating:

$$D_c(t) = D_c(0) - 3.3k_L t$$

and the time for complete dissolution is $t = 0.3D_c(0)/k_L$, where $D_c(0)$ is the initial particle diameter. Hence $t = 1.07\,\text{s}$. You should consider whether basing the calculation of the mass transfer coefficient on the initial conditions leads to an under- or overestimate of the dissolution time.

4.6.5 Bulk flow and diffusion: concentration polarization

In some situations the opposing effects of bulk flow and diffusion give rise to a phenomenon known as **concentration polarization**. As an example of this problem we discuss a simple model of a very important operation: the cross-flow ultrafilter. In this device (Fig. 4.9), which is frequently used for concentration or selective separation of macromolecules, process fluid is passed over a filtration membrane; as the pressure is higher in the feed side, there is a flow of permeate through the membrane, so that the feed-side solution (or retentate) leaving the membrane system will have a higher concentration of species unable to pass through the membrane.

Now consider what happens to species – such as a protein – unable to pass through the membrane. We suppose that the species concentration in the bulk stream is c_b; suppose also that the flowrate across the membrane is high in comparison to the permeate flow, so that the bulk concentration remains effectively constant in the membrane module. Recalling the basic fluid mechanics and heat transfer discussed above in Chapters 2 and 3, we assume that the stream flowing across the membrane comprises a well-mixed turbulent core and a thin boundary layer (Fig. 4.10). We assume that the concentration changes occur across the thin film. The flowrate of permeate is Q and the flux J of permeate is therefore Q/A, where A is the membrane area; suppose that none of the protein species is transported across the membrane.

If we consider the membrane as a porous body, then the permeate flux through it may reasonably be expected to follow Darcy's law (section 2.3.3):

$$J = \frac{\Delta P}{W_m} \tag{4.28}$$

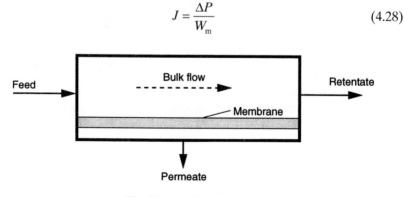

Fig. 4.9 Cross-flow filtration.

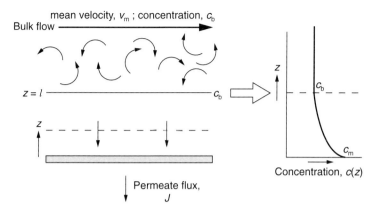

Fig. 4.10 Flows and concentration profile near the membrane.

where ΔP is the pressure drop and W_m is the hydraulic resistance of the membrane. As the discussion in Chapter 2 shows, this parameter depends on the membrane pore size distribution and voidage fraction, as well as on the viscosity of the permeate, equation (2.50).

The permeate, flowing at right angles to the bulk flow, transports dissolved species within it towards the membrane. If the protein concentration is c at some point in the boundary layer the bulk flux of the protein towards the membrane because of the permeate flow will thus be Jc. However, the protein cannot pass through the membrane and will tend to accumulate in the boundary film; because the concentration therefore increases towards the membrane surface, protein, following Fick's law, will tend to diffuse back towards the bulk. Thus if a steady state is established and a steady concentration profile is established within the boundary layer the fact that there is no net transfer towards the membrane implies that the bulk flux and the back, diffusional flux ($= -\mathcal{D}dc/dz$, by Fick's law, equation (4.6)) must be equal:

$$Jc\left(z\right) = -\frac{\mathcal{D}dc}{dz} \tag{4.29}$$

Integrating, and using the boundary conditions that $c = c_b$ at the edge of the boundary layer, $z = l$ and $= c_m$, say, at the membrane surface, $z = 0$ gives

$$J = \left(\frac{\mathcal{D}}{l}\right)\ln\left(\frac{c_m}{c_b}\right) \tag{4.30}$$

or

$$\frac{c_m}{c_b} = \exp\left(\frac{Jl}{\mathcal{D}}\right) \tag{4.31}$$

which relates the concentration at the surface to the permeate flux (Fig. 4.11).

Note that the higher the diffusion coefficient $\mathcal{D}$ and the thinner the boundary layer thickness l, the smaller is c_m for a given J. This results from the balance between the sweeping effect of the permeate flux J and the back-diffusional flow, which tends to reduce the concentration at the membrane. We see that the concentration necessarily increases towards the membrane surface: a phenomenon called concentration polarization. We shall also see below that it can have significant consequences for the performance of a cross-flow membrane.

In practice it would be extremely difficult to measure the boundary layer thickness (if indeed it really exists other than in the model-maker's mind), and it is common to lump the the two terms $\mathcal{D}$ and l into one – a mass transfer coefficient $k = \mathcal{D}/l$ – to give

$$J = k \ln\left(\frac{c_m}{c_b}\right) \tag{4.32}$$

Note that here the mean driving force over the boundary layer is the log-mean concentration difference.

Now consider one of the predicted consequences of concentration polarization. As we have seen, the theory predicts an inevitable increase in solute concentration towards the membrane. For a typical solute, such as a protein, there will be an upper limit (set by its solubility) to c_m. We write c_s to denote this saturation concentration; we further assume that the protein precipitates as a gel at this concentration, so that a gel layer forms at the membrane surface whenever $c_m = c_s$. From equation (4.30) we see therefore that there must be an upper limit to the permeate flux given by

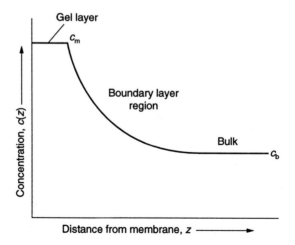

Fig. 4.11 Concentration profile near the membrane.

$$J = k \ln\left(\frac{c_s}{c_b}\right) = \text{constant} \tag{4.33}$$

This may seem incompatible with the fluid mechanics, equation (4.28). However, one theory explains how the two phenomena can be reconciled by accepting that the protein layer itself offers resistance to the passage of permeate, so that instead of equation (4.28) we have

$$J = \frac{\Delta P}{W_m + W_g} \tag{4.34}$$

where W_g is the additional resistance due to the gel layer, whose value (directly depending on the protein gel thickness) is such that equations (4.33) and (4.34) are satisfied simultaneously. If the pressure drop is increased – as the operator would be likely to do in order to increase the flux – there will be a brief increase in flux followed by a new steady state as the the protein gel layer builds up further resistance (Fig. 4.12).

The phenomenon whereby the permeate flux becomes independent of the applied pressure drop is an important and frustrating feature of polarized membranes.

4.7 Interphase transfer

4.7.1 Overall resistances and coefficients

As we have seen, many mass transfer operations involve more than one transfer step. First, we consider how a process involving a series of transfer

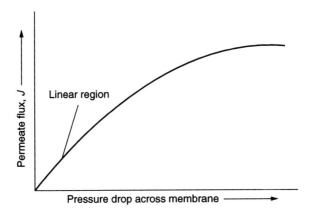

Fig. 4.12 Typical flux–pressure-drop curve.

steps can be reduced to a simpler single-stage process. Then we discuss the general, related problem of identifying the rate-limiting step. The first problem is parallel to the classic heat transfer problem of producing an overall heat transfer coefficient to describe a process involving more than one identifiable resistance to transfer (for example, in a heat exchanger, conductive transfer through the tube wall, through a fouling layer, and the convective transfer within the process fluid). In dealing with such heat transfer problems and some – but by no means all – mass transfer problems it can be helpful to consider an electrical analogy involving resistances in series. For example, the two-stage process in Fig. 4.13 illustrates a simple circuit, where the current flow I is driven by potential (voltage) differences $V_1 - V_2$ and $V_2 - V_3$ across resistances R_1 and R_2. The current flow is given by

$$I = \frac{1}{R_1}\left(V_1 - V_2\right) \tag{4.35a}$$

$$I = \frac{1}{R_2}\left(V_2 - V_3\right) \tag{4.35b}$$

As indicated in Fig. 4.13, we could represent heat or mass transfer processes in the same way. Thus the mass flux j across the transfer resistances would be given by

$$j = \frac{1}{R_1}\left(c_1 - c_2\right) = k_1\left(c_1 - c_2\right) \tag{4.36a}$$

$$j = \frac{1}{R_2}\left(c_2 - c_3\right) = k_2\left(c_2 - c_3\right) \tag{4.36b}$$

V_1, V_2, V_3 : voltage
R_1, R_2 : resistance
I : current

$$I = \frac{V_1 - V_2}{R_1} = \frac{V_2 - V_3}{R_2}$$

$$I = \frac{(V_1 - V_3)}{(R_1 + R_2)}$$

(a)

Fig. 4.13 Resistances in series: (a) electrical resistances; (b) heat transfer; (c) mass transfer.

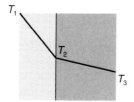

T_1, T_2, T_3 : temperature
$h_1, h_2,$: (film) heat transfer coefficients
Q : heat flux (= rate of heat transfer / area)
U : overall heat transfer coefficient

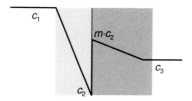

$$Q = h_1 (T_1 - T_2) = h_2 (T_2 - T_3)$$

(b) $$Q = \frac{(T_1 - T_3)}{[1/h_1 + 1/h_2]} = U (T_1 - T_3)$$

k_1, k_2 : (film) heat transfer coefficients
j : heat flux (= rate of heat transfer / area)
K_L : overall mass transfer coefficient

$$j = k_1 (c_1 - c_2) = k_2 (m \cdot c_2 - c_3)$$

(c) $$j = \frac{(c_1 - c_3/m)}{[1/k_1 + 1/m \cdot k_2]} = K_L (c_1 - c_3/m)$$

Fig. 4.13 *Continued.*

where k_1 and k_2 are the mass transfer coefficients (that is, reciprocal resistances) for the two stages.

The current flow indicated in Fig. 4.13a is readily found in terms of the overall voltage drop $V_1 - V_3$ by multiplying equations (4.35a) and (4.35b) by R_1 and R_2 respectively and adding the two equations:

$$I(R_1 + R_2) = V_1 - V_3$$

or

$$I = \frac{1}{R_1 + R_2}(V_1 - V_3) = \frac{1}{R}(V_1 - V_3) \tag{4.37}$$

where the overall resistance $R = (R_1 + R_2)$.

Carrying out the same operations for the hypothetical mass transfer process:

$$j\left(\frac{1}{k_1} + \frac{1}{k_2}\right) = c_1 - c_3$$

or

$$j = \left(\frac{1}{k_1} + \frac{1}{k_2}\right)^{-1}(c_1 - c_3) = K_L(c_1 - c_3) \tag{4.38}$$

where the overall mass transfer coefficient K_L is defined by

$$\frac{1}{K_L} = \frac{1}{k_1} + \frac{1}{k_2} \tag{4.39}$$

Note in particular that just as $R \to R_1$ when R_2 is small, so does $K \to k_1$ when k_2 is large (that is, the mass transfer resistance associated with step 2 is small), and $K_L \to k_2$ when k_1 is large.

The result corresponding to equation (4.39) for the overall heat transfer coefficient U in terms of the individual coefficients h_1 and h_2 is

$$\frac{1}{U} = \frac{1}{h_1} + \frac{1}{h_2} \tag{4.40}$$

While the procedure adopted above is correct in principle, it is not so easily applied to mass transfer problems because these often involve changes of phase (between water and a solvent, for example) between the different resistances. Because of the phase changes, solubility differences (see section 4.4.4 above) therefore imply concentration changes even at equilibrium in the region of the phase interface. We discuss that problem, and its solution summarized in Fig. 4.13c, in the following section.

4.7.2   Interphase transfer: the two-film theory

This theory, developed by Whitman, considers a solute being transferred across the interface between two separate adjacent phases. These could be two immiscible liquids, a liquid and a gas (see section 4.8 below), or a gas and a membrane (see above). In each case it is assumed that the resistance to transfer in each phase lies in a film parallel to the plane interface. The concentration profile of the solute in the phases is shown in Fig. 4.14; because the solute does not have the same solubility in the two phases the interfacial concentrations are different. The diffusivity of the solute may also be different in the two phases, as may the film thicknesses L_1 and L_2.

The fluxes (that is, transfer rate per unit area of interface) in each phase are given by

$$j_1 = k_1\left(c_1 - c_{1i}\right) \tag{4.41}$$

and

$$j_2 = k_2\left(c_{2i} - c_2\right) \tag{4.42}$$

respectively. As in the previous section we wish to derive an expression for the flux in terms of the overall driving force (determined by c_1 and c_2).

At steady state the fluxes in the two phases must be equal. In order to relate the interfacial concentrations we make another crucial assumption, that the concentrations at the interface are at equilibrium, so that

$$c_{2i} = mc_{1i} \tag{4.43}$$

where m is the partition (solubility) coefficient between the two phases.

Thus, as in the previous section, we can write for the flux j, which is the same in the two phases

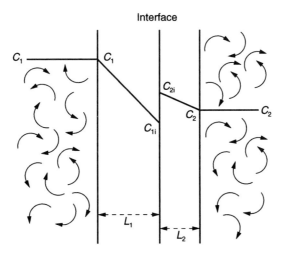

Fig. 4.14 The two-film theory.

$$\frac{j}{k_1} = c_1 - c_{1i} \tag{4.44}$$

and

$$\frac{j}{k_2} = mc_{1i} - c_2 \tag{4.45}$$

or

$$\frac{j}{mk_2} = c_{1i} - \frac{c_2}{m} \tag{4.46}$$

Adding equations (4.44) and (4.46) gives

$$j = K_1\left(c_1 - \frac{c_2}{m}\right) \tag{4.47}$$

where the overall transfer coefficient K_1 is given by

$$\frac{1}{K_1} = \frac{1}{k_1} + \frac{1}{mk_2} \tag{4.48}$$

Note the difference between this equation and equation (4.39): in particular note that the solubility m appears in the expression for the overall coefficient. Also, note that when $k_1 \ll mk_2$, $K_1 \to k_1$; when $k_1 \gg mk_2$, $K_1 \to mk_2$.

It is also important to note that the overall driving force is **not** $(c_1 - c_2)$ but $(c_1 - c_2/m)$. The reason for this is that the solubilities in the two phases are different and are therefore strictly incommensurate (that is, writing $c_1 - c_2$ is like writing 'apples minus oranges'). We can write the driving force as $(c_1 - c_1^*)$, where $c_1^* (= c_2/m)$ is the concentration in phase 1 that **would** exist if it were in equilibrium with c_2.

It will also be seen that equation (4.45) correctly represents what happens when equilibrium between the two phases is achieved. Under these conditions there is no net flux: the driving force is zero as then $c_2 = mc_1$, or $c_1 = c_1^*$.

Thus the overall form of the two-film representation is

$$j = K_1\left(c_1 - c_1^*\right) \tag{4.49}$$

where K_1 is given by equation (4.48) and the individual transfer coefficients are given by $k_1 = \mathcal{D}_1/L_1$ and $k_2 = \mathcal{D}_2/L_2$ respectively.

(It is also possible to derive the flux equation in terms of a driving force based on the concentration in the second phase: c_2 and mc_1 or c_2^*. Depending on which procedure we follow we call the appropriate overall transfer coefficient K_1 or K_2.)

EXAMPLE 4.5

Consider the solvent extraction of rape seed oil from a single seed, assumed diameter 1 cm, into a large pool of stagnant solvent.

Assume the following data:
Voidage fraction of seed = 0.5
Effective diffusion coefficient of oil in the seed, $\mathcal{D}_e = 2.5 \times 10^{-10}\, m^2\, s^{-1}$
Diffusion coefficient of the oil in the solvent, $\mathcal{D} = 10^{-9}\, m^2\, s^{-1}$
Partition coefficient between solvent and seed liquid, m = 20
Mass transfer coefficients:
Assume the internal coefficient is given by Sh = $k_1 d/\mathcal{D}_e$ = 10 (equation (4.27))
The external coefficient is given by Sh = $k_2 d/\mathcal{D}$ = 2 (equation (4.14))

(1) Calculate the overall mass transfer coefficient.
(2) Calculate the rate of transfer of oil from a seed with initial oil content 10 g l^{-1}. How much oil would be extracted in (a) 1 h, (b) 10 h?

First we calculate the internal and external transfer coefficients k_1 and k_2. The expression quoted for the internal coefficient is a useful approximation for the early stages of non-steady diffusion through a sphere (see section 4.4.3).

Internal coefficient
From $k_1 d/\mathcal{D}_e = 10$ we find that $k_1 = 2.5 \times 10^{-7}\, m\, s^{-1}$.
External coefficient
From $k_2 d/\mathcal{D} = 2$ we find $k_2 = 2 \times 10^{-7}\, m\, s^{-1}$ and $mk_2 = 4 \times 10^{-6}\, m\, s^{-1}$.

Thus from equation (4.48), the overall coefficient K_1 is

$$K_1 = \left(\frac{1}{k_1} + \frac{1}{mk_2} \right)^{-1} = \left(\frac{10^7}{2.5} + \frac{10^6}{4} \right)^{-1} = 2.35 \times 10^{-7}\, m\, s^{-1}$$

The rate of mass transfer at any moment is given by

$$J = (\text{Surface area of seed}) \times j$$

where the flux j is given by equation (4.47); thus

$$J = 2.35 \times 10^{-7}\, \pi 10^{-4} \left(c_1 - \frac{c_2}{m} \right)$$

The initial rate of transfer of oil from the seed is thus (per seed)

$$= 7.4 \times 10^{-10}\, kg\, s^{-1}$$

If we assume that the reservoir of solvent is large, so that its change in concentration is negligible, the rate of change in oil content c_1 of the seed is given by

$$0.5\left(\frac{10^{-2}}{6}\right)\frac{dc_1}{dt} = -2.35 \times 10^{-7} c_1$$

That is,

$$\frac{dc_1}{dt} = -2.82 \times 10^{-4} c_1$$

Integrating, with initial condition $c_1 = 10\,\text{kg m}^{-3}$ at $t = 0$:

$$c_1 = 10\,\exp(-2.82 \times 10^{-4} t)$$

Thus in 1 h and 10 h the oil concentration in the seed will have fallen to $3.6\,\text{kg m}^{-3}$ and $0.0004\,\text{kg m}^{-3}$ respectively.

4.7.3   Limiting resistances

From both a practical and theoretical point of view it is interesting to know which, if any, of the mass transfer resistances is dominant or limiting. In Example 4.5 we can see that the transfer coefficient for the diffusion in the seed (k_1) is 16 times smaller than the external contribution (mk_2), so that the overall coefficient K is actually not very different from k_1 (2.35×10^{-7} as opposed to $2.5 \times 10^{-7}\,\text{m s}^{-1}$). From a practical point of view this means that if we wish to increase the rate of transfer we should focus on the internal diffusional process rather than external transfer. For example, reducing the seed diameter by grinding would give a significant improvement in the rate of transfer, whereas agitating the solvent surrounding the seed would have only a minor effect. It also implies (cf. Chapter 3) that the concentration gradients inside the seed are much greater than those outside (Fig. 4.15).

In this situation we say that internal transfer controls or is limiting. Conversely, if $mk_2 \ll k_1$, K_1 is approximately equal to mk_2, in which case external transfer is limiting.

4.8   Aeration

There are many very important practical operations involving transfer of a solute from a gaseous phase to a liquid, or vice versa. In particular, oxygen transfer from an injected air jet or stream of bubbles is a key operation in fermentation processes. We can develop expressions for the rate of oxygen transfer using the same procedure as in the sections above.

We assume that there are only two significant resistances to mass transfer: on the gas side, within the bubble or jet; in the liquid between the bubble–liquid interface and the liquid bulk. Again, we work in terms of the transfer rate per unit area of interface, which for simplicity is represented as a plane in Fig. 4.16 showing the oxygen concentration profiles. As is usual,

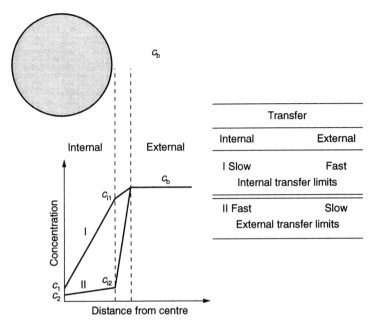

Fig. 4.15 The limiting resistance and concentration gradients. The diagram illustrates transfer from the bulk to a sphere. In Case I the resistance to internal transfer is high, so that there is a large concentration gradient inside the sphere. In Case II the main resistance to transfer is outside the sphere in the bulk, so the concentration gradient outside the sphere is high.

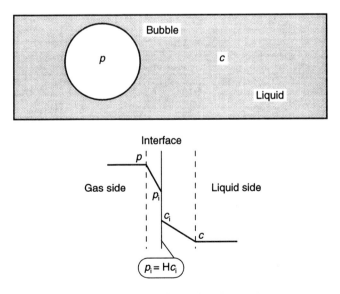

Fig. 4.16 Mass transfer from a bubble to a liquid.

partial pressure p is used as the measure of concentration in the gas phase. The dissolved oxygen concentration is denoted c.

Thus, as in section 4.7.2, the oxygen fluxes in the two phases are written:

$$j_1 = k_G(p - p_i) \tag{4.50}$$

and

$$j_2 = k_L(c_i - c) \tag{4.51}$$

where k_G and k_L are the gas-side and liquid-side film mass transfer coefficients.

The solubility or partition law for a gas such as oxygen in aqueous solution can be represented by **Henry's law** (cf. equation (4.43)):

$$p_i = Hc_i \tag{4.52}$$

where H is **Henry's constant**. At this stage we should note that oxygen is only sparingly soluble in aqueous solution; at atmospheric temperature and pressure its solubility in equilibrium with air (that is, with a partial pressure of 0.21 atm) is around $10\,mg\,l^{-1}$, so that for oxygen H is around $0.021\,atm\,l\,mg^{-1}$. The value of H for a more soluble gas such as carbon dioxide is much smaller.

Assuming equilibrium at the bubble–liquid interface, that is,

$$p_i = Hc_i \tag{4.53}$$

and following the same algebraic procedure as in section 4.7.2, in particular substituting p_i/H for c_i in equation (4.51), the steady flux of oxygen can thus be written in terms of an overall mass transfer and concentration driving force as

$$j = K_L(c^* - c) \tag{4.54}$$

where the overall mass transfer coefficient is given by

$$K_L = \left(\frac{1}{k_L} + \frac{1}{Hk_G}\right)^{-1} \tag{4.55}$$

and $c^* = p/H$; that is, the concentration which **would** exist in the liquid if it were in equilibrium with the oxygen in the air bubbles. Typically, therefore, c^* is around $10\,mg\,l^{-1}$. If the liquid phase is saturated then, of course, there is no net transfer. (If the liquid were sparged with, say, pure nitrogen so that the partial pressure of oxygen in the gas phase $p = 0$, equation (4.54) would describe the de-oxygenation of the liquid.)

Alternatively, instead of substituting for c_i in equation (4.51), we could substitute p_i by Hc_i in equation (4.50), to arrive at an equation for the flux with partial pressure as the driving force:

$$j = K_G\left(p - p^*\right) \tag{4.56}$$

where $p^* = Hc$ and

$$\frac{1}{K_G} = \frac{1}{k_G} + \frac{H}{k_L} \tag{4.57}$$

A little algebraic manipulation shows that these two methods of representation are formally identical, although the first, in terms of the liquid-side properties (that is, with concentration as the driving force) is more convenient and common.

The reason for this in the particular case of oxygen transfer to aqueous solutions is that typically k_L is approximately 10^{-5}–10^{-4}m s^{-1}, while k_G is approximately 9×10^{-4}mol cm^{-2}s^{-1}atm^{-1} (!) and, in this set of units, H is approximately 8×10^5atm cm^{3}mol^{-1}, so that Hk_G is approximately 7m s^{-1}.

Thus we see that $k_G H \gg k_L$: transfer is controlled by the liquid-side behaviour and to a very good degree of accuracy $K_L = k_L$. It must be emphasized that the same approximation may not be true with a more soluble gas such as carbon dioxide.

For oxygen transfer, therefore, we can write

$$j = k_L\left(c^* - c\right) \tag{4.58}$$

where k_L is the liquid-side film coefficient.

In a fermenter or aeration vessel of volume V the total interfacial area for transfer is aV, where a is the specific interfacial area; the oxygen transfer rate per unit volume of vessel is

$$Q = k_L a\left(c^* - c\right) \tag{4.59}$$

Both k_L and a depend on a range of factors, such as the physical properties of the liquid, the sparging and mixing conditions, and rather than correlate each parameter separately it is usual to use $k_L a$ as if it were a single parameter. Values of $k_L a$ for stirred sparged vessels range from 10^{-5} to 10^{-2}s^{-1}, but acceptable values are at the top end of this range. There are many correlations available for $k_L a$ in terms of geometrical and operating parameters such as air flowrate and specific power input to the vessel. A typical correlation for a stirred vessel (see Chapter 10) with coalescing bubbles is $k_L a = 2.6 \times 10^{-2}(P/V)^{0.4}U^{0.5}$ (s^{-1}); like many other correlations this is restricted to a specific range of vessel sizes and water-like liquids, is not properly dimensionless, and so must be used with caution.

EXAMPLE 4.6

A liquid food contains 20 mg l^{-1} of a volatile sparingly soluble compound responsible for an off-flavour. It is proposed to reduce the level of the *flavour to an acceptable level of 0.01 mg l⁻¹ by sparging a well-mixed tank of the liquid with a large excess of air. Under these conditions, $k_L a$ = 0.005 s⁻¹. It can be assumed that the liquid is saturated with oxygen. How long will it take to reduce the off-flavour to the desired value?*

The rate of transfer of the flavour compound to the gas phase is, per unit volume:

$$r = k_L a(c - c^*)$$

where c is the dissolved concentration and c^* its equilibrium concentration $= p/H$, where p is the partial pressure in the gas phase and H is Henry's constant.

If a large excess of air is used, $p \sim 0$ and $c^* \sim 0$.

Thus a mass balance on the compound in the liquid phase gives:

$$\frac{dc}{dt} = -k_L a c$$

that is,

$$c = c(0)\exp(-k_L a t)$$

where $c(0)$ is the initial concentration (= 20 mg l⁻¹). Substituting for c, $c(0)$ and $k_L a$ gives $t = 1520$ s, that is 25 min.

4.9   Mass transfer limitations

We now consider the situation where mass transfer and reaction occur in series: such as when a substrate like oxygen or glucose is transported to a microorganism, oxygen diffuses across a packaging layer to be taken up by a foodstuff in a spoiling reaction, or substrate is transferred to an enzyme immobilized in a porous matrix.

There are two ways of viewing the possible consequences of the interaction between transport and reaction. The reaction may speed up transfer by removing the transported species as it arrives, thus effectively increasing the driving force (Fig. 4.17): this is what was assumed in the example of glucose transfer to a microorganism (section 4.4.3). Alternatively, the transport process may not be able to deliver the reagent at anything like the rate at which it could potentially be reacted, so that the rate of reaction is controlled by the transfer process itself. In the following section we consider one important example to illustrate the phenomenon.

4.9.1   *Oxygen transfer in a fermenter*

We consider here the important question of oxygen transfer and oxygen limitation in a continuous fermenter (see Chapter 8 for the background to

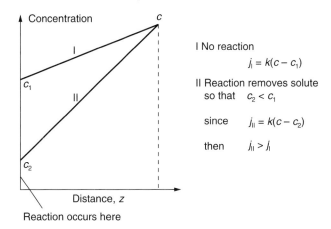

Fig. 4.17 Enhanced mass transfer by mass reaction at boundary.

this problem). Consider unit volume of fermenter. At steady state the rate of oxygen transport from the air to the liquid ($= Q$) must exactly balance the rate of consumption or demand (R) by the growing organisms, which have concentration $x\,\mathrm{kg\,m^{-3}}$ in the fermenter. Assuming that the organism growth follows Monod kinetics (equation (8.13)) and that (dissolved) oxygen with concentration c is the growth limiting substrate, the cell growth rate per unit volume of fermenter is thus

$$r_x = \frac{\mu_{\max} c x}{K_0 + c} \tag{4.60}$$

where K_0 is the Monod constant for oxygen. Further, assuming a constant yield coefficient Y_0 for cell growth in oxygen, the oxygen consumption rate necessary to sustain cell growth at r_x must be

$$R = \frac{r_x}{Y_0} = \frac{\mu_{\max} c x}{Y_0 (K_0 + c)} \tag{4.61}$$

Thus, using equations (4.58) and (4.60) and the fact that at steady state $Q = R$:

$$k_L a (c^* - c) = \frac{\mu_{\max} x c}{Y_0 (K_0 + c)} \tag{4.62}$$

The oxygen concentration c in the fermenter is the solution to equation (4.62) for given $k_L a$, c^* and growth kinetic parameters. If the solution to equation (4.62) has c close to c^* and $> K_0$, the rate of growth can be high, as under these conditions the specific growth rate μ tends to $\mu_{\max}$. However, if the solution to the equation is close to $c = 0$, microbial growth will be seriously slowed because of the limited rate of oxygen transfer. The solution to equation (4.62) is represented graphically in Fig. 4.18. The intersections (a, b, etc.) between the straight lines representing oxygen supply, Q, and the curves for the consumption rate, R, are the solution points, and $c(1)$, $c(2)$ etc. the corresponding oxygen concentrations.

Four situations are represented on the figure:

	Oxygen supply	Oxygen demand	Da	Oxygen concentration
a	Q_2 low	R_1 high	High	Low
b	Q_2 low	R_2 low	Quite high	Moderate/low
c	Q_1 high	R_1 high	Moderate	Moderate
d	Q_1 high	R_2 low	Low	High

An approximate idea of the importance or otherwise of transfer limitations can be obtained by comparing the maximum possible values of Q and R. The maximum value of Q, the oxygen transfer rate, occurs when the driving force is also maximum, i.e. $c \rightarrow 0$, and is

$$Q_{max} = k_L a c^* \tag{4.63}$$

The maximum demand or consumption rate of oxygen to sustain cell growth occurs when they are growing logarithmically, i.e. at μ_{max}, when $c \gg K_0$:

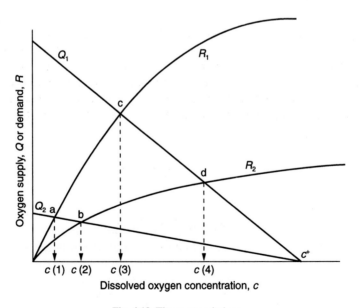

Fig. 4.18 The oxygen balance.

$$R_{max} = \frac{\mu_{max}x}{Y_0} \qquad (4.64)$$

If the ratio $R_{max}/Q_{max} << 1$, there are unlikely to be problems due to oxygen transfer; however, if $R_{max}/Q_{max} >> 1$, then oxygen transfer limitations are indicated. The ratio R_{max}/Q_{max} ($= \mu_{max}x/k_Lac^*Y_0$) is called the **Damköhler number**, Da, for which qualitative values are given in the table above.

To demonstrate this, equation (4.62) can be written

$$\left(1 - \frac{c}{c^*}\right) = \frac{Da(c/c^*)}{(K_0/c^*) + (c/c^*)} \qquad (4.65)$$

or

$$1 - f = \frac{Da\, f}{K + f}$$

Typically, $K(= K_0/c^*) \sim 0.1$; substituting this value and rearranging:

$$f^2 + (Da - 0.9)f - 0.1 = 0 \qquad (4.66)$$

For large Da, the solution to equation (4.66) is $f = c/c^* \approx 0$, so that the cell growth rate μ (equation (4.60)) is small. For small Da, the solution to equation (4.66) is $f \approx 1$, so that $\mu \approx \mu_{max}$.

EXAMPLE 4.7

Microbial cells are to be grown in continuous culture such that the specific growth rate $\mu = 0.15\,h^{-1}$. The maximum specific growth rate for the organism is $0.2\,h^{-1}$. What cell concentration would be achieved with $k_La = 0.0005\,s^{-1}$, if cell growth followed Monod kinetics under oxygen limitation with $K_0 = 0.1$, and the yield coefficient $Y_0 = 1\,kg\,cell/kg$ oxygen consumed? Assume all other nutrients are in large excess and that $c^* = 10\,mg\,l^{-1}$.

At steady state:

$$k_La(c^* - c) = \frac{\mu_{max}xc}{Y_0(K_0 + c)} \qquad (4.67)$$

so that

$$x = \frac{k_La Y_0(c^* - c)(K_0 + c)}{\mu_{max}c}$$

Also

$$\mu = \frac{\mu_{max}c}{(K_0 + c)} \quad \text{or} \quad c = \frac{K_0\mu}{(\mu_{max} - \mu)}$$

Hence $c = 0.3\,mg\,l^{-1}$; then substituting for the known parameters, $x = 116.4\,kg\,m^{-3}$. Under these conditions $Da \gg 1$.

Note that a lower value for $k_L a$ would lead to lower c and thus to a lower cell concentration at the same specific growth rate.

A final example illustrates the application of the same reasoning to another biological situation.

EXAMPLE 4.8

A biosensor for the in-line measurement of glucose concentrations consists of an ultra-thin film of enzyme immobilized onto a flat surface. The electrical output from the biosensor is directly proportional to the rate of enzymatic reaction of glucose on the sensor surface, which is given by

$$r = \frac{ke_0 c}{K_m + c}$$

In this equation r is the rate of reaction per unit area of biosensor surface; c is the glucose concentration – assumed uniform – at the enzyme film; e_0 is the enzyme concentration.

Under the process conditions where the biosensor is used the rate of mass transfer of glucose to the surface is given by $k_L(c_b - c)$, where c_b is the bulk glucose concentration, which it is hoped to measure.

The parameters have the following values:

$$ke_0 = 5 \times 10^{-4}\,kg \text{ glucose } m^{-2}\,s^{-1}$$
$$K_m = 0.01\,kg\,m^{-3}$$
$$k_L = 2.5 \times 10^{-4}\,m\,s^{-1}$$

(a) What is the Damköhler number appropriate to this situation?
(b) The biosensor is claimed to measure glucose concentrations from $50\,kg\,m^{-3}$ down to $0.1\,kg\,m^{-3}$, and it is claimed that high accuracy can be obtained. Is this true? What would be the observed glucose concentration (i.e. c) under these conditions?

At steady state, per unit area of biosensor, the flux of glucose towards the sensor surface = rate of reaction on the surface; that is,

$$k_L(c_b - c) = \frac{ke_0 c}{K_m + c} \qquad (4.68)$$

Hence $Da = $ max reaction rate/max transfer rate $= ke_0 / k_L c_b$

Thus when $c_b = 50\,kg\,m^{-3}$, $Da = 1/25$: there should be no serious transfer limitations. However, when $c_b = 0.1\,kg\,m^{-3}$, $Da = 20$: thus expect serious limitations, i.e. $c < c_b$.

The concentration c at the sensor is calculated as follows. Rearranging the glucose balance equation (4.68) and substituting for $k_L a$ etc. gives

$$c^2 + (2.01 - c_b)c - 0.01c_b = 0$$

with solution $c = 47.99\,kg\,m^{-3}$, when $c_b = 50\,kg\,m^{-3}$
$\qquad\qquad c = 0.0052\,kg\,m^{-3}$, when $c_b = 0.1\,kg\,m^{-3}$

We conclude that the accuracy of the biosensor is fair in the first case (at higher bulk concentrations), but very poor at lower bulk concentrations where there are very severe transfer limitations, resulting in serious underestimation of the measured concentration.

These examples illustrate how the physics of a process – in this case, the rate of mass transfer of a key nutrient – can determine the apparent kinetic and growth behaviour. The result can be generalized to many other important situations: in particular, ones involving immobilized enzymes and cells, where diffusional limitations on the rate of transfer can seriously constrain behaviour.

Conclusions

This discussion of some of the elements of mass transfer is no more than an introduction to a vast and hugely important subject. Here, we have only dealt with rather simple processes where concentration differences are the main driving force; we have dealt essentially with single rather than multicomponent transfer processes (and it should not be assumed that the effects of other solute transfers are merely additive); we have not touched on the very important situations, such as drying and the like, where heat and mass transfer are coupled. Some suggestions for further reading and study are given below.

   The processes of heat and mass transfer will have been seen to have much in common, despite the additional complications inherent in mass transfer operations. There is much in common between the processes of thermal diffusion (i.e. conduction) and mass diffusion, and the basic equations (Fourier's and Fick's laws respectively) are mathematically identical, so that solutions to many conductive heat transfer problems can be used, with the appropriate change of variable, for the equivalent mass transfer problem. Although these problems can generally be formulated in terms of an equivalent heat or mass transfer coefficient rather than a diffusion coefficient, this normally has little advantage for solving transient problems since it results in a time-varying transfer coefficient.

   As soon as interphase transfer is considered (such as in solvent extraction or solute extraction from solids or oxygen transfer between air bubbles and a solution) the problems become more complex. Convective transfer (in which the Schmidt number plays a similar role to the Prandtl number in heat transfer) is also an important mechanism in mass transfer – convection is invariably much faster than pure diffusion. You should understand the principles of and analogies, in so far as they exist, between the two processes. However, important differences between heat and mass transfer emerge. In both cases, the driving force for transfer is the deviation from equilibrium. In heat transfer, equilibrium always corresponds to equal temperatures in the two phases. In mass transfer problems, equilibrium does not imply equal concentrations in the phases, since solubilities are not the same. A consequence is that whereas in heat transfer problems the overall transfer process can always be defined in terms of an overall heat transfer coefficient and an overall temperature difference, the equivalent mass transfer rate is proportional to an overall transfer coefficient multiplied by an effective driving force. Moreover, whilst the overall heat transfer coefficient is obtained by summing the individual resistances, the resistance terms in the overall mass transfer coefficient include a solubility multiplier. You should, after reading this chapter, know the basic principles behind formulating overall mass transfer processes, and understand the meaning of a rate limiting process in this type of situation, and understand what it means to say that a combined process involving mass transfer and a reaction may be mass transfer limited. The other side of the same coin is that a reaction (which effectively increases the concentration driving force by removing a reagent) can enhance the rate of mass transfer. Most importantly, you should understand the implications of finding that transfer in one phase or another is rate-limiting, since this is the clue to improving the overall rate.

It is also noteworthy that some transfer processes are very fast in relation to the residence time in the equipment. In this ideal situation, overall process yields are determined only by the equilibrium conditions. This situation forms the basis of equilibrium stage analyses, which are a convenient and powerful means of designing or assessing many transfer operations.

Further reading

Coulson, J.M. and Richardson, J.F. (1977) *Chemical Engineering*, 3rd edn, Vols 2 and 3, Pergamon Press, Oxford.

Cussler, E.L. (1984) *Diffusion – Mass Transfer in Fluid Systems*, Cambridge University Press, Cambridge.

Haldane, J.B.S. (1985) On Being the right size, in *On Being the Right Size and Other Essays* (ed. J. Maynard Smith), Oxford University Press, Oxford, pp. 1–8.

King, C.J. (1984) *Separation Processes*, McGraw-Hill, New York.

Wesselingh, J.A. and Krishna, R. (1990) *Mass Transfer*, Ellis Horwood Ltd, Chichester.

5 Food rheology
C.D. RIELLY

Introduction

Fluids such as air and water have simple flow properties which are not functions of the previous process history of the material. Food materials are more complex, however, and their flow properties may be strong functions of the way in which they have been previously processed. For example, the flow behaviour of a yoghurt is a function of the bonding between the molecular chains of the protein aggregates which constitute it; if those bonds are disrupted by stirring or pumping, the flow properties of the material may change. This can be seen clearly by comparing a set and stirred yogurt bought from a supermarket and containing the same ingredients; the set material behaves essentially as a solid, whilst the stirred yoghurt has properties more like a liquid.

This chapter outlines approaches to the study of food rheology, the science of flow and deformation of materials. The simple fluids described up to now have had viscosities which are not functions of the fluid conditions: these are called Newtonian fluids. A series of models exist to describe more complicated, non-Newtonian, fluid systems, where the apparent viscosity changes with the process history and current conditions of the system. If the flow properties of a fluid can be described satisfactorily by such a model, then it is possible to carry out the sort of calculations introduced in Chapter 2, i.e. to predict flow rates, pressure drops and velocity distributions within systems.

Foodstuffs may exhibit non-Newtonian behaviour because they contain long-chain molecules, or solid particles, whose interactions depend on the rate at which the material is deformed. In some cases, the textures of water-based food products may be enhanced by addition of a polymer thickener: for example, addition of carboxymethyl cellulose (cmc) solutions to fruit drinks, or addition of xanthan gum to sauces or soups. These additives make the product appear 'thicker', something which in the mind of the consumer may be allied to higher concentration or better quality. However, they can also cause unacceptable changes to the foodstuff: the presence of 'wobbliness' caused by a large amount of elasticity, or 'stringiness' caused

Chemical Engineering for the Food Industry. Edited by P.J. Fryer, D.L. Pyle and C.D. Rielly.
Published in 1997 by Blackie A & P, an imprint of Chapman & Hall, London.
ISBN 0 412 49500 7

by having a large extensional viscosity (see section 5.1.5) may detract from the visual appearance of the product and its mouthfeel. The choice of these additives, from a rheological point of view, is critical to the formulation of textured foodstuffs, and one scientific method of determining the effect of various food additives on the perceived quality of food materials is to measure their flow behaviour in well-defined viscometric tests. In this chapter we shall discuss various concepts of non-Newtonian rheology and the engineering methods available to characterize the flow behaviour of complex food materials. Finally, we shall demonstrate how the various non-Newtonian constitutive equations can be incorporated into the solution of some engineering problems in the food processing industries.

Characterization

Many food materials have distinct physical properties in addition to their nutritional value, and it is often these rheological characteristics that make a significant contribution to the overall quality of the product. For example, to the consumer, the flow characteristics of tomato sauce pouring from a bottle may be as important as the taste; similarly the mouthfeel of a yoghurt (determined by its rheological properties) probably contributes as much to the pleasure of eating as does the flavour! It is therefore essential to be able to characterize the physical characteristics of the food in an exact and scientific way. Rheological testing may be carried out to ensure intermediate or final product quality control during prolonged batch or continuous operation (using in-line viscometers, which are accurate and can measure some non-Newtonian features of the fluid). It is also important to be able to correlate measured rheological parameters against consumer preference, allowing suitable choice of viscosity enhancers and giving a better understanding of ingredient functionality for new products. In the longer term it may be possible to correlate rheological characteristics against organoleptic properties determined by a taste panel, thereby producing a continuous and reproducible measurement of food texture.

Engineering processes

The rheological properties obtained from viscometric tests may be represented in terms of a constitutive equation (an equation relating material properties) describing the relationship between the rate of strain in the fluid and the applied shear stress. Solution of the momentum equations (see Chapter 2 for a discussion of Newtonian fluid mechanics) for fluid flow requires a knowledge of such a constitutive relation and allows prediction of the fluid flow behaviour in a number of engineering applications. Once foods have been rheologically characterized, then the same fluid mechanics approaches may (in principle) be used for non-Newtonian fluids, but using a different form of the constitutive equation relating the shear stress to the strain rate. In some cases it may be possible to treat the fluid as a Newtonian liquid, but in others this assumption could give seriously misleading predictions. We shall discuss the various forms of non-Newtonian behaviour and show which constitutive equations are best suited to model various rheological characteristics. Worked examples are used to illustrate use of these methods in realistic engineering problems: for example, calculation of the pressure drop for flow of a non-Newtonian fluid through a long pipeline.

Shear forces and viscosity

A fluid in motion can sustain both shear and normal stresses, which are determined by the rate of strain and physical properties of the fluid. A normal stress is one that acts perpendicular to a hypothetical plane (pressure is an example of an isotropic normal stress), whereas a shear stress acts tangentially to a plane. In this chapter we are mainly concerned with shear stresses. An example of a simple shear flow is shown in Fig. 5.1: fluid is sheared between a fixed lower plate and an upper plate moving at a velocity v.

For this situation, **Newton's law of fluid friction** relates the shear stress in the fluid, τ_{yx}, to the velocity gradient, dv_x/dy:

$$\tau_{yx} = \mu \dot{\gamma}_{yx} = \mu \frac{dv_x}{dy} = \mu \frac{v}{a} \tag{5.1}$$

where μ is a coefficient of viscosity, and $\dot{\gamma}_{yx}$ is the rate of strain (alternatively called the shear rate). In this simple case the rate of strain is equal to the velocity gradient dv_x/dy, and the shear stress acting in the fluid is constant. However, in general τ_{yx} depends on the distance y from the wall: for example, in pipe flow (see section 2.3.2), the shear stress increases linearly from zero on the pipe centreline to the wall shear stress value.

The SI units for viscosity are Pa s, or alternatively $N\,s\,m^{-2}$, the shear stress is given in Pa or $N\,m^{-2}$ and the shear rate is in s^{-1}. Many older texts use

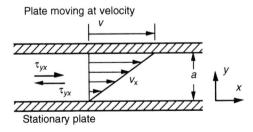

Fig. 5.1 Simple shear flow between two flat plates.

centipoise (cP) as the unit of viscosity, which is often convenient as water has a coefficient of viscosity at 25 °C of almost exactly 1 cP. To convert to SI units (which are used throughout this book) we use 1 cP = 0.001 Pa s. For Newtonian fluids the symbol μ represents the absolute viscosity; a kinematic viscosity, $v = \mu/\rho$ is also sometimes used in fluid mechanics and has units of $m^2 s^{-1}$.

Steffe (1992) gives some examples of the wide range of viscosities covered by Newtonian food fluids: water, 0.001 Pa s; coffee cream, 0.01 Pa s; vegetable oil, 0.1 Pa s; and honey 10 Pa s.

In more complicated three-dimensional flows there are six shear stresses and three normal stresses acting within the fluid. Figure 5.2 shows the stresses acting on three orthogonal faces of an element of fluid in Cartesian coordinates. The stresses σ_{xx}, σ_{yy} and σ_{zz} are known as the normal stresses, and for a Newtonian fluid in shear flow are equal to the isotropic pressure within the fluid, such that

$$\sigma_{xx} - \sigma_{yy} = 0$$

and

$$\sigma_{yy} - \sigma_{zz} = 0 \tag{5.2}$$

The shear stresses acting on the plane in the z direction (shown shaded) are τ_{zx} and τ_{zy}.

Thus for the simple shear flow of Fig. 5.1, $\tau_{yx} = \mu\dot{\gamma}_{yx}$ and $\tau_{xz} = \tau_{yz} = 0$. Note that the first subscript indicates the direction of the plane in which the shear stress lies and the second gives the direction in which it acts. By considering the moments of the forces due to shearing stresses it is also easy to show that

$$\tau_{xy} = \tau_{yx}, \qquad \tau_{xz} = \tau_{zx} \qquad \text{and} \qquad \tau_{yz} = \tau_{zy} \tag{5.3}$$

so that there are really only six independent stresses within the fluid. For most of the flows considered in this chapter it will be sufficient to work

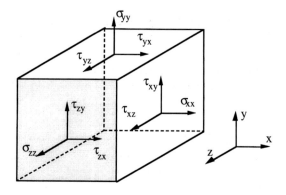

Fig. 5.2 Shear stresses and normal stresses acting in a fluid.

with one-dimensional fluid motion, and in this case we shall simply represent the appropriate shear stress by τ and the shear rate by $\dot{\gamma}$. The reader is referred to Barnes *et al.* (1989), Tanner (1985) or Tritton (1988) for more detailed discussions of three-dimensional rheology and fluid mechanics.

For Newtonian fluids the viscosity in equation (5.1) is a constant material property. However, the fluids that we shall consider in the remainder of this chapter have some internal structure, such that the viscosity depends on the rate at which the fluid is sheared; the viscosity may also depend on the time or history of the flow deformation. These are called non-Newtonian fluids, and in the next section we shall examine how the **apparent viscosity**, $\mu_a(\dot{\gamma})$, defined by

$$\mu_a(\dot{\gamma}) = \frac{\tau}{\dot{\gamma}} \tag{5.4}$$

changes with time and shear rate. In the notation used here, μ_a is the apparent viscosity of a non-Newtonian fluid at shear rate $\dot{\gamma}$, whereas μ represents a Newtonian coefficient of viscosity.

In the simple shear flow of Fig. 5.1 the shear rate in the fluid can be altered by changing either the separation of the plates or the velocity of the moving plate. For a non-Newtonian fluid the ratio $\tau a/v = \mu_a$ would not be constant, and would depend on the shear rate $\dot{\gamma} = v/a$, whereas for a Newtonian fluid $\tau a/v = \mu$ would be independent of $\dot{\gamma}$. This shear-dependent behaviour may be desirable in the formulation of a food product and is described in the following section.

5.1 Characteristics of non-Newtonian fluids

The characteristics of fluid flow behaviour described in this section are divided into a number of categories:

1. time-independent behaviour, in which the apparent viscosity is independent of the duration or previous history of the deformation;
2. time-dependent viscous behaviour, in which the viscosity changes with time of deformation, but the fluid exhibits no elastic effects; and
3. linear viscoelastic behaviour, in which the fluid exhibits some of the characteristics of a viscous liquid and some of those of an elastic solid.

These characteristics of non-Newtonian materials are discussed in terms of simple viscometric flows, such as the simple shear flow shown in Fig. 5.1. The final discussion in this section considers extensional flows, which involve no shearing, and it will be seen that again food materials exhibit different characteristics from those of Newtonian fluids.

5.1.1   Time-independent shear-thinning and shear-thickening fluids

The range of shear rates that a food fluid may experience during manufacture and consumption is large. For example, Table 5.1 shows shear rates for some typical operations (adapted from Barnes *et al.*, 1989), covering ten orders of magnitude.

In each operation the same fluid is expected to behave in a quite different manner. For example, during spreading the fluid should have a low apparent viscosity, but during chewing or swallowing it should have a higher value of μ_a, which gives a better mouthfeel. This is a fluid that exhibits **shear-thinning** behaviour, in which the viscosity decreases with increasing shear rate. Examples of such fluids are fruit purées, chocolate and meat pastes.

Figure 5.3 shows typical shear-thinning behaviour of a non-Newtonian fluid. At rest, the fluid has a microstructure (due either to interactions between particles within the fluid or to entanglement of macromolecules) that, as the fluid is sheared, is gradually broken down. In some cases the rheological behaviour is found to be independent of time, which means that this breakdown must be reversible, such that the structure is able to reform: that is, under steady shear conditions, time-independent non-Newtonian behaviour is a result of an equilibrium between the structural breakdown and reformation processes. As the shear rate increases, the equilibrium number of interactions or entanglements decreases, resulting in a lower apparent viscosity. This also means that when the rate of strain is decreased, a higher apparent viscosity is obtained as the structure recovers.

For the typical shear-thinning fluid of Fig. 5.3 there are two regions of Newtonian behaviour in which the viscosity is approximately constant, plus a region of decreasing, shear-thinning viscosity. Commonly, the shear-thinning region spans several decades of shear rate. The zero shear stress viscosity μ_0 corresponds to the viscosity of the fully structured fluid, whereas the high shear rate viscosity μ_∞ corresponds to that of the base fluid: that is, after all the structure has been broken down.

Table 5.1 Typical shear rates for food operations

Operation	Typical range of $\dot{\gamma}$ (s^{-1})	Examples
Settling of fine suspensions	10^{-6} to 10^{-4}	Salad dressings
Draining under gravity	10^{-1} to 10^{1}	Vegetable oils
Extrusion	10^{0} to 10^{2}	Snack foods, cereals
Pipe flow	10^{0} to 10^{3}	Chocolate, sauces
Chewing and swallowing	10^{1} to 10^{2}	Most foodstuffs!
Mixing or stirring	10^{1} to 10^{3}	Fruit squashes
Spreading	10^{2} to 10^{4}	Margarine, butter

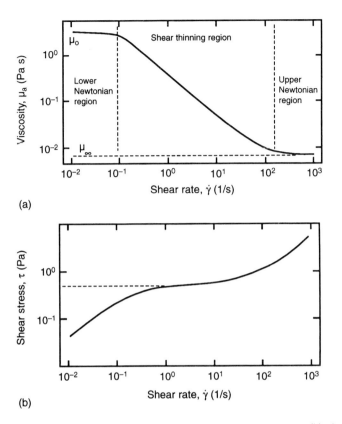

Fig. 5.3 Typical shear-thinning behaviour: (a) viscosity versus shear rate; (b) shear stress versus shear rate.

Cross (1965) developed a first-order model for the rates of breakdown and reformation of the structural interactions in a shear-thinning fluid, resulting in the following constitutive equation:

$$\frac{\mu_a - \mu_\infty}{\mu_0 - \mu_\infty} = \frac{1}{1 + \alpha(\dot{\gamma})^n} \tag{5.5}$$

Equation (5.5) is able to describe the whole range of shear-thinning behaviour including the Newtonian plateau; however, it requires fitting four parameters, μ_∞, μ_0, α and n, to experimental data for μ_a or τ versus $\dot{\gamma}$.

Often, however, it is sufficient to correlate these rheological data for shear stress versus shear rate over a limited range of shear rates using a simple power-law expression. Over the region of shear thinning – that is, for the range of viscosities $\mu_\infty \ll \mu_a \ll \mu_0$ – equation (5.5) becomes approximately

$$\mu_a = \frac{\tau}{\dot{\gamma}} = K(\dot{\gamma})^{n-1} \tag{5.6}$$

or

$$\tau = K(\dot{\gamma})^{n} \tag{5.7}$$

where K is the **consistency index** and n is the **power-law exponent**. These relationships are compared with Newtonian behaviour in Fig. 5.4.

For shear-thinning fluids the exponent n typically lies in the range 0.2–1, with $n = 1$ corresponding to a Newtonian liquid (compare equations (5.1) and (5.5)). Note that equation (5.7) is simply an engineering representation of the rheological behaviour over a given range of shear rates, and it would be unwise to extrapolate the power law outside this range into either the upper or lower Newtonian regions shown in Fig. 5.3. Usually the power-law equation would be reasonably accurate over two decades of shear rate (Nielsen, 1977).

Some examples of power-law rheological behaviour are given in Table 5.2 (data from Steffe, 1992). The power-law index gives a simple measure of the degree to which the fluid is non-Newtonian. For example, a value of n close to unity would act almost as a Newtonian fluid, whereas banana

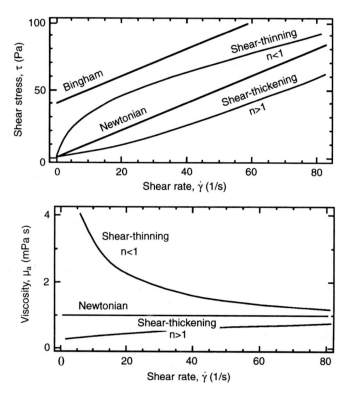

Fig. 5.4 Comparison of some typical Newtonian, shear-thinning and shear-thickening power-law fluids and a Bingham plastic fluid.

Table 5.2 Power-law parameters for various food fluids

Food fluid	T (°C)	n (–)	K (Pa s^n)	Range of $\dot\gamma$ (s^{-1})
Banana purée	22	0.28	107.3	28–200
Apple sauce	26	0.45	7.32	0.78–1260
Mayonnaise	25	0.60	4.2	40–1100

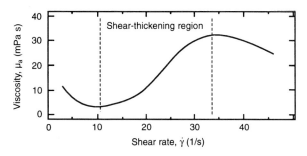

Fig. 5.5 Typical shear-thickening behaviour of a concentrated suspension of non-aggregating particles.

purée, which has a very low index, would exhibit extreme shear-thinning behaviour.

It is also possible for deformation of a fluid to cause rearrangement of its microstructure that results in an **increase** in viscosity with increasing shear rate. **Shear-thickening** fluids are less common than those with shear-thinning behaviour, although most concentrated suspensions of non-aggregating solid particles show some shear-thickening behaviour, given the correct conditions. For example, cornflour pastes and some honeys exhibit shear-thickening behaviour (Steffe, 1992). The explanation offered by Reynolds (1885) is that at rest the voidage fraction of the suspension is at a minimum and there is only just sufficient liquid to fill the voids between particles. At low shear rates the liquid lubricates the motion of one particle past another and the apparent viscosity is small. However, at larger shear rates the dense packing of the material is broken up, and the suspension dilates (the voidage fraction increases). There is now insufficient liquid to lubricate each particle and the apparent viscosity of the particulate mixture increases.

Figure 5.5 shows typical shear-thickening behaviour for a concentrated suspension of particles. Note that there is some shear-thinning behaviour at low shear rates and that shear thickening occurs over less than one decade of $\dot\gamma$. In this region, shear-thickening fluids can also be represented by the power law of equation (5.5), but with an exponent of $n > 1$ (see Fig. 5.4).

The next class of non-Newtonian fluids to be considered is **Bingham plastic fluids**, which appear to require a yield shear stress τ_y to be exceeded before fluid deformation takes place: that is, they contain a sufficiently rigid (solid-like) structure that any stress less than the yield stress can be resisted and no continuous motion results. Below the yield stress the material behaves as an elastic solid and stores energy at small strains; at stresses above the yield stress the structure disintegrates and the fluid deforms as a Newtonian fluid under an applied stress $\tau - \tau_y$. The constitutive equation for these fluids is

$$\tau = \tau_y + \mu\dot{\gamma} \qquad \tau > \tau_y$$

and

$$\dot{\gamma} = 0 \qquad \tau < \tau_y \tag{5.8}$$

and they have the stress–strain rate relationship shown in Fig. 5.4. As the Bingham fluid acts as an elastic solid for $\tau < \tau_y$, then it may be more appropriate to write the constitutive equation as

$$\tau = \tau_y + \mu\dot{\gamma} \qquad \tau > \tau_y$$

and

$$\tau = G\gamma \qquad \tau < \tau_y \tag{5.9}$$

where G is a shear modulus for elastic deformation (analogous to Hooke's constant for an elastic spring). The concept of a yield stress fluid is useful in many practical engineering applications (see section 5.4), but its existence is dubious; often, viscometric measurements cannot be made at a sufficiently low shear rate to determine whether a yield stress exists, or if there is extreme shear-thinning behaviour and a very large zero shear viscosity, in the limit, $\dot{\gamma} \to 0$. Figure 5.3(b) shows that if the measurements had been terminated at a strain rate of about $1\,\mathrm{s}^{-1}$, then no lower Newtonian region would have been observed and extrapolation to $\dot{\gamma} \to 0$ would suggest that the fluid possessed a yield stress. Barnes *et al.* (1989) discuss this question and conclude that there is no yield stress for dilute solutions and suspensions, but for materials such as ice cream or margarine the flow at very low applied stresses is so slow that motion cannot be observed and there is still some doubt as to the existence of τ_y. For many engineering situations, however, the assumption of Bingham plastic behaviour is a useful approximation, as will be illustrated in section 5.3.1.

The constitutive equations given above for time-independent fluids are the simplest available that characterize shear thinning, shear thickening and yield stress behaviour. Many other empirical equations have been proposed, but their use in solving engineering problems is algebraically more difficult than the simple Cross, power law and Bingham equations. Tanner (1985, p. 15) presents a number of alternative constitutive equations. The

Herschel–Bulkley equation is a useful model for fluids exhibiting both a yield stress and shear-thinning behaviour:

$$\tau = \tau_y + K(\dot{\gamma})^n \qquad (5.10)$$

Equation (5.10) now contains three fitted parameters, of which the yield stress is difficult to determine. The most common method of estimating the yield stress is to extrapolate the shear stress versus shear rate curves to $\dot{\gamma} \rightarrow 0$, but this is fraught with the difficulties of obtaining reliable data at low shear rates. Steffe (1992) discusses various other methods of estimating the yield stress. Non-linear regression to find the yield stress gives a result that is highly dependent on the form of the constitutive equation chosen to represent the data.

It is now generally accepted that molten chocolate can be modelled as a **Casson fluid** (Casson, 1959), which obeys a rheological equation of the form

$$(\tau)^{0.5} = (\tau_y)^{0.5} + K(\dot{\gamma})^{0.5} \qquad (5.11)$$

The following example, adapted from the calculation presented by Steffe (1992), illustrates the problem of estimating the yield stress and fitting the other model parameters to a given form of constitutive equation.

EXAMPLE 5.1

Using the following rheological data for molten chocolate at 40 °C (Prentice and Huber, 1983) obtain estimates of the yield stress using:

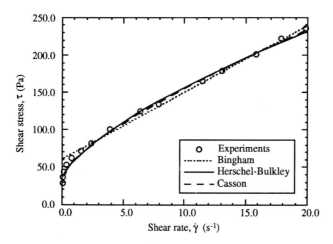

Fig. 5.6 Example 5.1: comparison of regression lines for molten chocolate.

(a) the Bingham plastic equation; (b) the Herschel–Bulkley equation; and (c) the Casson equation.

τ (Pa)	$\dot{\gamma}$ (s^{-1})	τ (Pa)	$\dot{\gamma}$ (s^{-1})
0.099	28.6	6.4	123.8
0.140	35.7	7.9	133.3
0.199	42.8	11.5	164.2
0.390	52.4	13.1	178.5
0.790	61.9	15.9	201.1
1.6	71.4	17.9	221.3
2.4	80.9	19.9	235.6
3.9	100.0		

The following equations were fitted using a non-linear regression method (for the case of the Bingham plastic, only data in the range $\dot{\gamma} = 0.79–19.9\,\text{s}^{-1}$ were fitted).

Model	τ_y (Pa)	K (Pa s^n)	n	R^2
Bingham	60.4	8.96	–	0.997
Herschel–Bulkley	33.0	25.5	0.69	0.995
Casson	30.5	2.19	–	0.996

Figure 5.6 shows that the Casson and Herschel–Bulkley equations give an almost indistinguishable fit to the data over the whole range of shear rates, and the two equations predict comparable yield stresses. The Bingham equation considerably overestimates the yield stress, partly because of the assumption of constant viscosity and partly because the low shear rate data were ignored to improve the overall fit of the equation.

5.1.2 Time-dependent non-Newtonian fluids

The fluids discussed in section 5.1.1 show no variation in rheological behaviour with the time that shearing is applied, or with repeated deformation: that is, all of their microstructure is recoverable and breakdown of structural interactions is a reversible process. The rheological behaviour of many real fluids also depends on the duration of the applied shear rate, as well as its magnitude. In this section we shall consider inelastic fluids with time-dependent behaviour; time-dependent effects may also result from the material having some elastic properties, similar to Hookean solids.

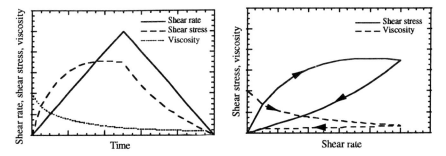

Fig. 5.7 Time-dependent non-Newtonian behaviour. This fluid shows hysteresis, characteristic of thixotropy during a ramp test.

Thixotropic behaviour is obtained from shear-thinning fluids in which no equilibrium is established between the structural breakdown and reformation processes, such that the number of structural interactions decreases continuously with time and the material suffers a permanent change as a result of shearing (for example, starch pastes, gelatins and mayonnaise). Figure 5.7 shows hysteresis loops typical of a thixotropic material for a test in which the shear rate is ramped up and then ramped down over the same time period. For a shear-thinning time-dependent material, initially, the shear stress would increase less than linearly with time. At the midpoint of the ramp test, the shear stress would decrease with time, but the pattern of behaviour would not be a simple reversal of the initial rise. The hysteresis loop for the shear stress is typical of thixotropic materials: here, because the material is both shear-thinning and time-dependent, the viscosity decreases continuously with time.

Similarly, **rheopectic behaviour** can be obtained with shear-thickening fluids in which the apparent viscosity increases with time of deformation. Typically this only occurs at low shear rates, as at higher shear rates the microstructure of the fluid is broken down irreversibly and does not reform.

Constitutive models such as the Herschel–Bulkley equation may be adapted to allow for thixotropic effects by introducing a structural parameter λ (Tiu and Boger, 1974):

$$\tau = \lambda \left(\tau_y + K(\dot{\gamma})^n \right) \tag{5.12}$$

The structural parameter has a value $\lambda = 1$ at $t = 0$ and may be described by a second-order decay equation:

$$\frac{d\lambda}{dt} = -k_1 (\lambda - \lambda_e) \qquad \text{for} \qquad \lambda > \lambda_e \tag{5.13}$$

where λ_e is the final value for complete breakdown of the structure and k_1 is a rate constant that depends on the shear rate. Experiments in which the fluid is sheared at various constant shear rates may be used to find values of k_1, λ_e, τ_y, K and n; Tiu and Boger (1974) describe these methods applied to a study of the thixotropic behaviour of mayonnaise.

5.1.3 Linear viscoelastic fluids

It was noted in the introduction that complex, structured fluids, such as foodstuffs, behave neither as pure Newtonian liquids, nor as Hookean solids: that is, they simultaneously show viscous and elastic behaviour, and hence are known as **viscoelastic fluids**. A Hookean solid behaves as a perfect spring, such that the shear stress (or force) applied is proportional to the shear strain (or extension). Many polymeric liquids deform in a viscoelastic way; their long chain molecules interact, forming chemical or physical cross-links. A deformation of one part of the fluid is transmitted throughout space to all other entangled chains and the fluid shows some elastic properties. These interactions can give rise to elasticity within the polymer network, large elongational viscosities (see section 5.1.5) and normal stress differences (see section 5.1.4), as well as shear-thinning behaviour. Viscoelasticity can give rise to a variety of effects: for example, in stirred flows, viscoelasticity can result in rod climbing (the **Weissenberg effect**) and flow reversal, which are described in section 10.4.4; and in extrusion processes die-swell is due to elastic effects (see section 5.1.4).

We begin by describing **linear** viscoelastic materials. By linear we mean that the mathematical principle of superposition can be applied to the system. The conditions required are:

1. the stress response of the material is proportional to the magnitude of the applied strain; and
2. the stress response is invariant to time translation; delaying the application of the strain signal by a time T results in the same measured stress, but also delayed by a time T.

These conditions are only likely to be satisfied by small strain deformations; non-linear behaviour would result from large strains.

Before we discuss methods of measuring this type of time-dependent response to deformation it is useful to examine a simple analogue model for linear viscoelastic behaviour. It is convenient to suppose that the fluid

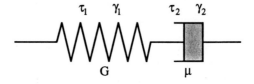

Fig. 5.8 A series-coupled spring and dashpot model: a single Maxwell element.

can be represented by elements exhibiting purely viscous and purely elastic behaviour. Appendix 5.A gives the derivation of a linear Maxwell viscoelastic material, comprising a series-coupled Hookean spring and Newtonian dashpot, as shown in Fig. 5.8. Here the spring has a shear modulus G and the dashpot contains fluid with viscosity μ. For the series combination shown, the shear stress in each element is the same, but the total shear strain is the sum of the shear strain in each part.

This model results in the linear differential equation (Appendix 5.A),

$$\frac{d\tau}{dt} + \frac{\tau}{\lambda} = G\dot{\gamma} \tag{5.14}$$

where $\lambda = \mu/G$ is the **relaxation time**. Equation (5.14) may be integrated to give

$$\tau(t) = G \int_{-\infty}^{t} \exp\left(-\frac{t-t'}{\lambda}\right) \dot{\gamma}(t') \, dt' \tag{5.15}$$

showing that the shear stress at time t depends on the previous history of the deformation $\dot{\gamma}(t')$ from $t' = -\infty$ to $t' = t$. (t' is a dummy integration variable and is used to distinguish the present time t from all previous times t'.)

The choice of a single spring in series with a single dashpot is simple but quite arbitrary; many other combinations of springs and dashpots have been formulated to give different viscoelastic responses. For example, the **Voigt model** comprises a parallel-coupled spring and dashpot combination. In practice, a single Maxwell element does not give a satisfactory representation of linear viscoelastic behaviour. However, because of the linear nature of equation (5.14) it is possible to superimpose a number of solutions from n parallel Maxwell elements (Fig. 5.9), each with its own relaxation time λ_i and shear modulus G_i to give the generalized model

$$\tau(t) = \sum_{i=1}^{n} G_i \int_{-\infty}^{t} \exp\left(-\frac{t-t'}{\lambda_i}\right) \dot{\gamma}(t') \, dt' \tag{5.16}$$

We can now apply this integral constitutive equation to predict linear viscoelastic behaviour for a number of deformation histories. Initially we consider a steady shear rate applied to a single Maxwell element:

$$\dot{\gamma}(t') = \dot{\gamma}_0 \qquad -\infty < t' < t \tag{5.17}$$

Substitution of equation (5.17) into equation (5.15) and integration gives

$$\tau(t) = \mu\dot{\gamma}_0 \tag{5.18}$$

So, the linear viscoelastic fluid behaves as a simple Newtonian under steady shear. This is one of the drawbacks of using linear models, as many real viscoelastic food fluids also exhibit shear-thinning behaviour, and the ratio $\tau/\dot{\gamma}$ should decrease with increasing shear rate: non-linear models

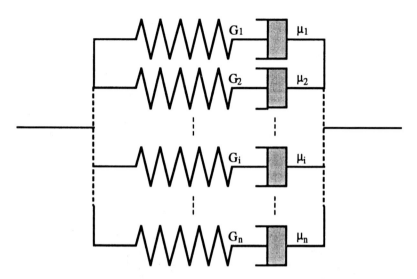

Fig. 5.9 An analogue model of a linear viscoelastic fluid: n parallel Maxwell elements.

are required to represent this behaviour, but are beyond the scope of this book.

Now let us consider the cessation of the steady shear at time $t' = 0$:

$$\dot{\gamma}(t') = \dot{\gamma}_0 \qquad t' < 0$$
$$\dot{\gamma}(t') = 0 \qquad t' \geq 0 \qquad (5.19)$$

Substituting equation (5.19) into equation (5.15) and integrating yields

$$\tau(t) = \mu \dot{\gamma}_0 \qquad\qquad t < 0$$
$$\tau(t) = \mu \dot{\gamma}_0 \exp\left(-\frac{t}{\lambda}\right) \qquad t \geq 0 \qquad (5.20)$$

The plot of equation (5.20) in Fig. 5.10 shows that even after deformation has stopped the fluid is able to sustain shear stresses, but that they decay exponentially to zero with a relaxation time λ.

This viscoelastic behaviour is quite different from that of a Newtonian fluid and is due to the existence of elastically loaded molecular entanglements, even after fluid motion has ceased. Figure 5.10 also shows the behaviour of (i) a Newtonian fluid where the shear stress drops to zero as soon as the rate of deformation ceases, and (ii) an elastic solid where the shear stress remains constant at the value at the cessation of shearing, which corresponds to $G\gamma$, where γ is the final strain.

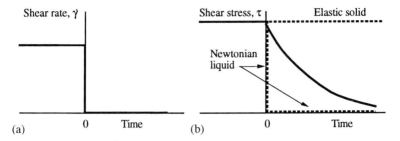

Fig. 5.10 Stress relaxation following the cessation of steady shear.

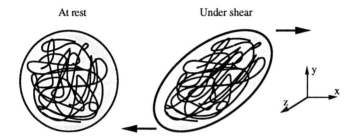

Fig. 5.11 Normal stresses generated by anisotropic structure under shear.

5.1.4   Normal stress differences

One part of the definition of a Newtonian fluid is that the normal stress differences are zero in simple shear flow (see equation (5.2)):

$$N_1 = \sigma_{xx} - \sigma_{yy} = 0$$

and

$$N_2 = \sigma_{yy} - \sigma_{zz} = 0 \qquad (5.21)$$

For linear viscoelastic fluids these normal stresses are also zero; they arise as second-order terms in $\dot{\gamma}$ and are associated with **non-linear viscoelastic effects**. Physically, the explanation for these normal stress differences is that at high shear rates the microstructure of the fluid becomes anisotropic (direction-dependent). Consider the schematic of a dilute polymer solution in Fig. 5.11: at rest the molecular envelope may be taken to be spherical and contains a number of entangled polymer chains, which are randomly oriented in space. Under shear the envelope deforms to an ellipsoidal shape and the molecules are stretched and partially aligned in the x direction.

The restoring forces in this deformed microstructure are anisotropic, such that usually the largest normal stress would be σ_{xx}: that is, in the direction of the flow. This leads to a positive first normal stress difference, $N_1 = \sigma_{xx} - \sigma_{yy} > 0$; generally the second normal stress difference $N_2 = \sigma_{yy} - \sigma_{zz}$ is much smaller than the first, $|N_2| \ll N_1$, and is of secondary importance. Over a range of strain rates the first normal stress difference may be written as a power-law function of $\dot{\gamma}$:

$$N_1 = A(\dot{\gamma})^m \qquad (5.22)$$

and it is not unusual for the ratio N_1/τ to be greater than 1, indicating a highly elastic state (Barnes *et al.*, 1989).

The existence of normal stress differences can give unusual flow effects in industrial applications (see also section 10.4.4). For instance, a rod rotating in a Newtonian fluid would cause a depression of the free surface because of formation of a surface vortex. In a viscoelastic fluid the normal stress differences causes a phenomenon known as the **Weissenberg effect**, in which the fluid actually climbs the rotating rod. Normal stress effects can also cause **reversal of the flow pattern** direction in impeller-driven tanks. In extrusion processes the phenomenon of **die swell** is due to the relaxation of normal stresses on exit from the die, and can give an increase in diameter of the extrudate by a factor of 2 or 3.

5.1.5 Elongational viscosity effects

Consider the element of fluid shown in Fig. 5.12, which is being stretched along its x axis at a constant rate $\partial v_x/\partial x = \dot{\varepsilon}$. In a purely elongational flow all the shear stresses are zero, $\tau_{xy} = \tau_{xz} = \tau_{yz} = 0$, and the normal stress components are equal in the y and z directions, $\sigma_{yy} = \sigma_{zz}$ (by symmetry). If the fluid is incompressible, its volume must be conserved, so that for an axisymmetric flow

$$\frac{\partial v_x}{\partial x} = \dot{\varepsilon} \quad \text{and} \quad \frac{\partial v_y}{\partial y} = \frac{\partial v_z}{\partial z} = -\frac{\dot{\varepsilon}}{2} \qquad (5.23)$$

(see Tritton (1988) for an explanation of the continuity equation for three-dimensional flow).

The normal viscous stress differences are given by

$$\sigma_{xx} - \sigma_{yy} = \sigma_{xx} - \sigma_{zz} = \mu_E \dot{\varepsilon} \qquad (5.24)$$

where μ_E is the **elongational viscosity**. In general, the elongational viscosity depends on the elongational strain rate $\dot{\varepsilon}$ and time. For a Newtonian fluid in uniaxial extensional flow the ratio of extensional to the shear viscosity is constant, $\mu_E/\mu = 3$, but for non-Newtonian fluids μ_E may increase (tension thickening) or decrease (tension thinning) with increasing $\dot{\varepsilon}$. Moreover, non-Newtonian fluids can have very large ratios of elongational to shear viscosity (orders of magnitude greater than for Newtonian fluids). These effects become very important in flows with converging streamlines (as shown in

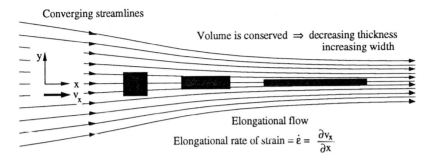

Fig. 5.12 An element of fluid undergoing elongational flow.

Fig. 5.12), where elongation of fluid elements takes place. For example, in the entrances to dies during extrusion, the flow is substantially changed by having a large elongational viscosity. Elongational flows also take place in valve homogenizers (used for emulsion formation), where the elongational strain is extremely efficient at causing droplet breakup. One of the more remarkable demonstrations of the effect of a large elongational viscosity is the open siphon experiment in which fluid can be sucked up from a reservoir, even though the tube is above the liquid free surface.

5.2 Viscometric flows

In the previous section we discussed some of the characteristics of non-Newtonian fluids under flow conditions in which either the rate of strain $\dot{\gamma}$ or the shear stress τ was controlled. In this section we shall examine the types of equipment suited to generating these flows and their use in determining rheological parameters in the constitutive equations. The flows described are known as **viscometric** as they are simple and well defined and are usually designed so that there is a controlled shear rate in a single direction. These flows would always be in the laminar flow regime (see Chapter 2). There are numerous devices for measuring the rheological behaviour of fluids, but here we shall concentrate only on those in which the rate of strain may be directly controlled. Devices such as the falling sphere or U-tube viscometer do not allow application of a prescribed shear rate and are really only suitable for use with Newtonian fluids. Many books (e.g. Steffe, 1992) describe the application of these measurement devices to Newtonian food fluids.

5.2.1 Measurement of shear viscosity: the concentric cylinder viscometer

Figure 5.1 shows an idealized simple shear flow between two flat plates, of which one is stationary and the other moves at a velocity v. The same flow field can be generated using the narrow-gap, concentric cylinder device shown in Fig. 5.13.

If the gap width $r_2 - r_1$ is small compared with the inner radius r_1, then the shear rate between the cylinders is approximately uniform and can be controlled by altering the rotational speed ω (rad s^{-1}) of the inner cylinder (see Appendix 5.B)

$$\dot{\gamma} = \frac{(2\omega/r^2)(r_1^2 r_2^2)}{(r_2^2 - r_1^2)} \approx \frac{r_1 \omega}{r_2 - r_1} \qquad \text{for} \qquad \frac{r_1}{r_2} > 0.96 \qquad (5.25)$$

Thus we shall assume that $\dot{\gamma}$ is independent of r in the narrow gap.

The shear stress in the fluid can be deduced from a measurement of the torque Γ_1 on the inner cylinder:

$$\tau = \frac{\Gamma_1}{2\pi r_1^2 L} \qquad (5.26)$$

(Other arrangements in which the outer cylinder rotates with the inner stationary, or in which the torque on the outside cylinder is measured, are also possible.) The design of these viscometers usually incorporates a recessed top and bottom to the inner cylinder so that the fluid shear stress acts only on the side walls. Using the definition of the apparent viscosity, given in equation (5.4), then (see Appendix 5.B for full analysis)

$$\mu_a(\dot{\gamma}) = \frac{\tau}{\dot{\gamma}} = \frac{\Gamma_1}{4\pi\omega L}\left[\frac{1}{r_1^2} - \frac{1}{r_2^2}\right] \qquad (5.27)$$

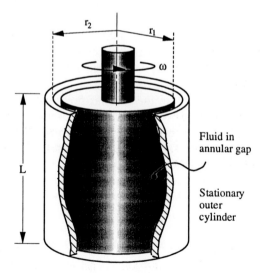

Fig. 5.13 Geometry of a concentric cylinder viscometer.

For food materials, in particular with suspended solid particles, it may not be possible to use a narrow-gap device, in which case the shear rate would vary with radius. Kreiger and Maron (1954) showed that for a power-law fluid the shear rate at the inner cylinder is

$$\dot{\gamma}_1 = \frac{2\omega}{n\left(1-\left(r_1/r_2\right)^{2/n}\right)} \tag{5.28}$$

and the viscosity at this shear rate is

$$\mu_a\left(\dot{\gamma}_1\right) = \frac{\Gamma_1 n\left(1-\left(r_1/r_2\right)^{2/n}\right)}{4\pi r_1^2 L\omega} \tag{5.29}$$

For a power-law fluid, the shear stress on the inner cylinder is

$$\tau_1 = K\left(\dot{\gamma}\right)^n = K\left[\frac{2\omega}{n\left(1-\left(r_1/r_2\right)^{2/n}\right)}\right]^n \tag{5.30}$$

and taking logs of equation (5.30) gives

$$\ln\left(\tau_1\right) = n\ln\omega + n\ln\left[K^{1/n}\frac{2}{n\left(1-\left(r_1/r_2\right)^{2/n}\right)}\right] \tag{5.31}$$

The second term on the right-hand side of equation (5.31) is independent of rotational speed, so a plot of $\ln(\tau_1)$ versus $\ln\omega$ has a slope n and an intercept related to the consistency index K. An alternative form of analysis is given in Example 5.2 below.

With wide-gap devices there is a danger that above a critical rotational speed **Taylor vortices**, a form of flow instability, may form in the gap, disturbing the simple shear flow pattern (see Tritton, 1988, p. 260). Measurements from such an unstable flow would not be performed in a simple shear field and would not yield useful information.

EXAMPLE 5.2

A concentric cylinder Couette viscometer is used to measure the rheological properties of a tomato juice. The inner cylinder rotates at a speed of N revolutions per second; the torque on the inner cylinder is

measured. The inner cylinder has a radius $r_1 = 0.025\,m$ and length $0.04\,m$.
The outer cylinder has a radius $r_2 = 0.026\,m$. Find an appropriate time-
independent constitutive equation that represents the fluid rheology over
the range of applied shear rates.

N (rps)	0.01	0.02	0.05	0.1	0.2	0.5	1	2	5
Γ, (Nm $\times 10^{-3}$)	2.37	3.58	5.72	7.80	1.04	1.49	1.97	2.64	4.09

Convert the above data to strain rates and shear stresses using, respectively, equations (5.25) and (5.26). Note that the ratio $r_1/r_2 = 0.96$, so the
approximate form of equation (5.25) will suffice, and the shear rate may be
assumed to be constant across the annular gap. Calculation of the apparent viscosity at each rotational speed shows that indeed this material
exhibits shear-thinning behaviour.

ω (rad s^{-1})	0.063	0.13	0.31	0.63	1.26	3.14	6.28	12.57	31.42
$\dot\gamma$ (s^{-1})	1.57	3.14	7.85	15.7	31.4	78.5	157.0	314.1	785.3
τ (N m^{-2})	1.51	2.28	3.64	4.97	6.61	9.48	12.51	16.80	26.02
μ_a (Pa s)	0.959	0.725	0.464	0.316	0.210	0.121	0.080	0.053	0.033

Plotting the shear stress versus the shear rate on a log–log plot reveals
that a power-law model would be suitable (Fig. 5.14). Linear regression of
the data gives that

$$\tau = 1.37\,\dot\gamma^{0.44} \qquad \text{for} \qquad 1.0\,s^{-1} < \dot\gamma < 1000\,s^{-1}$$

$$= 1.37\,\dot\gamma^{0.44} \quad \text{for } 1.0\,s^{-1} < \dot\gamma < 1000\,s^{-1}.$$

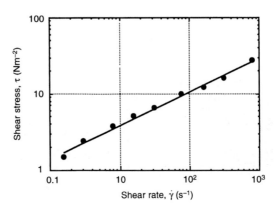

Fig. 5.14 Log–log plot for shear stress versus shear rate for a power-law fluid.

Final remark: the data for this example was 'artificially' created from the Cross model, using the form

$$\frac{\mu_a - 0.01}{0.2 - 0.01} = \frac{1}{1 + 0.8\,(\dot{\gamma})^{0.7}}$$

illustrating that equation (5.5) reduces approximately to the simple power-law form over the range of shear rates where shear-thinning behaviour is exhibited. However, extrapolation of the power-law outside this range of $\dot{\gamma}$ could give erroneous results.

5.2.2 Measurement of shear viscosity: capillary flow viscometers

For Newtonian fluids in laminar flow the pressure drop per unit length of capillary, $\Delta P/L$, is related to the volumetric flowrate w_L by the Hagen–Poiseuille equation (equation (2.37)) and the viscosity may be calculated from

$$\mu = \frac{\Delta P \pi a^4}{8 L w_L} \tag{5.32}$$

Unfortunately, the shear rate within the fluid depends on radial position:

$$\dot{\gamma} = -\frac{\Delta P r}{2 L \mu} \tag{5.33}$$

and so this device is more difficult to use with non-Newtonian fluids. Walters (1975) shows that the shear rate at the wall ($r = a$) is given by

$$\dot{\gamma}_w = \frac{4 w_L}{\pi a^3}\left(\frac{3}{4} + \frac{1}{4}\frac{\mathrm{d}\ln w_L}{\mathrm{d}\ln \tau_w}\right) \tag{5.34}$$

where the term in the bracket is known as the **Rabinowitch correction**. The wall shear stress τ_w is related to the pressure gradient by

$$\tau_w = \frac{a}{2}\frac{\Delta P}{L} \tag{5.35}$$

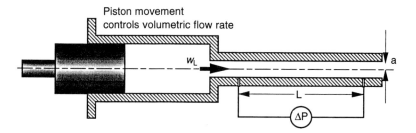

Fig. 5.15 Capillary flow viscometer.

so that the viscosity at the wall shear rate is

$$\mu_a\left(\dot{\gamma}_w\right) = \frac{\pi a^4 \Delta P/L}{8w_L\left(\dfrac{3}{4} + \dfrac{1}{4}\dfrac{d\ln w_L}{d\ln\tau_w}\right)} \tag{5.36}$$

Thus by measuring $\Delta P/L$ versus w_L the apparent viscosity of the fluid may be deduced. Additional problems associated with entrance effects are discussed by Mackley (1988) and Steffe (1992). Example 5.3 below shows how these equations may be used to characterize data from food fluids in capillary flow viscometers.

EXAMPLE 5.3

The following data were collected for orange juice concentrate in a 2 mm diameter capillary viscometer with a length of 0.25 m. Find the power-law index and consistency index from these data.

Raw data		Calculated data	
w_L $(m^3 s^{-1})$	ΔP (Pa)	τ_w (Pa)	$\dot{\gamma}_w$
1.0×10^{-7}	1.75×10^4	34.9	135.8
2.0×10^{-7}	3.03×10^4	60.5	271.6
3.0×10^{-7}	4.13×10^4	82.5	407.4
4.0×10^{-7}	5.27×10^4	105.3	543.1
5.0×10^{-7}	6.10×10^4	122.0	678.9
6.0×10^{-7}	7.18×10^4	143.5	814.7
7.0×10^{-7}	8.16×10^4	163.1	950.5
8.0×10^{-7}	9.26×10^4	185.2	1086.3
9.0×10^{-7}	9.86×10^4	197.2	1222.1
1.0×10^{-6}	1.06×10^5	212.0	1357.8

The tube length to diameter ratio is very large, so that end effects can be neglected. The first step is to calculate the wall shear stress, τ_w from equation (5.35) and then to plot w_L versus τ_w on a log–log plot (Fig. 5.16(a)). The slope of this line gives the Rabinowitch correction

$$\frac{d\ln w_L}{d\ln\tau_w} = 1.266$$

This allows the wall shear rate to be calculated from equation (5.34); a further regression of the wall shear stress versus the wall shear rate on log–log axes (Fig. 5.16(b)) gives the power law exponent and consistency index as

$$n = 0.79 \quad \text{and} \quad K = 0.72\,Pa\,s^n$$

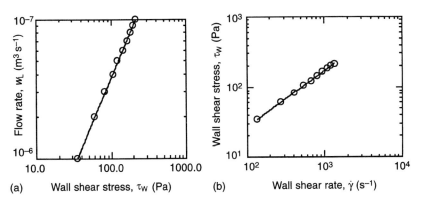

Fig. 5.16 Example 5.3: plot (a) is used to find the Rabinowitch correction and plot (b) is used to find the power-law parameters.

5.2.3 Cone and plate viscometers

Figure 5.17 shows the geometric arrangement of this viscometer: the fluid is held between a cone and a plate; the plate rotates at an angular frequency, ω (rad s^{-1}), while the cone remains stationary; the torque Γ on the cone is measured using a transducer. Provided that the cone angle θ is small ($<4°$), then the shear rate in the liquid is uniform and given by

$$\dot{\gamma} = \frac{\omega}{\tan\theta} \tag{5.37}$$

The shear stress is given by

$$\tau = \frac{3\Gamma}{2\pi R^3} \tag{5.38}$$

and so the viscosity may be calculated from (see Appendix 5.C for details)

$$\mu_a(\dot{\gamma}) = \frac{3\Gamma\tan\theta}{2\pi R^3\omega} \tag{5.39}$$

5.2.4 Parallel plate viscometer

The parallel plate viscometer (see Fig. 5.17) operates in a similar way to the cone and plate device, except that the shear rate in the gap is no longer uniform and analysis for non-Newtonian fluids becomes more difficult (see Barnes *et al.*, 1989).

5.2.5 Measurement of viscoelastic properties

Cone and plate and parallel plate viscometers are suitable for determining the shear viscosity of time-independent non-Newtonian fluids, but their

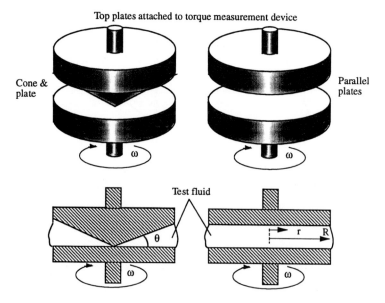

Fig. 5.17 Cone and plate and parallel plate viscometers.

main advantage is in oscillatory mode, for the measurement of viscoelastic properties. The lower plate is made to oscillate at a frequency ω (rad s^{-1}), giving a sinusoidally varying strain in the fluid, with a maximum amplitude of γ_o:

$$\gamma = \gamma_o \sin \omega t \qquad (5.40)$$

Differentiating equation (5.40) with respect to time gives the strain rate as

$$\dot{\gamma} = \frac{d\gamma}{dt} = \dot{\gamma}_o \, \omega \cos \omega t \qquad (5.41)$$

The shear stress, deduced from torque measurements, on the upper plate also varies sinusoidally, at the same frequency as the strain oscillation, but shifted out of phase by an angle δ:

$$\tau = \tau_o \sin(\omega t + \delta) \qquad (5.42)$$

or

$$\tau = \tau_o \cos\delta \sin(\omega t) + \tau_o \sin\delta \cos(\omega t) \qquad (5.43)$$

where τ_o is the maximum shear stress. At this point it is worth noting that if the material was a Hookean elastic solid, the angle δ would be zero as the shear stress would be in phase with the strain oscillation. Hooke's law for a solid material is

$$\tau = G\gamma = G\gamma_o \sin(\omega t) \tag{5.44}$$

where G is the shear modulus and γ is the shear strain.

However, if the material was a Newtonian fluid, the shear stress would be $\pi/2$ radians out of phase with the strain oscillation as

$$\tau = \mu\dot{\gamma} = \mu\gamma_o \omega \cos(\omega t)$$

$$\Rightarrow \quad \tau = \mu\gamma_o \omega \sin\left(\omega t + \frac{\pi}{2}\right) \tag{5.45}$$

To characterize the elastic and viscous components, we define the **elastic storage modulus** G' from the in-phase component of the stress in equation (5.43):

$$G' = \frac{\tau_o}{\gamma_o} \cos\delta \tag{5.46}$$

and the **loss modulus** G'' from the out-of-phase component of stress:

$$G'' = \frac{\tau_o}{\gamma_o} \sin\delta \tag{5.47}$$

For a perfectly elastic Hookean solid the shear stress ($\delta = 0$) and shear strain would be related by equation (5.44), giving an elastic storage modulus of $G' = G$ and a loss modulus of $G'' = 0$. Compare this with the response of a Newtonian viscous liquid ($\delta = \pi/2$), which has an elastic storage modulus of $G' = 0$ and a loss modulus of $G'' = \mu\omega$. Thus the relative values of the moduli G' and G'' from oscillatory tests yields information about the degree of elastic and viscous behaviour exhibited by the food material.

We can also define a **complex viscosity** μ^*, the magnitude of which is

$$|\mu^*| = \frac{\left(G'^2 + G''^2\right)^{1/2}}{\omega} \tag{5.48}$$

This is akin to the apparent viscosity defined in equation (5.4). These three parameters may then be used to describe the viscoelastic characteristics of a fluid. For most polymers, structured fluids and foodstuffs, G', G'' and $|\mu^*|$ are all functions of the oscillation frequency, and possibly also the strain amplitude γ_o and time.

The bulk and storage moduli may now be examined for a simple linear viscoelastic fluid, such as that discussed in section 5.1.3. For a single series-coupled Maxwell element the storage and loss moduli and complex viscosity are given by (see Appendix 5.A)

$$G' = \frac{G\lambda^2\omega^2}{\left(1 + \lambda^2\omega^2\right)} \tag{5.49}$$

$$G'' = \frac{G\lambda\omega}{\left(1+\lambda^2\omega^2\right)} \tag{5.50}$$

$$|\mu^*| = \frac{G\lambda}{\left(1+\lambda^2\omega^2\right)^{1/2}} \tag{5.51}$$

Figure 5.18 shows a schematic plot of these parameters for a single element, which can be compared with Figs 5.19 and 5.20, which show some typical strain and frequency sweeps for a polymeric foodstuff and a gel or suspension foodstuff. The Maxwell element represents linear viscoelastic behaviour in which G' and G'' are independent of the magnitude of the strain γ_0. G' is a monotonically increasing function of dimensionless frequency $\omega\lambda$, which becomes constant at high dimensionless frequency, and G'' has a maximum at $\omega\lambda = 1$. Figure 5.18 shows that at low dimensionless frequencies (slow deformation rates) the behaviour is viscous in nature ($G' \ll G''$), whereas at high dimensionless frequencies elastic effects dominate ($G' \ll G''$).

Figures 5.19 and 5.20 show that both the polymeric and gel foodstuffs show linear viscoelastic behaviour at low strains (G' and G'' are independent of the magnitude of the maximum strain γ_0), but non-linear response at higher strains. The gel foodstuff (yoghurt, for example) shows four separate regions (Steventon *et al.* 1991):

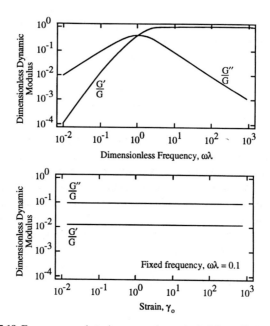

Fig. 5.18 Frequency and strain sweeps for a single Maxwell element.

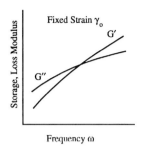 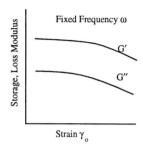

Fig. 5.19 Typical frequency and strain sweeps for a polymeric foodstuff.

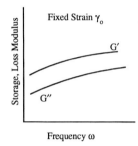 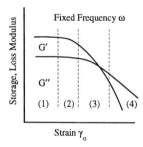

Fig. 5.20 Typical frequency and strain sweeps for a gel or suspension foodstuff.

1. a linear viscoelastic region in which G' and G'' are constant and the material is predominantly elastic ($G' \gg G''$);
2. a non-linear region in which G'' is fairly constant and G' starts to decrease, indicating breakdown of the elastic structure;
3. where G' and G'' cross over after the full elastic structure has been broken and the material becomes more viscous; and
4. where viscous behaviour dominates ($G'' \gg G'$).

It is clear that the single Maxwell element does not correspond to the behaviour of real polymeric foodstuffs. However, many parallel Maxwell elements with time constants λ_i and shear moduli G_i give an improved representation of real frequency-sweep behaviour (see Fig. 5.21) but not of the effect of strain on the loss and storage moduli. For n Maxwell elements the separate solutions of equations (5.49)–(5.51) can simply be added because of the linear nature of the constitutive equation:

$$G' = \sum_{i=1}^{n} \frac{G_i \lambda_i^2 \omega^2}{\left(1 + \lambda_i^2 \omega^2\right)} \qquad (5.52)$$

$$G'' = \sum_{i=1}^{n} \frac{G_i \lambda_i \omega}{\left(1 + \lambda_i^2 \omega^2\right)} \qquad (5.53)$$

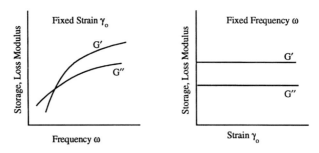

Fig. 5.21 Typical frequency and strain sweeps for n Maxwell elements.

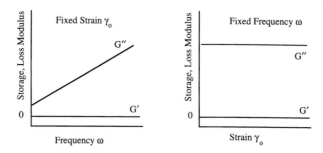

Fig. 5.22 Frequency and strain sweeps for a Newtonian fluid.

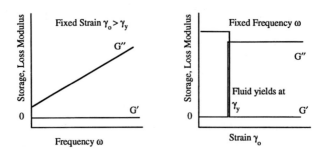

Fig. 5.23 Frequency and strain sweeps for a Bingham plastic.

and

$$\left| \mu^* \right| = \sum_{i=1}^{n} \frac{G_i \lambda_i}{\left(1 + \lambda_i^2 \omega^2\right)^{1/2}} \qquad (5.54)$$

For comparison, the frequency and strain sweeps for Newtonian and Bingham fluids have been included in Figs 5.22 and 5.23. For a Newtonian fluid the storage modulus should be close to zero, whereas the loss modulus should be proportional to the viscosity of the fluid and to the frequency. Both G' and G'' should be independent of the strain. This can be compared with the Bingham plastic, which exhibits elastic solid behaviour at small strains, and purely viscous behaviour at strains above the elastic limit.

Example 5.4 below shows how data from an oscillatory test in a cone and plate viscometer can be used to derive storage and loss moduli and Maxwell model parameters.

EXAMPLE 5.4

Tomato ketchup was sheared between the cone and plate of an oscillatory rheometer: the cone angle was $\theta = 0.07$ rad (4°) and the plate radius was $R = 12.5$ mm. The maximum amplitude of the oscillation was $\phi_o = 0.009$ rad. The data below give the maximum torque Γ_{max} and phase angle δ relative to the oscillatory strain

$$\gamma = \gamma_o \sin \omega t$$

At any radius r the maximum strain is given by the maximum displacement divided by the distance between cone and plate. That is:

$$\gamma_o = \frac{r\phi_o}{r\tan\theta} = \frac{\phi_o}{\tan\theta} = \frac{0.009}{\tan 0.07} = 0.13$$

which is independent of radius and thus the shear stress also should not be a function of r. The torque is given by

$$\Gamma = \int_0^R 2\pi r^2 \tau dr = \frac{2\pi R^3 \tau}{3} \Rightarrow \tau_o = \frac{3\Gamma_{max}}{2\pi R^3}$$

From equations (5.46) and (5.47)

$$G' = \frac{\tau_o}{\gamma_o}\cos\delta \quad \text{and} \quad G'' = \frac{\tau_o}{\gamma_o}\sin\delta$$

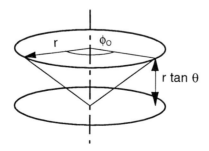

Calculating the storage and loss moduli gives the fifth and sixth columns of the table below.

Raw data			Calculated data		
ω (rad s^{-1})	Γ_{max} (N m)	δ (rad)	τ_o (N m^{-2})	G' (N m^{-2})	G'' (N m^{-2})
0.200	1.69×10^{-4}	0.126	41.23	3.19×10^2	4.03×10^1
0.600	1.85×10^{-4}	0.142	45.33	3.50×10^2	4.98×10^1

We shall attempt to use these data to fit a single element Maxwell model of the form

$$G' = \frac{G\lambda^2\omega^2}{\left(1+\lambda^2\omega^2\right)}$$

$$G'' = \frac{G\lambda\omega}{\left(1+\lambda^2\omega^2\right)}$$

The first data set at $\omega = 0.2$ rad s^{-1} gives $G = 324$ N m^{-2} and $\lambda = 39.6$ s, whereas the second data set at $\omega = 0.2$ rad s^{-1} gives $G = 357$ N m^{-2} and $\lambda = 11.7$ s, which are not in particularly good agreement. The reasons for this discrepancy are that: (a) a single Maxwell element is not sufficient to characterize the behaviour of most viscoelastic food stuffs; and (b) the maximum strain in this case is 13%, which is likely to be outside the range of linear behaviour.

5.3 Application to engineering problems

Non-Newtonian fluid rheology can lead to quite different flow behaviour from that of Newtonian fluids and has a profound effect on parameters such as pressure drop in pipeline flow, heat and mass transfer, mixing rate (see section 10.4.4) and residence time distribution. Some of the more dramatic observable changes have already been discussed in section 5.1. We shall conclude this chapter by applying some non-Newtonian constitutive equations to the problem of predicting the pressure drop for power-law and Bingham plastic fluids flowing through pipes.

5.3.1 Non-Newtonian pipe flows

As an example we consider flow of a power-law fluid through a round pipe, and we draw on the approach used in section 2.3.2. A force balance on a cylindrical element, as in Fig. 2.11, yields

$$\tau = \frac{r}{2}\frac{dP}{dL} \tag{5.55}$$

where now

$$\tau = K(\dot{\gamma})^n = K\left(\frac{dv_x}{dr}\right)^n \tag{5.56}$$

For convenience we shall call the pressure gradient

$$s = -\frac{dP}{dL} = \frac{\Delta P}{L} \tag{5.57}$$

noting that the pressure gradient has a negative value, but that the pressure drop ΔP is treated as being positive. Then

$$\left(\frac{sr}{2K}\right)^{1/n} = \left(\frac{dv_x}{dr}\right) \tag{5.58}$$

Integrating equation (5.58), using the boundary condition that $v_x = 0$ at $r = a$,

$$v_x(r) = \int_a^r \left(\frac{sr}{2K}\right)^{1/n} dr = \left(\frac{s}{2K}\right)^{1/n}\frac{n}{1+n}\left(r^{\frac{n+1}{n}} - a^{\frac{n+1}{n}}\right) \tag{5.59}$$

The volumetric flowrate may be obtained by integrating the velocity profile across the pipe:

$$w_L = \int_0^a 2\pi r v_x(r)dr = \int_0^a 2\pi r\left(\frac{s}{2K}\right)^{1/n}\frac{n}{1+n}\left(r^{\frac{n+1}{n}} - a^{\frac{n+1}{n}}\right)dr \tag{5.60}$$

Integrating gives

$$w_L = \frac{n\pi}{3n+1}\left(\frac{Ksa^{3n+1}}{2}\right)^{1/n} \tag{5.61}$$

Solving for the pressure drop gives

$$\frac{\Delta P}{L} = \frac{2K}{a^{3n+1}}\left(\frac{(3n+1)w_L}{n\pi}\right)^n \tag{5.62}$$

Substituting for the pressure gradient in equation (5.59) gives

$$v_x(r) = \frac{w_L(3n+1)}{\pi a^2(n+1)}\left[1 - \left(\frac{r}{a}\right)^{\frac{n+1}{n}}\right] \tag{5.63}$$

Figure 5.24 shows equation (5.63) plotted for various values of n, the power-law index. The important consequences of these for process engineering design are as follows.

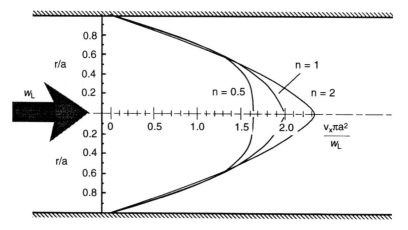

Fig. 5.24 Comparison of velocity profiles for Newtonian and non-Newtonian fluids.

- The residence time distribution of the fluid depends on the value of n. For $n < 1$ the velocity profile in Fig. 5.24 becomes flatter, resulting in more plug flow-type behaviour (see section 8.3). Similarly for $n > 1$ (shear thickening) the velocity profile becomes sharper, and a broader distribution of residence times would result.
- The pressure drop depends on the pipe radius a to the power $-(3n + 1)$, so for a Newtonian fluid $dP/dL \propto a^{-4}$ whereas for $n = \frac{1}{3}$, then $dP/dL \propto a^{-2}$, which would have important consequences for scale-up of a pipe flow.
- Heat transfer transfer coefficients may be directly correlated with the friction factor, which is related to the wall shear rate (see section 3.2, Reynolds, film and j-factor analogies). Thus shear-thinning behaviour can increase heat transfer rates, at the same throughput.

As a further example we shall investigate the behaviour of a Bingham plastic fluid in pipe flow. Following the same approach as above we can show that at a radius less than r_y, given by

$$r_y = \frac{4\tau_y}{\Delta P/L} \tag{5.64}$$

the fluid stress does not exceed the Bingham yield stress and the material moves as a central plug through the pipeline. At radii greater than r_y the fluid behaves as a Newtonian fluid and has a parabolic velocity profile, as shown in Fig. 5.25. Again, the residence time distinction and pressure drop are affected by the non-Newtonian behaviour of the fluid. Serious problems can occur with Bingham plastic fluids in more complex flow geometries: stagnant regions form where the fluid stress does not exceed the yield stress, resulting in poor rates of mixing and heat transfer.

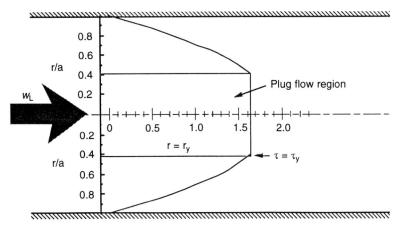

Fig. 5.25 Bingham plastic pipe flow velocity profile.

5.3.2 Complex fluid flow problems

Using the examples above it should now be obvious that laminar flow problems may be solved using similar approaches to those for a Newtonian fluid, but replacing the shear stress terms with a suitable non-Newtonian constitutive equation. The examples considered here are simple, one-dimensional problems, to which there are analytical solutions. For complex engineering geometries, the flows may be fully three-dimensional, or un-steady, and an algebraic solution to the resulting set of equations may not be possible. This is also true of many Newtonian flows; however, recent advances in computational fluid dynamics have resulted in a number of commercial software packages that are able to calculate numerical solutions to these problems. These packages solve the Navier–Stokes and continuity equations (the full three-dimensional equations of fluid motion) and are able to handle simple rheological models, such as a power-law fluid. The ability to perform calculations with viscoelastic fluids is limited, although a few (more academic) packages are available. Currently much research is being carried out on the appropriate forms of constitutive equation to model real non-linear viscoelastic materials and also to extend the current techniques of fluid mechanics to higher Reynolds number flows, even into the turbulent regime.

Appendix 5.A   Linear viscoelastic Maxwell element

Referring to Fig. 5.7, the total shear stress and strain are

$$\tau = \tau_1 = \tau_2 \tag{A5.1}$$

and

$$\gamma = \gamma_1 + \gamma_2 \tag{A5.2}$$

so that

$$\dot{\gamma} = \dot{\gamma}_1 + \dot{\gamma}_2 \tag{A5.3}$$

For the Hookean spring

$$\dot{\gamma}_1 = \frac{\dot{\tau}_1}{G} \tag{A5.4}$$

and the Newtonian dashpot

$$\dot{\gamma}_2 = \frac{\tau_2}{\mu} \tag{A5.5}$$

which leads to

$$\frac{d\tau}{dt} + \frac{\tau}{\lambda} = G\dot{\gamma} \tag{A5.6}$$

where $\lambda = \mu/G$ is a relaxation time.

Solving this first-order ordinary differential equation using an integrating factor:

$$\tau(t) = G \int_{-\infty}^{t} \exp\left(-\frac{t-t'}{\lambda}\right) \dot{\gamma}(t') \, dt' \tag{A5.7}$$

Suppose now that

$$\gamma = \gamma_0 \sin \omega t \tag{A5.8}$$

giving a strain rate of

$$\dot{\gamma} = \gamma_0 \omega \cos \omega t \tag{A5.9}$$

which on substitution into equation (A5.7) and integrating gives

$$\tau(t) = \frac{G\lambda^2 \omega^2}{\left(1 + \lambda^2 \omega^2\right)} \gamma_0 \sin \omega t + \frac{G\lambda \omega}{\left(1 + \lambda^2 \omega^2\right)} \gamma_0 \cos \omega t \tag{A5.10}$$

or

$$\tau(t) = G' \gamma_0 \sin \omega t + G'' \gamma_0 \cos \omega t \tag{A5.11}$$

Appendix 5.B   Concentric cylinder viscometer

Referring to Figs 5.12 and 5.26:

$$\dot{\gamma} = \frac{(r+dr)(\omega+d\omega)-(r+dr)\omega}{dr} = r\frac{d\omega}{dr} \tag{A5.12}$$

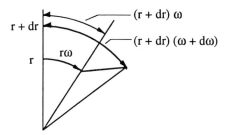

Fig. 5.26 Fluid motion in a circular path.

In steady shear

$$\Gamma_1 = -2\pi r^2 \tau L \qquad (A5.13)$$

where τ is the fluid shear stress at radius r, and

$$\tau = \mu_a \dot{\gamma} \qquad (A5.14)$$

If the gap is small, then $\dot{\gamma}$ and μ_a are almost constant. Then

$$\mu_a r^3 \frac{d\omega}{dr} = \frac{-\Gamma_1}{2\pi L} \qquad (A5.15)$$

and integrating using the boundary conditions $\omega = \omega$ at $r = r_1$ and $\omega = 0$ at $r = r_2$ gives

$$\mu_a = \frac{\Gamma_1}{4\pi\omega L}\left[\frac{1}{r_1^2} - \frac{1}{r_2^2}\right] \qquad (A5.16)$$

The shear stress varies as

$$\dot{\gamma} = \frac{(2\omega/r^2)(r_1^2 r_2^2)}{(r_2^2 - r_1^2)} \approx \frac{r_1 \omega}{r_2 - r_1} \qquad (A5.17)$$

for $r_1/r_2 > 0.96$.

Appendix 5.C   Cone and plate viscometer

Referring to Fig. 5.14, in a cone and plate viscometer, the shear rate is constant, independent of radius r:

$$\dot{\gamma} = \frac{\omega r}{r \tan \theta} = \frac{\omega}{\tan \theta} \qquad (A5.18)$$

The torque acting on an elemental area of $2\pi r\, dr$ is

$$d\Gamma = 2\pi r^2 \mu_a \dot{\gamma} dr = \frac{2\pi r^2 \omega \mu_a}{\tan \theta} dr \qquad (A5.19)$$

Integrating from $r = 0$ to $r = R$ gives

$$\mu_a = \frac{3\Gamma \tan \theta}{2\pi R^3 \omega} \qquad (A5.20)$$

Conclusions

In the introduction to fluid mechanics in Chapter 2, the discussion centred on two idealized models of a fluid: one in which it could be assumed to be frictionless and the other in which it was assumed to have Newtonian properties. A Newtonian liquid is one whose rheology is described by a single constant parameter – its viscosity.

Many food materials don't fall into either of these categories, and instead also exhibit some of the properties we usually associate with deformable or elastic solids. This chapter has dealt with ways of characterizing and classifying such non-Newtonian fluids. The quantitative models for these fluids, that is the relationships between the shear stress (or apparent viscosity) and shear rate are known as the constitutive equations. You should understand the difference between fluids whose properties are time-independent and time-dependent. Three principal categories of time-independent fluid were introduced here: shear thinning, shear thickening and Bingham plastics. The latter are fluids which behave like solids when the shear is small, but begin to flow or yield at some critical shear stress. This chapter should have given some physical insight into why these different types of behaviour exist as well as introducing some of the simpler mathematical models to describe them. Two different types of time-dependent behaviour were also introduced. Thixotropic and rheopectic fluids are examples of the first, in which changes in the physical structure lead to changes in viscosity with time. Another category of fluid exhibits both Newtonian and elastic properties, and this also results in a response to deformation which is time-dependent. These are the viscoelastic fluids. As well as meeting these different classes of fluid and real examples of food materials which approximate to them, you will have encountered some of the more common methods of measuring their properties, that is of estimating the parameters in the constitutive equations. The final part of the chapter shows how the behaviour of some of these fluids in simple pipe flow can be predicted using the methods of Chapter 2. As a result you should be able to recognize how the velocity distribution of a fluid being pumped along a pipe depends on its rheology, and how the power requirements for pumping can be predicted.

References and further reading

Barnes, H.A., Hutton, J.F. and Walters, K. (1989) *An Introduction to Rheology*

Casson, N. (1959) A flow equation for pigmented-oil suspension of the printing ink type, in *Rheology of Dispersed Systems* (ed. C.C. Mill), Pergamon Press, New York, pp. 84–104.

Cross, J.M. (1965) Rheology of non-Newtonian flows: equation for pseudoplastic systems. *Journal of Colloid Science*, **20**, 417–437.

Kreiger, I.M. and Maron, S.H. (1954) Direct determination of flow curves on non-Newtonian fluids. *Journal of Applied Physics*, **25**, 72–75.

Mackley, M.R. (1988) in *The Physical Principles of Rheological Measurement* (eds A.A. Colyer and D.W. Clegg), Elsevier, Chapter 1.

Nielsen, L.E. (1977) *Polymer Rheology*, Marcel Dekker.

Prentice, J.H. and Huber, A.N. (1983) Measuring rheological properties of foodstuffs, in *Physical Properties of Foods* (eds R. Jowitt, F. Escher, B. Hallstrom, H.F.Th. Meffert, W.E.L. Spies and G. Vos), Applied Science Publishers, pp. 123–184.

Reynolds, O. (1885) *Philosophical Magazine*, [5] **20**, 469.

Steffe, J.F. (1992) *Rheological Methods in Food Process Engineering*, Freeman Press, Michigan.

Steventon, A.J., Parkinson, C.J., Fryer, P.J. and Bottomley, R.C. (1991) The rheology of yoghurt, in *Rheology of Food, Pharmaceutical and Biological Materials with General Rheology* (ed. R.E. Carter), Elsevier Applied Science, pp. 196–210.

Tanner, R.I. (1985) *Engineering Rheology*, Clarendon Press, Oxford.

Tiu, C. and Boger, D.V. (1974) Complete rheological characterization of time-dependent products. *Journal of Texture Studies*, **5**, 329–338.

Tritton, D.J. (1988) *Physical Fluid Dynamics*, 2nd edn, Chapman & Hall, London.

Walters, K. (1975) *Rheometry*, Chapman & Hall, London.

6 Process design: heat integration
P.J. FRYER

Introduction

The principles of thermal balances, heat and mass transfer and fluid flow developed in the previous chapters are well suited to the outline design of flowsheets and the design of individual plant items. It is much more difficult to consider the flowsheet as a design problem, and to decide whether the whole process is optimal. The simple economic analysis developed in Chapter 1 will tell whether a plant will make money, but will not produce better designs that make more money. To a large extent, optimization still depends on the skills of the engineer designing the plant. However, in some areas considerable progress has been made in developing design techniques that search for cost-optimal solutions to problems. These techniques are computer based and complex. However, one of them is conceptually very simple, and the principles can be developed without the use of computers. Any process plant will require some heat input and need some cooling. Some of this can be provided from within the plant, i.e. the cooling need on one process stream can be provided by the heating of another; but how much? It is possible, using thermodynamic principles, to find the maximum amount of heat which can be recovered from a system, and thus to design a process which needs the minimum amount of external heating and cooling. This chapter describes the problem, and then develops the solution using a worked example to demonstrate the method.

6.1 Design of process plant

The techniques of material and thermal balances described in Chapter 1 can be used to determine the mass and molar flows and the heat loads within a plant. However, this type of analysis does not indicate whether the plant is optimal: that is, whether a better design could be produced. There are several stages in the design of a food process plant. Each piece of equipment must be designed individually to carry out the job required; however, it is also important to consider the design of the whole system and the way

Chemical Engineering for the Food Industry. Edited by P.J. Fryer, D.L. Pyle and C.D. Rielly. Published in 1997 by Blackie A & P, an imprint of Chapman & Hall, London. ISBN 0 412 49500 7

in which the individual pieces of process plant can interact for example, making sure that the process is simple to control. The food industry has, historically, tended to design flowsheets one part at a time, and then assemble the parts into a whole. If plants are designed one part at a time, they can be inefficient.

As an example, consider the simple flowsheet shown in Fig. 6.1, in which:

1. a process stream is heated up to some required temperature,
2. a sterilization reaction is carried out at that temperature; and
3. the process stream is cooled.

In Fig. 6.1(a) the stream is heated and cooled by external steam and water. This requires two process units (heat exchangers) and expense in both heating and cooling. If some of the waste heat from the hot fluid is used to heat the cold fluid, however, as in Fig. 6.1(b), it is possible to reduce the heat

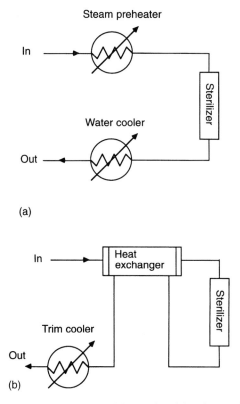

Fig. 6.1 A simple flowsheet for a process requiring feedstock heating, sterilization and cooling of product: (a) inefficient plant; (b) efficient plant.

load and thus save operating costs. It is unlikely that the heating and cooling loads will be the same; the figure includes a trim cooler designed to bring the outlet stream to the right temperature. Although the number of process units is the same, the second plant is more efficient.

The example in Fig. 6.1 is a very simple one in which the solution is obvious; less obvious would be the optimization of a case in which there were (say) 50 process units and 400 streams. Techniques have been developed in the petrochemical industry to consider the design of whole plants; these have been given the general name **process integration**. The use of these techniques to design a very large-scale plant can be very complex and involve the use of very large computer programs. Research into systematic design techniques is under way in both academia and industry. Some of the methods are conceptually very simple, however. The aim of this section is to introduce some of the techniques, using as an example the ways of making heat transfer within process plant as efficient as possible.

There are two basic design problems;

- **process synthesis**, in which the aim is to create a new process, and
- **process analysis**, where the aim is to understand how an existing process works.

The latter is easier than the former; there is no 'right answer' to a process design problem, and millions of possible solutions. The approach of chemical engineers has always been to start with a flowsheet for the process, and to analyse the flowsheet rather than considering the design of each element. It would be ridiculous to suggest that there is any infallible way of solving a synthesis problem using the same sort of easy steps. However, it is important when designing a plant to be able to screen out undesirable options as rapidly as possible, so that time can be spent as usefully as possible, considering only designs that are sensible.

Process synthesis proceeds in five basic steps: development, planning, basic design, detailed design, and improvements. A series of **design estimates** are made during the course of a project. The first stage of the design begins with an order-of-magnitude estimate, with costs accurate to about ±40%. These estimates are then refined through a series of design stages to reach a detailed estimate, which is given to the contractor, which should be accurate to within ±3%. The systematic approach to the preparation of flowsheets and then design estimates has become known as the **hierarchical approach** to design in chemical plant design. Although developed for the chemical industry, it is equally applicable to the food industry. It involves making a series of decisions, as follows.

1. **Should the process be batch or continuous?** The structure of batch process flowsheets is inherently different from that of continuous flowsheets, and it is necessary to decide which to use right at the outset.

Continuous processes are inherently more efficient, but many processes in the food industry, such as beer brewing or whisky distilling, are carried out batchwise because it has proved impossible to produce product continuously with the same texture or quality.

2. **What is the input/output structure?** At this stage an overall material balance on the process should be conducted using the principles described in Chapter 1. A control surface is considered that surrounds the whole process. Into this control surface go raw materials, and out of it come the products and by-products of the process. At this stage the first estimation can be made of the efficiency and thus the economics of the process and any possible environmental problems involved.

3. **What is the recycle structure?** As described in section 1.1.4 on material balances, recycle streams are often necessary: for example, when the conversion in a reaction is low, in which case the unused reactants are recycled back into the process. Requirements for recycles can be determined using the reaction kinetics of the process. Local material balances can be performed at this stage to determine all the flows within the system.

4. **Separation system.** In many cases in the process industries, products must be separated from the outlet stream and concentrated into an economic form. Once the conversion in the reactor is known, the type and size of any separation system needed can be worked out. In general, it is convenient to consider **vapour recovery** (condensation, ab- or adsorption, membranes) and **liquid recovery** (distillation, extraction, membranes) as separate systems. Most food engineering processes are based around liquids rather than gases, of course: only liquid recovery systems are needed.

5. **Heat integration.** Once the structure of the process is known fully, **heat loads** can be considered. Techniques have been developed that minimize the heat needs of a plant; these are outlined below.

The above type of approach is commonly used in computer-aided design processes; however, it is equally applicable to hand design and analysis. The process can be used in reverse to analyse the basic structure of existing flowsheets:

1. remove the heat exchangers;
2. group the distillation columns and separation systems;
3. analyse the resulting recycle structure;
4. consider the overall material balance.

6.2 Second-law analysis: heat integration

Most of the techniques of process design are complex, and beyond the scope of this book. One area, however, is very simple to study, and uses very simple physical principles. The design of structures of heat exchanger networks (HENs) that maximize the amount of energy recovery has been systematized. This is stage 5 of the above scheme. Mathematically it is possible to state the problem of energy recovery quite precisely:

> A set of cold streams initially at supply temperatures T_C^{IN} are to be heated to target temperatures T_C^{OUT} while a set of hot streams at T_H^{IN} are to be cooled to target temperatures T_H^{OUT}. Determine the structure of a network of heat exchangers that will bring all their streams to their target temperatures while minimizing the cost of equipment, steam and cooling water.

The problem is simple to state but much more difficult to solve. Even for very small numbers of process streams the number of possible permutations of networks is enormous, so using a computer program to consider all the possible alternatives is impossible in practice. It is necessary to find solutions that satisfy maximum energy recovery (usually described as MER) together with the minimum number of heat exchangers. This combination will minimize both the operating and capital cost of the flowsheet.

The insights made into this design problem have been developed from both thermodynamic principles and from the mathematics of network theory. The technique identifies pinch points in the system where heat transfer is most difficult; these are the most critical points of any network.

The analysis is based on the second law of thermodynamics. This is always regarded as much less easy to understand than the first law, but is based on a very simple observation: heat can only flow in one direction, from a system with a high temperature to one with a low temperature. The amount of heat contained with a body, which can be found from the first law, is not relevant to the direction of heat flow; a red-hot needle dropped into a swimming pool heats up the pool, despite the fact that the pool contains a much greater amount of heat. The first law of thermodynamics is a statement of conservation of energy; it makes no statement about the direction of heat flow. The second law defines that direction, via the definition of temperature. The core of the second law analysis is the experimental fact that heat can only move in the direction of decreasing temperature. It might be thought from a first-law analysis – the thermal balances studied in Chapter 1 – that heat at a low temperature could be supplied to a fluid at a high temperature; the second law says that this is impossible.

The second law governs the techniques of heat integration. The best way to study this is by an example. A test problem, of four process streams of defined start and end temperatures will thus be solved to demonstrate and explain the method.

6.2.1   Stage 1: identify the process streams

Table 6.1 shows four streams. The table includes the capacity flowrate of the streams, given as $kW\,K^{-1}$. The capacity flowrate, wc_P, is the product of the

Table 6.1 Process streams

Stream number	Supply temperature (°C)	Target temperature (°C)	Heat capacity flowrate (kW K⁻¹)
1	400	60	0.6
2	210	40	1.0
3	20	160	0.8
4	100	300	1.2

mass flowrate and the heat capacity, and is the power required to raise the temperature of the stream by 1 degree.

Determination of the streams is in many ways the most important step in the method. The start and end temperatures are fixed, for example by:

- design requirement within the flowsheet (the need to bring a stream to a sterilization temperature will mean that the upper temperature is set);
- the temperature at which the stream enters the flowsheet;
- the temperature at which the stream leaves the flowsheet (which may be to waste or to some other process) – environmental considerations may determine this.

There is no need for the streams to be materially different: for example, the streams to and from the reactor in Fig. 6.1 are different streams in a heat integration sense because they start and end at different temperatures although they are the same in mass balance terms.

6.2.2 Stage 2: thermodynamic analysis

The example above consists of four streams, two to be cooled and two to be heated. The second law states that heat at any temperature can be transferred to a system at a lower temperature. Two **composite curves** can thus be constructed from the data, representing the net amount of heat available at a given temperature. The **hot composite curve** is the thermodynamic sum of the two streams that are to be cooled; there is

$0.6\,kW\,K^{-1}$ available at temperatures between 400 and 210°C (stream 1 alone) then
$1.6\,kW\,K^{-1}$ between 210 and 60°C (both 1 and 2) and then
$1.0\,kW\,K^{-1}$ between 60 and 40°C (stream 2 alone)

The **cold composite curve** is the sum of the two streams that have to be heated; there is

$0.8\,kW\,K^{-1}$ required between 20 and 100°C (stream 3) then
$2.0\,kW\,K^{-1}$ required between 100 and 160°C (both 3 and 4) and then
$1.2\,kW\,K^{-1}$ required between 160 and 300°C (stream 4 alone).

These two curves can be represented graphically on a temperature–enthalpy diagram, as in Fig. 6.2. The horizontal axis is an arbitrary one; the two curves can be moved sideways relative to one another. Any overlap between the two represents the amount of heat recovery that is possible: that is, the amount of heat that can be transferred from the hot streams to the cold. Figure 6.2 thus represents the case where there is no heat recovery: that is, where all heating and cooling duties are satisfied by external heating and cooling analogous to Fig. 6.1(a). In Fig. 6.3, there is some overlap, corresponding to the amount of heat recovery that occurs.

The vertical distance between the curves is the temperature driving force between the streams. This can be used in the basic heat transfer equation:

$$Q = UA\,\Delta T \tag{6.1}$$

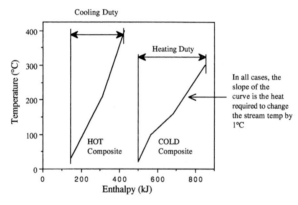

Fig. 6.2 Hot and cold composite curves, showing no heat recovery; all the heating and cooling must be done externally.

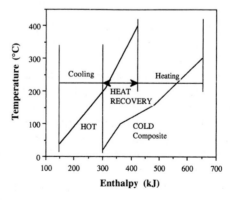

Fig. 6.3 Hot and cold composite curves, showing some heat recovery – overlap of the two curves.

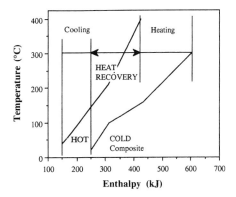

Fig. 6.4 The overlap between the two composite curves again represents the heat recovery; different approach temperatures give different recovery to that of Fig. 6.3.

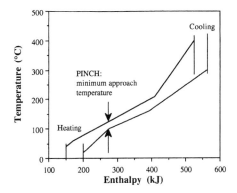

Fig. 6.5 At the chosen minimum approach temperature, heat recovery is maximized.

and is thus a measure of the heat transfer possible. It is only possible to transfer heat from hot to cold streams. Depending on the ΔT selected between the two streams, different amounts of heat can be recovered; compare Figs 6.3 and 6.4, where the overlap of the two composites is different, and the temperature between the two streams is also different.

The smaller the temperature difference between the two streams, the greater is the amount of heat transferred. The selection of a **minimum approach temperature**, or minimum temperature driving force (often written ΔT_{min}) is an important step in the analysis of the system. From equation (6.1) it can be seen that the smaller the driving force the larger is the heat transfer area. In the limit of no temperature difference between the two streams the area required becomes infinite, from equation (4.1). The chosen case corresponds to the composite curves moving until they are separated by the ΔT_{min}, as in Fig. 6.5. The point where the curves are closest is the **pinch point** for the system. If the two curves are overlapped further, then they will cross, implying that the fluid to be cooled will in fact be heated. This is the key point in the system, where heat transfer is most difficult. The core of the pinch design technique lies in finding this point – once the network is designed to ensure heat transfer in this region can be carried out efficiently, all other heat exchange will be easier. For engineering practicality, a finite ΔT_{min} must be selected. Small ΔT_{min} leads to a very high heat recovery, but low driving forces imply a large heat transfer area and thus capital cost. If a large ΔT_{min} is selected, however, then the heat transfer area is small and the capital cost is low, but the heat recovery is less.

In the example, 20 °C is taken as the ΔT_{min}. To ensure that this require-ment is not violated, and to simplify the arithmetic, it is common to adjust the temperatures of the streams; hot-stream temperatures have $\Delta T_{min}/2$ subtracted from them and cold-stream temperatures have $\Delta T_{min}/2$ added to them. This is purely a convenience, but makes the thermodynamics much clearer. It is now possible to plot the hot and cold composite curves on axes of enthalpy versus **adjusted** temperature, as in Fig. 6.6. At the pinch point, where in reality the temperature driving force is ΔT_{min}, the two adjusted curves touch: this makes the pinch point evident. This leaves an overlap at each end of the curve. Above the pinch point the two curves do not overlap; process heating Q_H is required to bring the cold composite curve to the required temperature. Below the pinch point process cooling Q_C is needed to bring the hot composite curves down to the required temperature. These two values can be seen in the figures.

The second-law analysis thus defines the minimum heat loads for a given approach temperature. For the example of Fig. 6.6, a 20 °C approach results

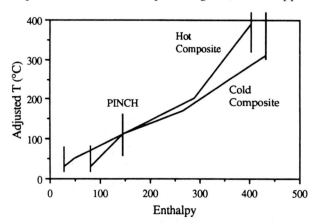

Fig. 6.6 Data of Fig. 6.5 replotted as adjusted temperature: at the pinch point, the two composites touch.

in a heating duty of 30kW and a cooling duty of 52kW; this can be seen from the diagram (but is difficult to read!). If cooling greater than Q_C is given to the system, this will lead to an increase in the process heat Q_H required: this effectively corresponds to the horizontal displacement of the composite curves. This involves a direct transfer of heat from Q_H to Q_C: the thermodynamics suggests that for MER no heat should be transferred across the pinch.

Manipulation of the composite curve in the manner described above is possible for simple systems, and is very useful to demonstrate the concepts of the method. It is less easy to use for larger numbers of streams. In general it is best to construct a **problem table** as in Fig. 6.7. The table includes all the streams at their adjusted temperatures. The left-hand side of the diagram shows the problem as a cascade, with streams shown vertically between

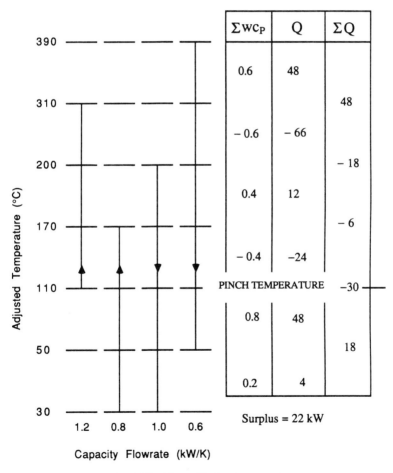

Fig. 6.7 Problem table for the example.

their adjusted temperatures. The diagram defines a series of temperature intervals: in each interval the net capacity flowrate and the net energy requirement are calculated with cooling as positive. For example, between 170 and 200°C, the net capacity flowrate is $(1.0 + 0.6 - 1.2)\,kW\,K^{-1} = 0.4\,kW\,K^{-1}$, and so the heat evolved by the system between these two temperatures is 12 kW. At any temperature, the second law says that heat can be transferred only to lower temperatures. A heat cascade can be thus be produced with the energy requirements or surpluses from one interval carried down to the next: this is the ΣQ column in the table. The pinch point is that where the net flow is the most negative. As heat cannot be transferred 'uphill' – that is, from a low temperature to a hot – heat must be added to the top of the cascade to make the system operate; 30 kW must be added as hot utility making the net flow of heat zero at the pinch, and rejecting $22 + 30\,kW = 52\,kW$ as cold utility. This again emphasizes that the two halves of the system are separate, and that no heat should be transferred across the pinch; if extra heating had been added as hot utility it would be transferred down the cascade out to the cold utility.

This method is in general an easier way to find the heating and cooling loads than the composite curve technique, especially for large numbers of streams.

6.2.3 Stage 3: design for MER

The thermodynamics has defined the maximum heat recovery; it is now necessary to design a system of heat exchangers between the streams that produces that recovery. The pinch-adjusted temperature is 110°C; the pinch temperature of the hot stream is thus 120°C and that of the cold stream is 100°C. No heat must flow across the pinch for MER. It is best to design the heat recovery system in two halves:

- **Above the pinch** all hot streams must be cooled from their supply temperatures to the pinch, and all cold streams heated from the pinch to their target temperatures. This must be done without utility cooling.
- **Below the pinch** all hot streams must be cooled from the pinch temperature to their target temperatures, and all cold streams heated from their supply temperatures to the target temperatures. This must be done without utility heating.

Design thus starts at the pinch and works out. To minimize the number of heat exchangers needed, it is important to match heat loads so that, if possible, the whole need of the stream is satisfied in one unit. Care must also be taken to avoid infeasible matches which give a temperature driving force below the minimum:

- exchangers just above the pinch should have $(wc_P)_H < (wc_P)_C$, so that heat transfer increases the temperature difference between the streams;
- those just below the pinch must have $(wc_P)_C < (wc_P)_H$.

Figure 6.8 shows the MER solution obtained following these rules. Each heat exchanger is represented as a vertical line with two circles connecting two horizontal streams; the number in the top circle is the number of the heat exchanger and the number in the bottom circle is the heat load in the exchanger in kW. The structure of the network is obtained using the following sequence of steps:

- **Cold end below the pinch:** All the heat needed to heat stream 3 can be supplied by cooling stream 2 in exchanger 4. No other heat can be used (as stream 4 begins at the pinch!) so the other cooling duties, 36 kW on stream 1 and 16 kW on stream 2, are supplied by cold utility, indicated by C.
- **Hot end above the pinch:** The whole heat duty of 3 can be supplied by stream 1 through exchanger 3, and the whole cooling duty of 2 can be supplied by 4 through exchanger 2. The rest of the duty on 1 can then be used to heat 4 by exchanger 1, leaving a 30 kW heating load to raise 4 to the correct temperature, indicated by H.

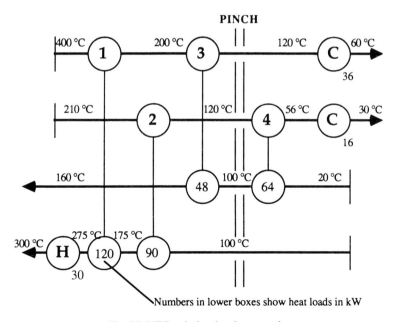

Fig. 6.8 MER solution for the example.

6.2.4 *Stage 4: relaxing the solution*

The above satisfies MER but contains four heat exchangers and three heaters and coolers. This has the lowest operating costs but may have an excessive capital cost. Network theory – a branch of pure mathematics – can be used to optimize the system, by minimizing the number of process units. The **minimum number of units** possible can be calculated; it is $N-1$, where N is the number of streams plus the number of utilities, here 6: so the minimum number of units is 5. Network theory also gives a way of identifying which units can be lost, by identifying loops in the system as shown in Fig. 6.9. A loop is a set of connections that can be traced through the network that starts from one exchanger and returns to the same exchanger (for example, loop A in Fig. 6.8), or which passes through a utility, as does loop B, which goes through the two coolers and four heat exchangers. Breaking these loops is possible by removing units.

Design decisions are required here. The MER solution is optimal in terms of the heat loads; other criteria control what, if any, relaxation is made. To make the network controllable, it is probably best to leave the coolers intact. So the loop to be broken is that with the four exchangers. It is best to start by removing the unit with the smallest duty, here exchanger 3. Examination of the loop shows that removal will add 48 kW to loads on 1 and 4, while subtracting 48 kW from 2. This results in smaller ΔT than is allowed; extra heater and cooler duties are needed, as shown in Fig. 6.10. The result is a network with a smaller capital and maintenance cost, but which costs more to operate; the final decision, as in all things, must be made on cost, as discussed in Chapter 1.

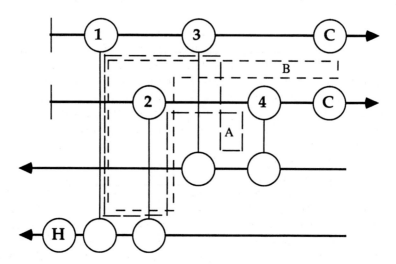

Fig. 6.9 Loops in the MER solution for the example.

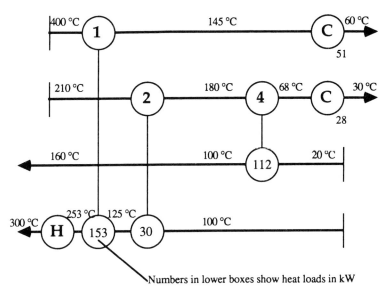

Fig. 6.10 Relaxed solution for the example.

6.3 Heat and process integration in the food industry

The above worked example demonstrates the use of the 'pinch' design technique. The technique has been widely used in the petrochemical industry and has been shown to yield significant energy savings. A petrochemical plant such as an oil refinery contains many heat exchangers and uses a wide range of temperatures, as in the above example. However, a typical food plant will probably contain fewer heat exchangers, and their inter-use may be limited. For example, there may be objections on safety grounds if cannery waste water is used to preheat material for canning; if the exchanger were to leak it is possible that microbes could cross between the two streams. Chemical process plant can involve a number of processes to produce many products; heat generated in one place can be used in another. Food plants tend to be smaller, reducing the opportunities for integration. However, some food plant is already integrated; a plate heat exchanger used as a sterilizer will commonly preheat the feed by exchange with hot product, along the lines of Fig. 6.1.

Another area of interest to the food industry is control of plant, as discussed in Chapter 7. Integrated plant is more difficult to control than unintegrated plant. For example, if the final network of Fig. 6.10 is examined it can be seen that stream 3 is heated only by stream 2. If stream 2 changed its temperature as a result of a problem elsewhere in the process, or if the efficiency of heat exchanger 3 changed as a result of fouling, then it would be difficult to control the 160 °C outlet temperature of stream 3.

However, if the heat were provided by process steam, reaching the required temperature would be simple (but more expensive!).

In practice, the final design may be easy to control and flexible enough to deal with changes in both input conditions and the efficiency of heat transfer; this is termed **process operability**. The pinch design approach is well suited to continuous plants with heat sources and sinks. Many of the operations of the food industry are still batch or semibatch, and when operation is continuous the plant is frequently shut down for cleaning. Unless great care is taken in their design, integrated plants are more difficult to start up and shut down than less thermally efficient systems. Deciding the optimal compromise between operability and operating cost is very difficult, not least because difficulties in operating process plant are not always obvious until the plant has been working for some time.

The integration of batch processes is more complex still: for example, if a biscuit factory has to make 15 products from four lines, what is the most efficient operating strategy, given the shelf-life of the product? It is necessary to design efficient operating schedules to maximize both usage of the plant and profit. This needs an understanding both of the profit resulting from each action and of the limits to the operation of the plant such as the time needed in cleaning shutdowns. This sort of information is common in the fine chemicals industry but less so in the food industry.

Note that, unlike much of the basic work described in this book, such as material and thermal balances, second-law analysis, and ways to develop optimal designs, are an active research area and are thus being continually developed. The example described above is deliberately simple; an attempt to explain the concepts of the method. It has been developed into a complex design tool which can be applied to designing very large-scale plant. More recently, a similar type of analysis has been applied to the study of waste streams from process plant, in an attempt to maximize waste recovery and minimize disposal costs.

Since this area is being actively researched, basic textbooks are scarce. One text which goes into detail of the design of chemical plant is:

Douglas, J.M. (1988) *Conceptual Design of Chemical Processes*, McGraw-Hill, New York.

Conclusions

The ways of calculating energy requirements, that is of setting up energy balances around processing operations, and their basis in the first law of thermodynamics were introduced in the first chapter of this book. Anyone faced with designing or operating a food processing plant will have come across important problems to which those methods don't appear to give an answer. Two such problems are:

- how can we make best use of the various hot streams throughout a plant?
- what is the absolute minimum amount of energy or work that is needed for a particular set of operations?

The second law of thermodynamics is needed to answer these questions, but the first of them can in fact be solved with little new theory beyond that developed on Chapter 1. This chapter has focused on that problem, that is, of energy integration, and has outlined the principles and techniques of 'pinch' technology which can be employed in its solution. The thermodynamic principle underlying the technique is that heat energy cannot flow 'uphill': in other words, heat is only transferred **down** a temperature gradient. Since the rate of heat transfer (and ultimately therefore the size of any heat exchanger) is proportional to the driving force it is not economically or technically feasible to attempt to reduce the temperature difference between a hot and cold stream to zero: in reality a minimum temperature approach (typically 15 to 20 °C) is chosen. The problem is then addressed by preparing composite curves representing the temperature versus heat energy or enthalpy of the hot and cold streams respectively, and adjusting these to maximize the heat recovery from one to the other. The pinch point is the point at which the composite curves come closest to each other, i.e. the minimum temperature approach. The method is illustrated graphically by a simple example, and its extension to more complex and more realistic problems is briefly outlined.

You should now appreciate the difference between the first and second laws of thermodynamics, and be able to analyse plant so as to recognize where opportunities for heat recovery might arise. Whilst the methods of handling complex problems are beyond the scope of this text, we believe that an understanding of the principles behind the technique is of great importance to anyone involved with designing or operating real processes, where energy conservation is economically and environmentally more and more important.

7 Process control

D.L. PYLE and C.A. ZAROR

Introduction

Up to now, most of the examples studied have been for plants in a steady state; conditions in the process have not been changing. In practice, no process is in a steady state; processes are always unsteady and require continual control action to keep the product within specification. Process control requires accurate measurement of process parameters, together with some understanding of the ways that changes to the inlet conditions of the process will affect the product. When a process is designed, it is important that it be easy to control; it is best to consider the controllability of a plant at the outset, rather than attempting to design a control system after the rest of the plant has been developed.

This chapter introduces the ideas of process control. Of necessity this is a mathematical subject, but the principles are easy to understand. Once the objectives of a control system have been identified, then it is possible to develop a control model for the process, which identifies the outputs to be controlled and the input variables which can be changed. Depending on how well the process is understood, different types of control model can be developed; if the process can be accurately modelled then it may be possible to produce a **feed-forward** model in which the effect of changes in input variables on the output can be directly predicted; however, if the process is not well-understood, then **feedback** control, in which the change in output conditions with changes in inputs is measured and then used to change the inputs, may be the only one possible. Feedforward control is more efficient and rapid in theory, but requires much better knowledge of the process, and therefore is rarely used in practice. Analysis of process controllability can also help suggest how to design processes to be more easily controlled. As always in food processing, the better understood is a system, the more likely it is to be operated in a profitable manner.

More and more, computers are being used for 'on-line' control; it is now possible to carry out data processing, optimization and the adjustment of process and control parameters in real time. Hierarchical control structures, in which process control and overall process management are closely inte-

Chemical Engineering for the Food Industry. Edited by P.J. Fryer, D.L. Pyle and C.D. Rielly. Published in 1997 by Blackie A & P, an imprint of Chapman & Hall, London. ISBN 0 412 49500 7

grated, are now becoming common. These structures encompass conventional control techniques at the lowest level of the process, through production control right through to management policy. At the process level the data are processed through software control algorithms and the control signals are fed back to the process. In this sense the computer can be seen as a replacement for traditional control systems. The application of on-line control will undoubtedly continue apace, with huge implications for process efficiency. Nevertheless, the basic principles of process control theory will remain valid, and they will be the focus of this introductory chapter.

Although there are many types of control problem and many different reasons for needing to control a process, two preconditions for any control scheme are that:

1. it must be possible to measure some key indicators; and
2. it must be possible to alter or correct the process behaviour in a predictable and stable way by manipulating one or more inputs.

For example, the composition of a blender product stream might be controlled by altering the flowrate of one of the input streams, or biscuit quality may be controlled by manipulating the heat input to part of the oven. Sometimes it is easy to see which input must be manipulated: the obvious way to control the temperature of a heated vat is to manipulate the heat input. In other cases, such as in controlling a batch dough mixer, it is more difficult to see how to control the process. Measurement is a very important issue for the food industry, but unfortunately there is no space here to discuss such problems: instead the focus will be mainly on issue (2): modelling and controlling processes. Within that framework, the primary emphasis will be on controlling continuous rather than batch or discrete processes.

Some aspects of the material in this chapter are illustrated in the control simulation included on the disk accompanying this text. The example simulates the feedback control of a continuous well-mixed heater, and details of the model and the simulation are given in section 11.12.

Some sections of this chapter (7.4–7.6 in particular) are more mathematical than the others and can be omitted on a first reading. Sections 7.1–7.3 introduce some key concepts of linear systems. Sections 7.7 and 7.8 are concerned respectively with some common controller types and actions (whose principles should be understood) and with a few issues involved in controlling complete processes as opposed to single units.

7.1 What is the control problem?

There are several stages in developing an adequate control strategy for a process. These include:

- defining the main control objectives;
- defining appropriate control structures (identifying potential disturbances and defining what to measure and what to manipulate) at the level
of individual units and the whole process;
- specifying the appropriate control laws (relations between the measurement and the magnitude and rate of change of the control variables);
- translating the definition into hardware and software.

7.1.1   Control objectives

Classical control theory has traditionally concentrated on two classes of
control objective. The first is to maintain a key parameter constant in the
face of disturbances. For example, it might be necessary to maintain the fat
content of a milk stream at a constant value despite batch-to-batch variations. There are many problems of this type (called the **regulator** problem)
in continuous processes. In extreme cases control may actually be needed to
stabilize the plant in the face of disturbances. Sometimes the uncontrolled
process output changes because of fluctuations in process inputs, such as the
raw materials quality or feedrate, or because of changes in demand for
process services such as the steam supply. Some of these fluctuations could
be rapid, or high-frequency; others may be much slower, such as variations
in the outside temperature. Some may occur as more-or-less random variations about a mean value; others may result from longer-term changes.
The food industry is particularly prone to fluctuations in raw material
quality and supply.

An obvious first strategy in dealing with this sort of problem is to try to
eliminate or minimize those disturbances that **can** be controlled. For example, changes in flow or composition can often be reduced or damped by the
judicious use of intermediate storage or buffer tanks.

The second type of control problem, sometimes called the **servo problem**,
arises with processes where the conditions **have** to change. In many operations, such as batch mixers and cookers, or batch fermentations, it is necessary to sequence the addition or rate of addition of some components or to
adjust an operating parameter – such as mixing speed or heat input – to
achieve the desired product quality. The essential problem is to 'steer' the
process along a more-or-less defined path towards a final objective, in
contrast to the regulator problem, where the aim is to remain within a small
region of the desired steady state. The same problem also arises when a
change in production volume or quality is called for. It may also arise in a
different guise if the process performance changes (for example, because of
exchanger fouling). Many processes rely on historical or design information
to provide the basis for sequencing: typically – as embodied in many simple
programmable logic controllers (PLCs) – valves or motors are switched on
or off at predetermined times. This sort of process does not have any built-
in mechanism for corrective control action.

It is often assumed that accuracy is synonymous with process control. This is not always true: sometimes all that is needed is to maintain some parameter within a broad band. With a storage tank, for example, it is usually sufficient to ensure that the vessel doesn't overflow or run dry. More generally, means must be found to ensure that a process, or chain of processes, doesn't run out of key inputs during the production cycle. At the process level, this is called **material balancing**.

It will be appreciated, then, that there exists a range of control objectives. From the cases mentioned above it will be clear that it is necessary to consider the dynamic behaviour of the process, and how this is modified by the control system. This presupposes a process model. Linear models usually suffice for regulatory control, but non-linear models may be needed when significant changes in operating conditions are involved, such as in servo control. Here we shall concentrate on some basic ideas of classical theory, which developed around linear **single input single output** (or SISO) systems.

Three complementary methods have traditionally been used. **Time domain methods**, which typically examine the system response to (for example) a step disturbance, focus on the transient behaviour using criteria such as the rise and settling times, degree of oscillation in response, overshoot and offset as the basis for design and tuning. In **frequency domain methods** the system's response and stability are characterized in terms of its frequency response, bandwidth, and gain and phase margins (which measure how close the system is to unstable, highly oscillatory behaviour). The importance of these two methods stems essentially from the use of transfer functions to describe system behaviour, and the ease with which they can be manipulated algebraically. However, a disadvantage is that, in dealing with complex systems, they lead to mathematically high-order functions. **Root locus methods**, which provide a bridge between the two other methods, are the basis of a third set of techniques. Here we shall touch on the first two methods only. First, however, we outline some typical control structures.

7.1.2 Some basic control structures

We can illustrate some of the basic concepts involved in process control by considering the control of a single unit, in this case a continuous mixer–blender (Fig. 7.1(a)). In this example two (liquid) streams with different fat contents X and Y are blended continuously to produce a product stream with fat content Z. We assume that the principal objective is that Z should be controlled as closely as possible. For this example we assume that $X > Y$, so that $Y < Z < X$. In the regulatory problem, the desired value of the outlet fat content is constant. The servo problem corresponds to the case when a new fat product is desired: that is, Z changes. For simplicity, most of the discussion below focuses on the regulatory problem, but we shall see that it is also relevant to the situation where the desired fat content is changed.

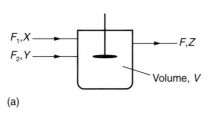

(a)

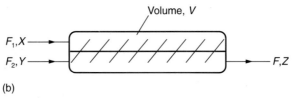

(b)

Fig. 7.1 Continuous blenders.

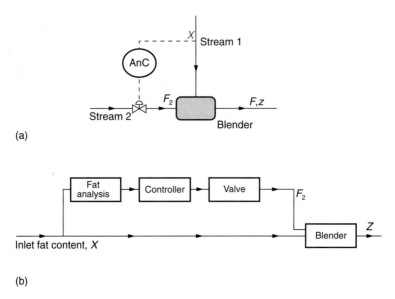

(a)

(b)

Fig. 7.2 Feedforward control of blender: (a) process flowsheet; (b) block diagram of control loop. AnC: analysis controller.

First we have to devise a control structure: what to measure and what to manipulate. Suppose that all flowrates and fat contents can be measured. The only possible manipulated variables are the two inlet flowrates and the mixer speed or motor power. Changing the mixer speed cannot, of itself, alter the average exit fat content; all it can do is affect the quality of the blend. This leaves us with the flowrates as possible manipulated variables. In theory, if the feed fat contents and flowrates were measurable, one or both of the inlet flows could be altered so as to ensure constant outlet fat content. For example, it would be possible to measure the fat contents X and Y, and one feedrate, say F_1, and then adjust the flow of the other stream F_2 to maintain Z constant. This would be a **feedforward control** scheme. In order to implement it one needs to know how F_2 (the **manipulated variable**) affects the other variables. A simplified version of a feedforward scheme, built around the assumption that significant disturbances would only occur in the fat content of stream 1 (that is, X), is shown in Fig. 7.2(a). Note that, without taking additional measurements, it couldn't be guaranteed that Z was actually at its desired value as, for example, F_1 might deviate from its assumed value, or the actual value of F_2 could be in error. An analogy might be a rally driver who had such confidence in her navigator that she relied only on instructions read from the map.

An alternative scheme would involve measuring the **outlet** fat content Z and then, depending on whether Z was below or above its desired value, adjusting the feedrate of streams F_1 or F_2 to restore Z to its target value. (A similar process could be used independently to control the quality of the blend by manipulating the mixer power.) The principle behind the fat content control scheme is shown for one adjusted flowrate only in Fig. 7.3(a). In practice there would also be a time lapse between realizing that Z was drifting from its desired value and being able to do something about it before it was too late. Assuming that the dynamic problem is not a serious limitation it will be recognized that this scheme – **feedback control** – has the

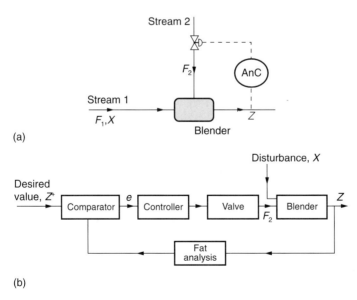

(a)

(b)

Fig. 7.3 Feedback control of blender: (a) process flowsheet; (b) block diagram of control loop.

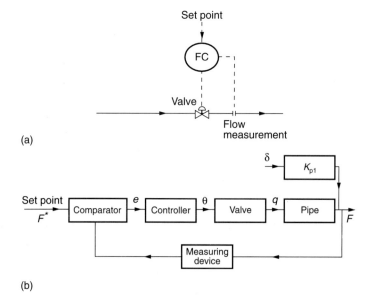

Fig. 7.4 Flow control. FC: flow controller.

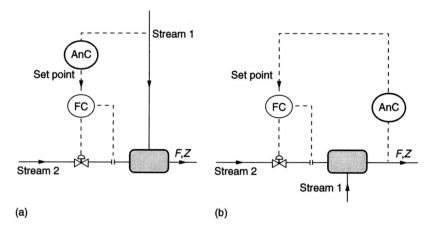

Fig. 7.5 Cascade control: (a) feedforward cascade; (b) feedback cascade.

intuitive advantage that it is based on the actual parameter that it is desired to control. A rough analogy is the strategy we use to adjust the heater setting in the shower: we trim the setting more or less violently in response to the sensation on the top of our head. We soon learn to compensate for the delay between changing the setting and feeling hotter or colder. The full scheme involving the two manipulated streams (that is, changing the flows of stream 1 or 2 depending on whether an increase or decrease in Z was required) would be known as **split-range control**, as different manipulated variables may be used depending on the measured deviation in Z.

In feedforward control (Fig. 7.2) a control signal alters the setting of the valve controlling the flow F_2. As noted above, this involves the assumption that the valve stem moves to precisely the correct position to give the desired flow. Many valves are equipped with positioners to ensure this. A more secure system would employ a **secondary feedback loop**. Figure 7.4 illustrates a flow control loop in which the reading from a measurement device just downstream from the valve is compared with the desired value or set point. Figure 7.5 shows how a secondary loop could modify the set point of the flow control loop in response to changes in the measured fat content X (or, in a feedback system, Z). Such a 'nested' scheme is called **cascade control**.

Sometimes, when two or more streams are blended, it is their flowrates that are subject to change rather than their compositions, and then the desired output consistency will be assured by using **ratio control** to hold the flows in a fixed ratio to each other (Fig. 7.6).

All feedback schemes involve comparison of a measured output with its **desired value** or **set point**, which in the discussion above is assumed constant. If it is desired to change from one output fat content to another or to change the flowrate of a particular stream in some way, this could be achieved by changing the set point either stepwise or in a programmed way. A good design will then ensure that the system output is able to track this change: which, of course, is an example of servo control.

Most of these loops (and, indeed of those used in practice) have a single controlled input and a single output (SISO schemes). However, the fact that more complicated arrangements might be needed can be realized by looking at another feature of the blender: that is, the existence of multiple 'linkages' between the various inputs and some or all of the outputs. As

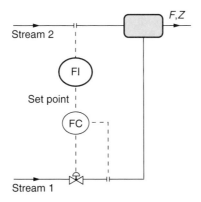

Fig. 7.6 Ratio control. FI: flow indicator.

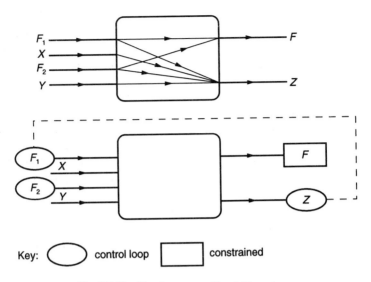

Fig. 7.7 The blender as a multivariable system.

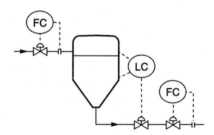

Fig. 7.8 An impossible control scheme. LC: level controller.

shown schematically in Fig. 7.7, changing either of the input flows will lead to a change in both the product flowrate and its composition; however, changes in the inlet composition only affect the composition and **not** the flowrate of the output stream. Where the interactions are weak, this presents no problem, and the whole system can be controlled by a set of independent SISO control loops. In other cases control system design must take account of the multivariable nature of the process in order to ensure that the desired objectives are met.

The ideal design consists of the minimum set of independent control loops. It is tempting to attempt to control everything, whether it is strictly necessary or not. Figure 7.8, showing a continuous liquid buffer tank, illustrates two important considerations. First, any control system must be feasible: the scheme shown, which implies **independent** control of the inlet flow, the level in the separator and the outlet flowrate, is clearly impossible, as there are insufficient degrees of freedom for all three variables to be independent of each other. Controlling the inlet flow and the level means that the outlet flowrate cannot also be varied independently. Second, as noted above, precise control is often **not** necessary. For example, it usually necessary to control the liquid level in a holding tank only within wide margins, as all that is needed is to ensure that the tank doesn't overflow or empty. Recognition of this can provide an important degree of flexibility in a system. It is recommended that, before detailed control of **quality measures** is undertaken, consideration be given first to ensuring adequate **mass balancing** throughout the plant: that is, to ensuring that pumps are always fed and that storage and process vessels don't run dry. Most important of all is to define the control objectives!

From the examples above we can distinguish between the following types of parameter or variable.

- **Disturbances**, such as the inlet concentration X. These fall into two categories: those that are measurable and those that aren't. Note that it would be very dangerous to assume that there was only one disturbance: in the case of the blender, we must ask what **would** happen if the inlet flowrate of milk **did** change?
- **State variables**, which are indicators of the state of the process, and which may include some **measured variables** (such as the outlet concentration Z) or **outputs**. Not all of these variables may be measurable on line; it may be possible to infer some from other readings or by computation. In what follows it will normally be assumed that the measured values provide analogue rather than either/or (open/closed, for example) information.
- **Manipulated or controlled** variables, such as the flowrate F_2.

Note also that in each case there has to be an appropriate **control law**: that is, a defined relation between the measured variable (or realistically its variation from the desired or target value) and the magnitude (and rate) of the change in the manipulated variable. In the example of the shower, the amount by which we change the heater setting in response to the sensation of burning reflects the control law, which we have learned through hard experience. You will see that this law reflects the model of the system: we would respond in one way with a modern, fast-acting shower and in another with an older less powerful type.

Two other features of control systems should also be noted. The first, obvious, point is that the control signals in a plant, such as flowrates, are constrained and not limitless. The second point is that control loops must be integrated into the emergency/alarm system appropriate to the plant. Alarms need to be built in to protect against process or control system failure; control valves should be chosen so that, wherever possible, they fail safe; overrides to shut down process flows in an emergency must also be built in.

7.2 Block diagrams

We can represent the control schemes described above by means of their block diagrams. For linear systems (see below) we shall see that this method of representation is a very powerful tool for control system analysis.

For example, Figs 7.2(b) and 7.3(b) are block diagrams for the feedforward and feedback schemes for blender control. The boxes, or blocks, represent the various components in the control loop. Each block has one or more inputs (such as a flowrate) and an output (for example, a composition or, from a transducer, an electrical signal); the arrowed lines show the direction of signal flow (that is, input → output). Most control systems will have blocks corresponding to the following hardware units:

- the process unit (the blender, holding tank etc.);
- a process sensor;
- a unit (the comparator) where the measured output is compared with the desired value (put in by the operator) to generate an 'error' signal;
- the controller itself, which, in response to the error signal, sends a signal to the final element:
- an actuator (most typically a valve) whose output is the manipulated control variable, usually a flowrate.

In practice the comparator and controller form a single unit, which might nowadays be a computer or programmable logic controller (PLC) device.

The algebra of block diagrams, which is the basis for many techniques for analysing control systems, is developed further in section 7.6.4.

7.3 Process dynamics

Processes and instruments can never react instantaneously to changing inputs. A few types of dynamic behaviour recur very frequently; these can be used to characterize many more complex processes and to explain the elementary principles of regulatory process control.

Two of these – the **first-order lag** and the **dead-time** or **transportation lag** – are particularly important. The difference between them can be grasped qualitatively by comparing the behaviour of a constant-volume well-mixed tank and a pipe (Fig. 7.9).

Consider the effects of a change (assumed a step jump) in the composition of the inlet stream to the two units. The first device is well mixed, so that, instantaneously, the compositions of the output stream and the average composition in the vessel are the same. As we shall see in Chapter 8, well-mixedness implies a very broad spread (from zero to infinity) in the residence times of individual material elements. A change in the composi-

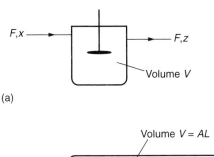

(a)

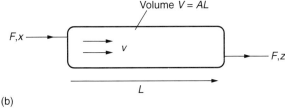

(b)

Fig. 7.9 (a) First-order and (b) transportation lags.

tion of the inlet flow will therefore be sensed immediately in the outlet
because of the short residence time of some material. However, the full
consequences of the inlet change will only be seen some time later. In
contrast, material is assumed to be transported without axial mixing along
the length of the pipe in Fig. 7.9(b); no change in outlet composition is
expected until the transportation lag time has elapsed. We now examine
these two systems quantitatively.

7.3.1 First-order systems

As illustrated in Fig. 7.9(a) we assume one input and outlet stream, flowing
at a constant rate F through the unit whose volume is V. This could, for
example, represent a holding tank for a continuous milk feed whose composition (protein or fat concentration), fluctuates. x and z are the instantaneous concentrations of the species of interest in the inlet stream and the
vessel (and in the outlet). The only disturbance considered is a change in
inlet concentration x. An instantaneous species balance is, in words:

Rate of accumulation = flowrate in − flowrate out

That is,

$$\frac{V dz}{dt} = Fx - Fz \tag{7.1}$$

or

$$\frac{\tau dz}{dt} + z = x \tag{7.2}$$

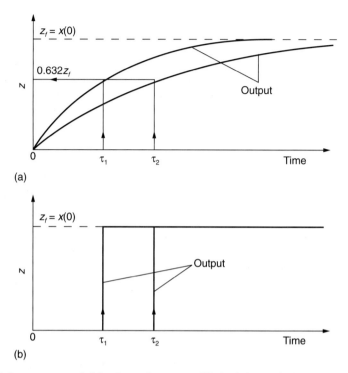

Fig. 7.10 Step response of: (a) a first-order system; (b) dead time. z_f is the final value of the output $z(t)$.

This is a first-order system (as it is described by a first-order linear ordinary differential equation). τ is the system time constant: here it is the mean residence time, V/F.

If the system is subjected to a step change of magnitude $x(0)$ in the inlet concentration, the response (which is readily checked by back-substitution) is

$$z(t) = x(0)\left[1 - \exp(-t/\tau)\right] \tag{7.3}$$

where the final value of the outlet concentration is, of course, the same as the inlet, $x(0)$. The response, $z(t)$, is shown in Fig. 7.10(a) for two different values of τ. The larger the system time constant, the slower the response. Note that the effects of the change in inlet concentration are observed immediately in the outlet stream, where the initial rate of change in concentration is $x(0)/\tau$. Two useful results are that z reaches 63.2% of its final value within one time constant and 95% within three time constants.

Many simple processes (such as the flow response of a holding tank or a simple thermocouple) demonstrate, or approximate to, first-order dynamics: that is, they are characterized by a single time constant.

7.3.2   Dead times or transportation lags

Now compare the result above with a **dead time** or **transportation lag** (Fig. 7.9(b)) (sometimes also called the **distance/velocity lag**). A pipeline with turbulent flow is a good approximation to this. Equation (7.1) no longer holds, as the contents are not perfectly mixed. A first approximation to the flow behaviour is that the contents flow at a constant mean horizontal velocity $u = F/A$ through the process unit, just as in the plug flow reactor (Chapter 8, section 8.3.3). A is the pipe cross-sectional area. A change in inlet concentration propagates through the unit with velocity u, appearing unaltered in magnitude at the exit a time $L/u = V/F$ later. Thus, although the system has the same characteristic time constant as the well-mixed process, its behaviour is very different (Fig. 7.10(b)). With a first-order system the first effects of an input change are seen immediately in the outlet stream, although the full effect is not seen until a few time constants have elapsed. With a pure time delay there is no attenuation in the outlet signal, and there is no intimation of a disturbance until one time constant has elapsed. In the case examined here, a step change in inlet concentration would result in the same final exit concentration from both systems.

7.3.3   Series of lags

The step response of a system comprising a first-order lag preceded **or** followed by a dead time τ_1 would follow the curve given by equation (7.3) but shifted by a time τ_1, as shown in Fig. 7.11(a):

$$z(t) = 0, \qquad t < \tau_1$$

$$z(t) = x(0)\left\{1 - \exp\left[-(t - \tau_1)/\tau\right]\right\}, \qquad t \geq \tau_1 \qquad (7.4)$$

This has significant implications for control system design. If a measuring element is placed some distance downstream from the process, the lag between a change occurring and its effects being recognized can have serious consequences for control quality.

It will be obvious intuitively that a system of first-order lags in series would give rise to an increasingly sigmoidal series of responses to a step input to the first unit, as shown qualitatively in Fig. 7.11(b). The response to a step input can never give rise to an oscillatory response.

7.3.4   Second-order lags

Examples of the **second-order** (or **quadratic**) **system** that are often quoted include a damped oscillator and the U-tube manometer. An example of the first would be a load cell. The force on the load cell is resisted by a restoring force from the spring (proportional to its compression) and a viscous damp-

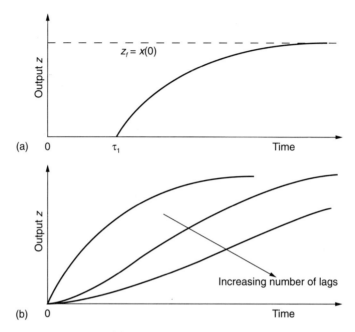

Fig. 7.11 Step response of: (a) first-order lag plus dead time; (b) series of first-order lags.

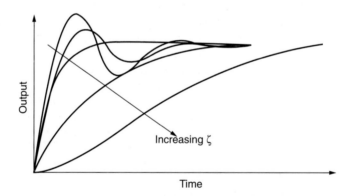

Fig. 7.12 Step response of a second-order system.

ing force, proportional to the rate of compression or movement of the cell. A force balance on both these systems leads to an equation of the form

$$\tau^2 \frac{d^2x}{dt^2} + \zeta \frac{dx}{dt} + x = F(t) \tag{7.5}$$

where x is the deflection (output) and F is the imposed, forcing function.

A feature of this is that the step response, sketched in Fig. 7.12, shows regions of non-oscillatory, or over-damped, response corresponding to $\zeta >$

1, and increasingly oscillatory (or underdamped) behaviour as ζ decreases for $\zeta < 1$. The frequency of this oscillation is related to the two parameters τ and ζ by $\omega\tau = \sqrt{(1 - \zeta^2)}$. In the absence of any viscous damping the system behaves as a simple harmonic oscillator with natural frequency $\omega = 1/\tau$. Two first-order lags in series (for example, one holding tank feeding another) give non-oscillatory behaviour, and exactly correspond to a system with $\zeta > 1$.

In practice, this form of response is far more important than the two examples quoted might suggest, because many closed-loop control systems behave in a qualitatively similar way. The choice of control parameters is often governed by a search for an appropriate compromise between the speed of response (favoured by lower values of ζ and τ) and the extent of oscillatory response that is acceptable.

7.4 Multiple inputs and linearization

All the examples above are based on linear processes. If, in the example used to develop the idea of a first-order lag, the flowrate F was allowed to vary, however, the system would be non-linear because of the product terms $F(t)x(t)$ and $F(t)z(t)$. Many processes are inherently non-linear: for example, the output (pressure signal) from an orifice flowmeter varies with (flowrate)^2 (equation (2.14)); the flow through an orifice or valve is, by the same token, proportional to (pressure drop)$^{0.5}$. However, it is always possible to approximate the process by a linearized model to allow the use of the large body of linear theory. This process is illustrated here. *This section and the following example can be omitted on a first reading.*

Consider the well-stirred blender shown in Fig. 7.1(a). We assume that the materials are incompressible, that the volume is maintained constant and that all flows and compositions may vary with time. Instantaneous material balances on the flows of total material and of fat both have the form:

Rate of accumulation = Sum of flows in − Sum of flows out

which, with the constant volume assumption, give

$$F_1(t) + F_2(t) = F(t) \tag{7.6}$$

and

$$V\frac{dZ}{dt} = F_1(t)X(t) + F_2(t)Y(t) - F(t)Z(t) \tag{7.7}$$

$$= F_1X + F_2Y - (F_1 + F_2)Z \tag{7.8}$$

for the total flow and fat respectively. The explicit dependence on time has been suppressed in equation (7.8), where equation (7.6) has been used to eliminate the outlet flow F.

If all of the inlet compositions or flowrates vary with time, equation (7.8) is non-linear. It is often hard to solve, and does not have a general solution. If the only disturbances were due to changes in the fat compositions X and Y, equation (7.8) would be a linear first-order differential equation with constant coefficients (A, B, C), of form

$$\frac{dZ}{dt} = AZ(t) + BX(t) + CY(t)$$

However, the equation can be reduced to an approximate linear form in **all** the variables by working in terms of changes (or deviations) rather than the absolute values of the variables. To do this we write each variable in the form

$$W(t) = W(0) + w(t)$$

where $W(0)$ is the initial (assumed steady) value and $w(t)$ is its deviation from the initial value. For example, we write

$$X(t) = X(0) + x(t)$$

and

$$F_1(t) = F_1(0) + f_1(t)$$

It is also assumed that $w(t)$ is small, so that, where necessary, products of small variables (such as $f_1(t)x(t)$) can be neglected to eliminate non-linear terms. Thus equation (7.8) becomes

$$V\frac{dz}{dt} = \left[F_1(0) + f_1\right]\left[X(0) + x\right] + \left[F_2(0) + f_2\right]\left[Y(0) + y\right]$$
$$- \left[F_1(0) + f_1 + F_2(0) + f_2\right]\left[Z(0) + z\right] \tag{7.9}$$

Some of the terms in equation (7.9) cancel because at steady state

$$F_1(0)X(0) + F_2(0)Y(0) = \left[F_1(0) + F_2(0)\right]Z(0) \tag{7.10}$$

Substituting from (7.10) in (7.8) and neglecting the small terms f_1x, f_2y, f_1z, and f_2z gives the general linearized dynamic model:

$$V\frac{dz}{dt} = \left[X(0) - Z(0)\right]f_1 + \left[Y(0) - Z(0)\right]f_2 + F_1(0)x$$
$$+ F_2(0)y - \left[F_1(0) + F_2(0)\right]z \tag{7.11}$$

which has the linear form

$$V\frac{dz}{dt} = Af_1 + Bf_2 + Cx + Dy - Ez \tag{7.12}$$

Suppose, for example, that all the inputs are constant except the fat composition of stream 1; equation (7.11) reduces to the simple first-order equation

$$V\frac{dz}{dt} = F_1(0)x - [F_1(0) + F_2(0)]z \qquad (7.13)$$

which can be written in the simpler form (cf. equation (7.2))

$$\tau\frac{dz}{dt} + z = K_p x \qquad (7.14)$$

where, as before, τ is the system time constant, here $= V/[F_1(0) + F_2(0)]$
$= V/F(0)$. The constant $K_p = F_1(0)/F(0)$; this is the 'static' gain.

If the system is subjected to a step change of magnitude $x(0)$ in the inlet
fat content, the response is as before:

$$z(t) = z(\infty)[1 - \exp(-t/\tau)] \qquad (7.15)$$

where the final value of the outlet fat content $z(\infty) = K_p x(0)$.

The time constant for changes in exit fat content (the blender volume
divided by the flowrate) is the same for all possible disturbances in the
model. However, changes in inlet flowrate are reflected by instantaneous
changes in the outlet flowrate F.

The assumption that fluctuations are small is often justified in the analysis
of control systems, on the grounds that a well-designed regulatory control
scheme will ensure that deviations are kept small. It is less likely to be
generally true, however, when set point changes are introduced, as in the
case of so-called servo control, as this often implies significant changes in
operation.

EXAMPLE 7.1: THE DYNAMICS OF A HOLDING TANK

*A tank, cross-sectional area $1\,m^2$, is used as a buffer tank. The steady-
state flow through the tank is $0.1\,m^3\,min^{-1}$; the output flow is related to
the liquid height in the tank by $F_o = 0.1\sqrt{H}$. How would the outlet flow and
liquid height respond to a step change in inlet flowrate from 0.1 to
$0.12\,m^3\,min^{-1}$?*

We first derive the general linearized model for a holding tank, using the
symbols defined in Fig. 7.13, with

$$F_o = K\sqrt{H} \qquad (7.16)$$

Small changes in flowrate from the steady value f_o are related to small
changes in liquid height h by taking the first terms in the Taylor series
expansion of equation (7.16):

$$F_o(0) + f_o = K\sqrt{H(0)}[1 + 0.5h/H(0) + \ldots]$$

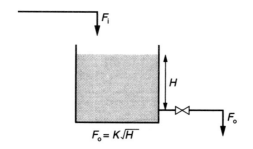

Fig. 7.13 Example 7.1: flow through a holding tank.

That is,

$$f_o = 0.5Kh = h/R_v \qquad (7.17)$$

where R_v is the linearized resistance of the outlet valve.

A linearized input–output relation for the flows through the tank then follows directly by substituting for $h = R_v f_o$ (equation (7.17)) into the mass balance:

$$A\frac{dh}{dt} = f_i - f_o \qquad (7.18)$$

That is,

$$AR_v\frac{df_o}{dt} + f_o = f_i \qquad (7.19a)$$

or

$$\tau\frac{df_o}{dt} + f_o = f_i \qquad (7.19b)$$

The system time constant $\tau = AR_v = 2AH(0)/F(0) = 2V/F(0)$. (The factor 2 appears here as a consequence of the non-linear flow/height relation.) Variations in the liquid height follow the equation

$$AR_v\frac{dh}{dt} + h = R_v f_i \qquad (7.20)$$

which, not surprisingly, has the same time constant but a different 'static' gain K_p.

Here, $K = 0.1$ and $f_o = 0.05h$, the valve resistance $R_v = 20\,min\,m^{-2}$, and the time constant $= 20\,min$. The step change in inlet flow thus results in:

$$f_o = 0.02\left[1 - \exp\left(\frac{-t}{20}\right)\right] \qquad (7.21a)$$

and

$$h = 0.4\left[1 - \exp\left(\frac{-t}{20}\right)\right] \qquad (7.21b)$$

The liquid height would change by 0.4 m; it would reach 0.25 m within 20 min and be almost steady at its new value within 1 h of the change. If the tank were much smaller or the steady flowrate higher, the speed of response (measured by the time constant) would be correspondingly faster.

7.5   Frequency response

The example above illustrates the ideas underpinning time domain analysis. The principles of frequency response analysis are briefly illustrated here. This section may be omitted on a first reading. We consider the response of a first-order system governed by equation (7.2) or (7.14) to a sinusoidal input $x = x(0) \sin \omega t$. Here ω is measured in radians/time; it is related to the frequency f (cycles/unit time) by $\omega = 2\pi f$. Once the immediate, transient, effects of the disturbance have died down, it can be shown that the output $z(t)$ itself settles down to an oscillatory form given by

$$z(t) = A \sin(\omega t + \phi) \qquad (7.22)$$

where the amplitude of $z(t)$ is

$$A = \frac{z(\infty)}{\left(1 + \omega^2 \tau^2\right)^{0.5}} = \frac{K_p x(0)}{\left(1 + \omega^2 \tau^2\right)^{0.5}} \qquad (7.23a)$$

and the phase shift is:

$$\phi = -\tan^{-1}(\omega\tau) \qquad (7.23b)$$

The physical significance of A and ϕ is illustrated in Fig. 7.14.
   Note the following.

- The output is also a sine wave with the same frequency as the input.
- The output amplitude is **reduced** from its steady-state or asymptotic value ($= K_p x(0)$) by a factor $1/(1 + \omega^2\tau^2)^{0.5}$: the higher the frequency, or the smaller the system time constant (that is, the faster it is able to respond), the greater is the reduction in the output amplitude, reflecting the combination of resistance and capacity in the system.
- The output signal **lags** the input by an angle ϕ, or a time $\phi/360f = \pi\phi/180\omega$.

   The effect of the process dynamics on the magnitude of the outlet is very important. Consider the effect of the holding tank on the outlet flow, for example: here $K_p = 1$. When the frequency of fluctuations in the inlet flow

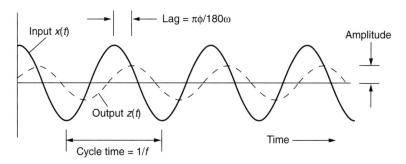

Fig. 7.14 Response to sinusoidal input.

is low in relation to the tank time constant (that is, $\omega \ll 1/\tau$), the magnitude of oscillations in the outlet will be the same as those in the inlet and there will be no time lag between them. If the frequency of the disturbances is high, the tank–valve system exerts a significant damping effect, reducing the magnitude of the variations. For example, if $\omega = 1/\tau$, the outlet flow oscillations are reduced by a factor $1/\sqrt{2}$; if $\omega = 10/\tau$, the amplitude is reduced to approximately one tenth of its inlet value. This is why buffer tanks, if correctly designed, can significantly reduce fluctuations, and effectively decouple one part of a process from the remainder downstream.

It also explains why, if a system is disturbed by, or expected to cope with, quickly varying variables, it is important to ensure that the dynamics of the various process elements (sensors and the like) are also fast. A thermocouple with a time constant of 1 s will have no problem in accurately following the changes of bulk temperature in a large vat of sauce; it may be less satisfactory in coping with a small gas-fired oven.

7.6 Feedforward and feedback control

We now return to a discussion of the control systems introduced earlier in section 7.4. To simplify matters we base the discussion around the blender control problem. This section may also be omitted on a first reading.

7.6.1 Feedforward control

First, consider feedforward control of the blender output, with the single feedforward scheme shown in Fig. 7.2. In order to respond to a variation in X it is necessary to know how X and Z depend on F_2. In other words, we need a model of the process, which has already been derived above:

$$F_1(t) + F_2(t) = F(t) \tag{7.6}$$

and

$$V\frac{dZ}{dt} = F_1(t)X(t) + F_2(t)Y(t) - F(t)Z(t) \tag{7.7}$$

$$= F_1 X + F_2 Y - (F_1 + F_2)Z \tag{7.8}$$

for the total flow and fat respectively.

The objective of the control scheme is to ensure that the effects of deviations in X are eliminated from Z. It is further assumed that neither F_1 nor Y varies from its steady value $F_1(0)$ or $Y(0)$. How then should F_2 be changed when a change in the inlet fat content X is detected, to ensure that Z remains at its steady value (that is, $dZ/dt = 0$)? The answer from equation (7.8) is that $dZ/dt = 0$ provided F_2 is

$$F_2(t) = \frac{F_1(0)X(t) - F_1(0)Z(0)}{Z(0) - Y(0)}$$

The flowrate of the added stream should always be proportional to the inlet fat content X. It is obvious in this case that the change in flowrate ($= f$) is also proportional to the change in fat content:

$$f = K_c x \tag{7.24}$$

where

$$K_c = \frac{F_1(0)}{Z(0) - Y(0)} \tag{7.25}$$

This is an example of **proportional feedforward** control. Note that the value of K_c, the controller gain, is fixed. If the model is wrong, or the flowrate F_1 is different from the value assumed in calculating K_c, the control system won't respond correctly to changes in inlet fat content, and the controlled value of X will be different from its desired value. The flow must also respond **immediately** to changes in X to achieve the desired objective.

EXAMPLE 7.2: FEEDFORWARD CONTROL

Consider a continuous blender, capacity 100 kg, with the following steady design conditions:

$$F_1(0) = 1000\,kg\,h^{-1}$$
$$X(0) = 0.06\,kg\,fat/kg\,milk$$
$$Y(0) = 0.01\,kg\,fat/kg\,milk$$
$$Z(0) = 0.05\,kg\,fat/kg\,milk$$

The fat content X(t) of the stream inlet F₁ may vary between 0.05 and 0.07 kg/kg. Design a proportional feedforward system to ensure that Z remains constant.

From the steady-state version of the mass balances (equations (7.6) and (7.9)):

$$F_2(0) = 250\,\text{kgh}^{-1} \quad \text{and} \quad F(0) = 1000\,\text{kgh}^{-1}$$

Then from equation (7.25):

$$K_c = \frac{1000}{0.04} = \frac{25\,000\,\text{kg}}{\text{kg fat/kg milk}}$$

Suppose that the inlet fat content jumps instantaneously from 0.06 to 0.061 kg/kg; then F_2 must also change instantaneously by $f_2 = (25\,000)(0.001) = 25\,\text{kgh}^{-1}$, so that $F_2 = 275$ and $F = 1275\,\text{kgh}^{-1}$, to ensure the correct value of Z.

However, if the blender was actually working with an inlet milk flow different from the assumed value of $1000\,\text{kgh}^{-1}$, or the fat content of stream F_2 was not 0.1 kg/kg, or the proportional control constant was not 25 000, Z would not be at its desired value, unless the control action was changed to allow for this.

Example 7.2 shows the power of feedforward control. However, for it to be effective every disturbance must be measured and the plant model must be accurate. It is useless, however, in the face of unmeasured plant disturbances, and is sensitive to the accuracy of the plant model.

7.6.2 Feedback control

Some of the key features of any feedback control system can be discussed by first exploring the behaviour of a process whose dynamics are so fast that, in a first analysis, they can be neglected. As noted earlier it is convenient to work in terms of **changes** in key variables rather than their absolute values, not least because it allows us to work with linear models: the object of the control scheme is then, if possible, to reduce the deviation in the measured output to zero. Consider the flow control loop in Fig. 7.4.

In the absence of any control a disturbance δ in the pressure upstream or downstream causes a change f in the uncontrolled flowrate, where

$$f = K_{p1}\delta \tag{7.26}$$

(K_{p1} would be positive for upstream pressure changes and negative for downstream fluctuations.)

With control the effect of the disturbance is compensated by a movement in the valve opening. The measured value f is compared with its desired value (the set point) f^*; the difference between these two, the error signal

$e = f* - f$, is the input to the controller. The output from the controller causes the valve opening to change to compensate the measured deviation. We assume that a proportional controller is used: that is, a controller whose output $\theta = K_c e$. Further, we assume that the valve itself is linear so that its output flow $q = K_v \theta$. As we are neglecting dynamic effects, the pipe between the valve and measuring point has no effect on the flowrate (that is, with no disturbance, $f = q$; the gain of the pipe or process, $K_p = 1$). Then

$$f = K_{p1} \delta + q \tag{7.27a}$$

$$= K_{p1} \delta + K_v K_c e \tag{7.27b}$$

$$= K_p \delta + K_v K_c \left(f* - f \right) \tag{7.27c}$$

Rearranging:

$$f = \frac{K_{p1} \delta}{1 + K_v K_c} + K_v K_c \frac{f*}{1 + K_v K_c} \tag{7.28}$$

This is the 'closed loop' relationship: that is, when the process is controlled, between changes in the flowrate, the disturbance and the set point. Note that the effect of feedback control is to reduce the sensitivity of the output to the input changes. Comparison of equations (7.26) and (7.28) shows that, for a given disturbance, the outlet flow is reduced from its 'open-loop' value (its value without feedback control) by $1/(1 + K_v K_c)$. If the pipe had a static gain K_p this term would become $1/(1 + K_p K_v K_c)$.

At first sight, perhaps the most surprising feature is that it is **not** possible with this control scheme to ensure perfect control. For example, if the system is upset by a disturbance that remains at a finite value, then f must also be finite. If the set point is changed, the output flow f can never exactly equal its desired value! However, the higher the value of the proportional control constant or gain (that is, the more sensitive the control action), the lower the value of f. The larger $K_v K_c$ is the smaller is the effect of a disturbance, as for large $K_v K_c$, $f \approx (K_p/K_v K_c)\delta$; also, the outlet approaches the set point more closely as $f \approx f*$. The phenomenon whereby the output is always slightly displaced from the desired value is a general feature of all **proportional** feedback control schemes. It is known as **offset**. The reason for offset is that the flow generated by the valve to counteract the effects of disturbances must result from a finite change in the measured variable: if there was no change there would be no control action. One implication of this is that we should look to other forms, apart from proportional control, of control action.

EXAMPLE 7.3: FEEDBACK BLENDER CONTROL

A single feedback control loop, shown in Fig. 7.3, is used to control the same blender as in Example 7.2. What proportional control constant will ensure that the outlet fat content Z remains within 0.001 kg/kg of its desired value in the face of disturbances in the fat content, X, of stream 1 of up to 0.01 kg/kg?

The diluent flowrate F_2 is manipulated in response to measured changes in the **outlet** fat concentration Z (Fig. 7.3) by altering the flowrate in direct proportion to the error signal. As before the steady compositions and flowrate are:

$F_1(0) = 1000\,\text{kg h}^{-1}$	$F_2(0) = 250\,\text{kg h}^{-1}$	$F(0) = 1250\,\text{kg h}^{-1}$
$X(0) = 0.06\,\text{kg/kg}$	$Y(0) = 0.01\,\text{kg/kg}$	$Z(0) = 0.05\,\text{kg/kg}$

It is assumed that all process dynamics are very fast, so that even when inputs are changing the process is always at the corresponding steady state.

First we require the closed loop relationship, analogous to equation (7.28), between z, x and f_2 (working with perturbation variables, as before). From the fat balance (equation (7.11)), setting $dz/dt = 0$ because of the quasi-steady state assumption:

$$F(0)z = \left[Y(0) - Z(0)\right]f_2 + F_1(0)x$$

That is,

$$z = -0.000032f_2 + 0.8x \tag{7.29}$$

which is the model for the block marked 'blender' in Fig. 7.3. The flowrate from the combination of controller and valve is proportional to the error signal; that is,

$$f_2 = K_c K_v\left(z^* - z\right) \tag{7.30a}$$

so that the closed-loop relationship is:

$$z = -0.000032 K_c K_v\left(z^* - z\right) + 0.8x \tag{7.30b}$$

That is,

$$z = -0.000032 K_c K_v\left(1 + 0.000032 K_c K_v\right)^{-1} z^*$$
$$+ 0.8\left(1 + 0.000032 K_c K_v\right)^{-1} x \tag{7.31}$$

Thus, for constant set point, i.e. $z^* = 0$ and for a change in inlet fat content $x = 0.01\,\text{kg/kg}$, the condition from equation (7.31) for z to vary by only $0.001\,\text{kg/kg}$ is that:

$$1 + 0.000032 K_c K_v = 8$$

That is,

$$K_c K_v = 218750\,\text{kg h}^{-1}/(\text{kg/kg})$$

A higher value will ensure a smaller offset from the ideal, $z = 0$. With this control setting the relation between z and the desired value (corresponding to servo control) is $z = (7/8)z^*$. That is, there would be a steady offset of $0.125z^*$ following a change z^* in the set point.

Note that, as in the first example of proportional feedback control, the term $(1 + K_p K_c K_v)^{-1}$ plays a crucial role in determining the system sensitivity.

7.6.3 Dynamics and control

Now we consider how the process dynamics affects feedback control. Intuitively we might expect the controlled variable to respond to a step change in a disturbance or set point by settling down to the value predicted from the static analysis. This will usually be true, provided the control system is stable (which can only be established from analysis of the dynamics); however, it will also be clear intuitively that the dynamics of the process and the various units in the feedback loop, such as the measuring element, must affect the control behaviour.

Again, we consider the example of the mixer–blender, but with the important difference from Example 7.3 that the dynamics of the blender itself are included. We assume that all other parts of the closed loop have very fast dynamics in comparison with the blender.

Thus the appropriate open-loop model is now a linearized dynamic model for the blender. Again we consider only one disturbance (x) and one manipulated variable (f_2). Then equation (7.6) becomes

$$f_2(t) = f(t) \tag{7.32a}$$

and equation (7.11) is

$$V\frac{dz}{dt} = \left[Y(0) - Z(0)\right]f_2 + F_1(0)x - F(0)z \tag{7.32b}$$

$$= Af_2 + F_1(0)x - F(0)z \tag{7.32c}$$

where $A = Y(0) - Z(0)$. As before

$$f_2 = K_c K_v\left(z^* - z\right) \tag{7.30a}$$

so that

$$V\frac{dz}{dt} = -\left[AK_c K_v + F(0)\right]z(t) + K_c K_v z^*(t) + F_1(0)x(t) \tag{7.33}$$

Equation (7.33), describing the closed loop, has exactly the same first-order form as the open-loop system (equation (7.14)), with the exception that there are two possible 'forcing' functions or inputs, z^* and x. For example, if we wish to examine the response of the system to a step change only in the inlet fat content x (so that $z^* = 0$), equation (7.33) becomes

$$\tau \frac{dz}{dt} + z(t) = Kx(t) \qquad (7.34)$$

where the time constant $\tau = V/[F(0) + AK_cK_v]$ and the closed-loop static gain $K = F_1(0)/[F(0) + AK_cK_v]$. These can be compared with the corresponding open loop values (equation (7.14)) $\tau = V/F(0)$ and $K_p = F_1(0)/F(0)$. Feedback proportional control **reduces** the apparent time constant for the system – that is, speeds up the response – and reduces the ultimate effect of a permanent change on the output, without eliminating it completely, as the offset $= Kx(0)$.

EXAMPLE 7.4

Consider the same blender as in Example 7.3. Compare the open- and closed-loop responses to step and sinusoidal changes in the inlet fat content, X, with the same control setting as in the previous example. As before the steady compositions and flowrates are:

$F_1(0) = 1000\,kg\,h^{-1}$	$F_2(0) = 250\,kg\,h^{-1}$	$F(0) = 1250\,kg\,h^{-1}$
$X(0) = 0.06\,kg/kg$	$Y(0) = 0.01\,kg/kg$	$Z(0) = 0.05\,kg/kg$

The open-loop characteristics are (see equation (7.14)):

$$\tau = \frac{V}{F(0)} = 0.08\,min \qquad \text{and} \qquad K_p = \frac{F_1(0)}{F(0)} = 0.8$$

As in the previous example, $K_cK_v = 218750\,kg\,h^{-1}/(kg/kg)$. Note that, in equation (7.33), $A = Z(0) - Y(0) = 0.04\,kg/kg$ and $AK_cK_v = 8750\,kg\,h^{-1}$.

The time constant of the controlled system is (equation (7.34)), $\tau = 0.01\,min$, and $K = 0.1$: both reduced eightfold from the open-loop values. The response of the system to a step change in inlet fat content $x(0) = 0.01\,kg/kg$ is, from equation (7.3):

$$z(t) = Kx(0)\{1 - \exp{-t/\tau}\}$$
$$= 0.008\{1 - \exp{-12.5t}\} \qquad \text{(open loop)}$$
$$= 0.001\{1 - \exp{-100t}\} \qquad \text{(closed loop)}$$

The step responses of the uncontrolled (open loop) and controlled (closed loop) blender are shown in Fig. 7.15.

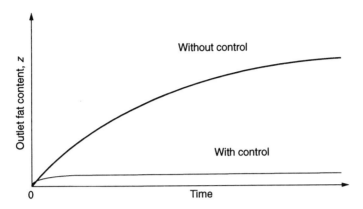

Fig. 7.15 Example 7.4: step response of blender, with and without control.

Note that, as expected, the final value of z is the value calculated from the static analysis. We can also easily obtain the responses of the system to sinusoidal changes in inlet fat content. We assume the same disturbance amplitude ($=0.01$) as the step disturbance. The amplitude $|z|$ and the phase shift ϕ of the output concentration calculated from equations (7.23a) and (7.23b) (namely $|z| = K_p x(0)/[1 + \omega^2\tau^2]^{0.5}$ and $\phi = -\tan^{-1}(\omega\tau)$) are tabulated below for disturbance frequencies $\omega = 1$ and 1000 rad min^{-1} respectively:

		Frequency, ω		
	1		1000	
	Open loop	Feedback	Open loop	Feedback
$|z|$	0.008	0.001	0.0001	0.0001
ϕ	4.6°	0.6°	89.3°	84.2°

When the disturbance varies slowly, the amplitude of the controlled outlet fat content is the same as the steady result following a step change; however, for a rapid disturbance the combined effect of the process dynamics and the feedback loop is the virtual complete elimination of the disturbance, even though it does now lag the input by almost 90°. Note, too, that with this control setting the main improvement over the uncontrolled system is seen at lower frequencies. This is because the blender itself 'irons out' high-frequency disturbances.

Remember that the great advantage of feedback control is that its efficacy does not depend on being able to measure or even identify the principal disturbances. Although the example above was developed on the assumption that there was only one disturbance, the same qualitative behaviour would result if the system was upset by changes in any of the other inputs, such as the flowrate F_1.

Note also that the results above all depend on the assumption of proportional control; below we shall discuss what other forms of controller action are available and how they might be expected to influence process behaviour.

7.6.4 Block diagram representation: the algebra of closed loops

In the examples above, the input–output relationships for the controlled system were found by incorporating equations to represent the proportional control action into the unsteady-state model. Long-winded mathematical derivations for each new problem can be avoided by deriving input–output relationships directly from a block diagram representation of the system. It will be seen that this allows some of the key results above to be generalized.

Block diagrams for various control schemes are shown in some of the diagrams above. The blocks or boxes usually represent a piece of equipment such as the process itself, the controller or a valve. The arrowed lines represent the direction of signal flow, which does not always coincide with the direction of material flow; for example, fluctuations in downstream pressure could act as a disturbance to the flow control system in Fig. 7.4. Nevertheless, this is properly represented as an 'input' ($= \delta$ in Fig. 7.4) to the process, affecting the 'output': the measured flow.

The lines in the block diagram represent the 'signals' (flowrates, temperatures etc.) and their direction. The signals (and the blocks) must obey the rules of dimensionality: we can add two flowrates but not a flowrate and a temperature. Junctions of lines represent addition and subtraction of signals, as shown in Fig. 7.16.

For linear systems each block represents an operator on the input, defined so that output = $G \times$ input, i.e. $\theta = G_1 q$ etc. The **transfer function** G has the dimensions of [output]/[input]. For example, if the input is a flowrate ($kg\,h^{-1}$) and the output is a temperature (°C), G has the units °C/($kg\,h^{-1}$).

The input and output variables (for example x, y and z in Fig. 7.16) are always defined as **deviation** or **perturbation variables**, which are therefore zero at steady state. In the simplest cases the transfer function G is a constant, but it can in fact be any operator, or combination of operators, that obeys the rules of linearity: namely, that if a is a constant the output y corresponding to an input ax [i.e. $G \times (ax)$] is $y = aGx$, and that $G \times (x + z) = Gx + Gz$. For example, the differential operators d/dt ($= D$), d^2/dt^2 ($= D^2$) etc. are linear operators. G need not be a scalar quantity: multivariable

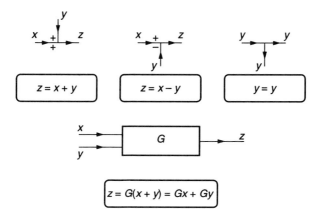

Fig. 7.16 Block diagram and signal flow notation.

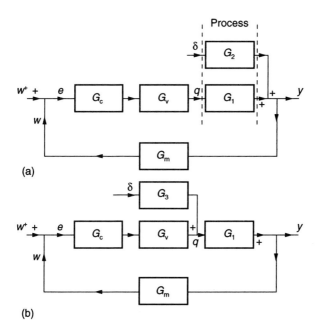

Fig. 7.17 A feedback control system.

systems can be represented by vectors of inputs and outputs linked by transfer function matrices.

Consider Fig. 7.17(a), representing a typical feedback control system. The transfer functions G_1 and G_2 represent the process: they relate changes in the controlled flow q and the disturbance δ to the uncontrolled process output. Without feedback and with $q = 0$ the output would be $y = G_2\delta$. We can easily derive the closed-loop transfer functions between the output, the disturbance and the set point, since

$$y = G_1q + G_2\delta \tag{7.35a}$$

$$= G_1G_vG_ce + G_2\delta \tag{7.35b}$$

Now the error e is

$$e = w^* - G_my \tag{7.36}$$

so that

$$y = G_1G_vG_cw^* - G_1G_vG_cG_my + G_2\delta \tag{7.37}$$

or

$$y = \frac{G_1G_vG_cw^*}{1+G_1G_vG_cG_m} + \frac{G_2\delta}{1+G_1G_vG_cG_m} \tag{7.38}$$

That is,

$$y = H_1w^* + H_2\delta \tag{7.39}$$

This is the **closed-loop transfer function** for the system. If the set point is constant and unchanged, $w^* = 0$ and $y = H_2\delta$. Each of the individual **closed-loop** transfer functions H_1 and H_2 has the same structure:

$$H = \frac{\text{Product of transfer functions between input and output}}{1+\text{Product of all transfer functions within the loop}}$$

We call the product term in the denominator, $G_1G_vG_cG_m$, the **system open-loop transfer function**, L.

Thus the closed-loop transfer function H between **any** input x_1 and **any** other signal x_2, such as the controlled output, defined by $x_2 = Hx_1$ is (with negative feedback)

$$H = \frac{G_f}{1+L} \tag{7.40}$$

where G_f is the product of the transfer functions between the input and the output **in the direction of signal flow** (that is, the forward path transfer function). Positive feedback (generating a signal $e = w^* + w$) produces a closed-loop transfer function of form $G_f/(1 - L)$, which is often unstable, as the control signal reinforces rather than cancels the effect of the disturbance.

Note that the two block diagrams in Fig. 7.17 are exactly equivalent provided that $G_1G_3 = G_2$.

In general, the larger the value of L the more effective is the control loop in attenuating the effects of a disturbance on the output (as in Fig. 7.17(a) $y = G_2\delta/[1 + L]$), and the closer does the output track the set point, for a given G_2. We can apply the same reasoning – that the smaller the magnitude of $G_2/(1 + L)$ the better – to the dynamic behaviour of a control system. In this case the system frequency response is particularly useful; recall from Example 7.4 that the ratio of the amplitudes or magnitudes of output and input sinusoids is frequency-dependent. The amplitude or modulus of $G_2/(1 + L)$ must be considered as a function of frequency. (For most (proper) systems the amplitude of any transfer function tends to the static gain (K) at low frequencies and towards zero at high frequencies.)

The denominator term $1 + L$, which is called the **characteristic equation**, plays a very important role: the classical methods of stability analysis and control system design are based around this equation.

7.6.5 Feedback and feedback system sensitivity

One important feature of feedback control is its influence on the system sensitivity. Consider a system (Fig. 7.18) with output y and input x; G_f is the forward path transfer function. In the absence of feedback, $y = G_f x$ or $y/x = G_f$.

Differentiation and a little algebra lead to the open-loop result that

$$\left[\frac{d(y/x)}{(y/x)} \right]_{OL} = \frac{dG_f}{G_f} \tag{7.41}$$

With feedback, $y = G_f x/(1 + L) = G_f x/(1 + G_f G)$, where G is the feedback transfer function. Thus

$$\frac{y}{x} = \frac{G_f}{1 + G_f G} \tag{7.42}$$

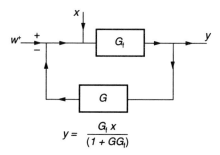

$$y = \frac{G_f x}{(1 + GG_f)}$$

Fig. 7.18 Simple closed loop.

Differentiating with respect to G_f gives the closed-loop result:

$$\left[\frac{d(y/x)}{(y/x)}\right]_{CL} = \frac{dG_f}{G_f(1+G_fG)} \tag{7.43}$$

which $\ll dG_f/G_f$ for $G_fG = L \gg 1$.

The ratios $d(y/x)/(y/x)$ and dG_f/G_f are sensitivity coefficients. Equation (7.43) shows the improvement (reduction) in sensitivity of the relation between x and y – that is, $[d(y/x)/(y/x)]_{CL}$ – because of feedback. The sensitivity of the closed loop is less than the sensitivity of the open loop. Also, the sensitivity of the closed loop to a small change (or modelling error) in the forward path transfer function dG_f/G_f is low. These are most important results: they tell us (what we have already seen above in the discussion of the proportional gain) that the larger L (that is, G_fG) the better in terms of control performance; it also tells us that the result is normally not very sensitive to modelling errors in the process transfer function (unlike feedforward control, which is extremely sensitive to the model).

7.6.6   Feedback cancellation and stability

Figure 7.19 shows a generalized SISO feedback control loop. In the absence of feedback the process output $y = y_p$ is due solely to the effect of the disturbance.

With feedback control the output is the sum of y_p and the compensating output y_c. Ideally, $y_c = -y_p$ as this would ensure that $y = 0$. Now consider how y_c and y_p are related: to do this we can apply the general result for the closed-loop transfer function (equation (7.40)) to give

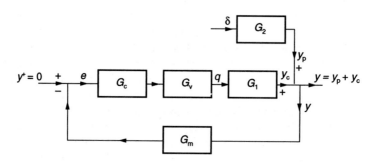

Fig. 7.19 Cancelling signals in feedback control.

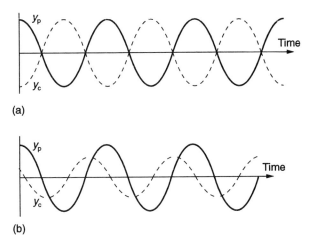

Fig. 7.20 Cancelling effect of controller input: (a) perfect and (b) imperfect cancellation of effect of disturbance.

$$y_c = -\left(\frac{G_1 G_v G_c G_m}{1 + G_1 G_v G_c G_m}\right) y_p \qquad (7.44)$$

$$= -\left(\frac{L}{1 + L}\right) y_p$$

$$= -\frac{y_p}{1/L + 1} \qquad (7.45)$$

For any disturbance $y_c \to -y_p$ provided $L \gg 1$. When the dynamics of all the elements in the loop are fast the transfer functions G_1, G_v etc. are constants (the static gains K_1, K_v etc.) and, theoretically, it is possible to realize the ideal of cancelling the disturbance, provided only that the static open loop gain $K_L = K_1 K_v K_c K_m$ is very large. This is illustrated in Fig. 7.20 for a sinusoidal y_p. The two outputs cancel each other exactly.

However, to be realistic we cannot neglect all the process dynamics. Earlier we saw that the effect of the system dynamics is to change either or both of the amplitude and the phase angle between the input and output signals (a dead time introduces a phase shift only; first-order and higher transfer functions also change the gain). Figure 7.20 also illustrates qualitatively how this can affect the behaviour: the net output y is now longer zero (in fact it is also a sine wave with the same frequency as y_p). Moreover, when the phase shift (which is in general frequency-dependent) reaches 180°, the two signals y_c and y_p are exactly out of phase, and the feedback control reinforces the effects of the disturbance. This situation is potentially unstable and many of the classical control design methods were evolved to ensure that stability is ensured. Although the mathematics involved is beyond the scope of this text we can note that a system in which L has only first-order dynamics (such as a proportional controller and a first-order process) can never become unstable as the maximum phase shift is, as we have seen, 90°. Systems of higher order than 2 or where a dead time is present may, however, become unstable with feedback control. Good design will always attempt to minimize any dead times occurring in the loop.

7.7 Types of controller action

So far, all the discussion has centred on the use of proportional control, partly because we have wanted to avoid unnecessary difficulties with the mathematics. However, we have come across one limitation on proportional action: the existence of offset. High proportional gain leads to lower offset, but it may lead towards instability, or be impractical. In the following section we briefly summarize some other types of control action. The simulation accompanying this book will be found useful in illustrating some of the ideas mentioned below.

7.7.1   On–off control

If the gain K_c of a proportional controller is made very high, its output switches from one extreme to another in response to very small variations in the error signal. Effectively, then, the valve operated by the controller will either be fully open or fully closed according to whether the error signal is negative or positive. (Note that the analyses above did not allow for the constraints to which valves are subject in practice.) In practice, on–off control is implemented by a simple switching relay. It has several advantages: it is cheap; response is usually rapid as the control is either fully on or off; and it is simple (but the relay must be robust to go through many thousands of switching operations). A disadvantage is that the quality of control is usually inferior to that achieved with continuous controllers. It is a form of control that will be familiar to many readers from their domestic heating systems. Anyone who has played with the thermostat on such a system will know that the relay doesn't switch on and off immediately the temperature rises above or drops below the thermostat setting: this would result in continuous high-frequency chattering. Instead there is a small dead zone over which the relay is insensitive.

Figure 7.21 illustrates an on–off controller, together with the effect of the dead band on its behaviour. Figure 7.22 shows how an on–off controller could be used to control the continuous blender that we have examined above. Rather than switch between zero and maximum flow of the control

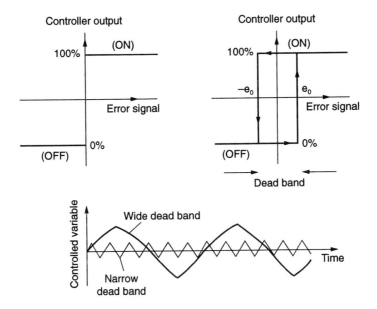

Fig. 7.21 On–off controller: ideal and with dead band.

stream F_2 it is often convenient, as shown here, to maintain a steady 'background' flow with an additional stream as the controlled input.

7.7.2 Integral action: eliminating offset

Although offset can sometimes be effectively eliminated by making K_c as high as possible, in practice the system dynamics often make this impossible, as increasing the controller gain can lead to increasingly oscillatory behaviour and ultimately to instability. It can also lead, as we have seen above, to violent swings in the valve stem position. However, if the controller output signal depends not only on the actual value of the error signal e but on its time **integral**, then offset can be removed, as the signal to the valve will continue to increase so long as the deviation continues. This is known as **integral action**, and is usually implemented in combination with proportional control as a **proportional plus integral** (P + I) controller whose ideal output is

$$v = K_c \left[e + \left(\frac{1}{T_I} \right) \int e \, dt \right] \tag{7.46}$$

T_I is the **integral action time**. (Its inverse is called the **reset rate**.) The smaller its value is the more significant is the integral term. The disadvan-

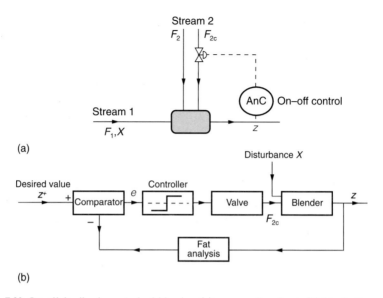

(a)

(b)

Fig. 7.22 On-off feedback control of blender: (a) process flowsheet; (b) block diagram of control loop.

tage of integral action is that, for a given proportional gain, it tends to make the system response more oscillatory and unstable.

At this stage readers should find it helpful to experiment with the control simulation on the disk accompanying this book and discussed in section 11.12. The example allows the step response of a stirred tank heater (a first-order system) to be examined with and without feedback control. The open loop system has a time constant of 10 min. The controlled behaviour can be examined with proportional or proportional plus integral control; the consequences for control performance and stability of a dead time within the control loop can be examined in some detail.

7.7.3   Derivative action: speeding up response

Another common type of controller action is realized by adding to the controller output a term that is proportional to the **rate of change** of the error signal. The idea is to speed up the control system response to deviations. This type of controller signal is, not unnaturally, called **derivative** action; a simple ideal two-term (P + D) controller would have an instantaneous output:

$$v = K_c \left[e + T_D \left(\frac{de}{dt} \right) \right] \tag{7.47}$$

T_D is the **derivative action time**: the larger its value is the greater is the weight given to the derivative signal. The effect of derivative action is to decrease oscillatory tendencies and to speed up the response (for example, by reducing the settling time following a step disturbance). It does not, however, alter the offset. The derivative action time must be chosen with some care: too high a value can produce an over-sensitive response from the controller, whereby every noisy fluctuation provokes a change in the controller output and in the correcting element.

7.7.4 The three-term controller

The classical **three-term** or P + I + D controller involves contributions, which can be tuned at the controller panel or, nowadays, at the control computer, from all three terms:

$$v = K_c\left[1 + \left(\frac{1}{T_I}\right)\int e\,\mathrm{d}t + T_D\left(\frac{\mathrm{d}e}{\mathrm{d}t}\right)\right] \qquad (7.48)$$

In practice real controllers are approximations to, rather than exact realizations of, these ideal types. They will incorporate constraints on the control parameters, and hardware or software approximations to the derivative and integral terms. Nonetheless, the main principles outlined above remain valid.

Many methods exist for 'tuning' standard controllers – that is, selecting the most appropriate values of the control parameters – but the techniques used are beyond the scope of this chapter. Where approximate process models are available, probably the most widely used methods are those, like the Ziegler–Nicholls criteria, based on frequency response analysis; details are found in all the standard texts (see further reading section). Root locus methods are also used. Alternatively, in the absence of a process model, an approximate model can be identified experimentally, and used as the basis for controller tuning. In any event, a satisfactory set of controller settings will ensure process stability, while also ensuring a rapid, but not over-oscillatory, response to process disturbances or changes in set point. In practice, the final values of the controller settings are established on line by trial and error around the design values.

Figure 7.23 shows qualitatively how the different control modes influence the dynamic behaviour. The addition of integral action removes the offset associated with proportional control, but at the expense of increased oscillation, for the same proportional control constant. Derivative action will improve the system response over that of the two-term P + I controller. The behaviour of a proportional and a P + I controller can be compared and contrasted by using the simulation with this book. Further comparison will be found in many of the standard textbooks referred to in the bibliography.

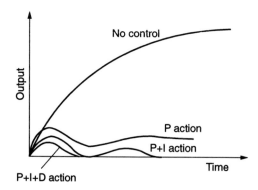

Fig. 7.23 Qualitative step responses of various systems.

7.7.5 *Adaptive control*

The classical methods for linear systems design can be unsatisfactory for processes with parameters that change with time, such as a heat exchanger subject to fouling, or for non-linear processes, where the assumption that only small changes occur is not valid; at some point the relative insensitivity of feedback loops to process changes is no longer sufficient, and control performance may deteriorate with time. Sometimes, inherent non-linearities can be effectively cancelled by incorporating a compensating non-linear element in the control loop. The correct choice of control valve characteristics (that is, the precise relation between valve lift and flowrate) is a good example. Adaptive controllers respond to changes in the process by automatically adjusting their parameters, such as the proportional gain, so as to compensate for variations in the process characteristics. This is one area where theoretical ideas from a couple of decades ago are now a practicality because of developments in computer hardware and software.

Another area where on-line computation helps is in coping with situations where key process outputs are not measurable but, provided good process models are available, can be inferred using 'soft sensors' from other measurements. Some areas where inferential techniques have been used in control include the control of fermenters and distillation columns (where key concentrations can be inferred from temperatures, flows and pressures). Some of these techniques use mechanistic process models; others are based on 'black box' statistical models, using techniques including neural networks.

7.7.6 *Multivariable control*

Many processes have several inputs and outputs (MIMO [= multi-input multi-output] in control jargon), and the first problem is to choose the best

set of connections between the measurements and the manipulated variables. Figure 7.7 shows the continuous blender (excluding the level) as a
MIMO system; note that changes in inlet flowrate affect **both** the output
flow and fat content, while changes in the inlet fat contents affect **only** the
outlet fat composition. As described earlier, a possible feedback strategy
(illustrated schematically) would be to control the product quality by varying the flowrate of one stream. The flow of the other stream could be
controlled independently or (not shown) used to control the level of the
contents on the blender. In either case, the output flow **cannot** be controlled, as its (average) value is determined by the two input flows. An ideal
control system will have the minimum number of single-input single-output
loops; these loops should be non-interacting, in the sense that when one
loop is active it doesn't influence (or worse, conflict with) another; the
response of the system should be fast, direct and stable. Sometimes process
interactions are such that this ideal cannot be realized. Often, intuition and
a basic understanding of the way the process operates is enough to develop
an appropriate control structure, as in the blender example. Another example, showing two schemes to control the temperature and level of a continuous liquid heater, is illustrated in Fig. 7.24. Whether it is possible to control
the input flow (L_i) depends on the operations (if any) further upstream,
illustrating the point that the whole system and its dynamics must be
considered.

Quantitative methods now exist to guide MIMO system design: the simplest of these, such as the relative gain array method, essentially try to
establish the control configuration on the basis of the relative sensitivity
(that is, the gains) of the various interconnections. Other methods apply
frequency response methods to the whole system. Useful rules of thumb in
selecting the control configuration include the following.

- Select manipulated variables that have a direct and fast effect (usually
  implying a high gain) on the controlled variable.

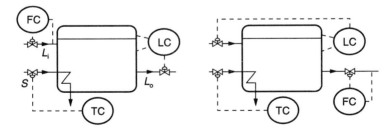

Fig. 7.24 Two configurations for heater control. L_i, L_o, output flows; S, steam rate; Q, heat
input; θ, disturbance.

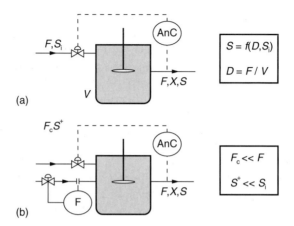

Fig. 7.25 Continuous fermenter: decoupling inputs.

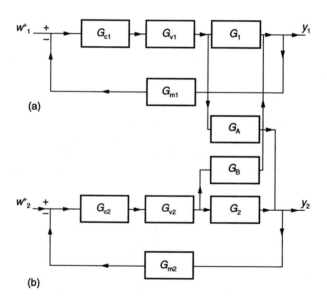

Fig. 7.26 Block diagram of interacting system.

- Where possible, avoid interactions between control loops.
- Minimize time delays within the loops.

Sometimes interactions can be decoupled by careful engineering design. For example, the performance of a continuous fermenter can depend both on the inlet substrate concentration and the feed flowrate (that is, the dilution rate). Scheme (a) in Fig. 7.25, to control the residual substrate concentration by changing the dilution rate via the inlet flowrate, is less than ideal for this reason, as the two variables cannot be changed independently. However, scheme (b), in which a highly concentrated stream of substrate is used as an additional feed (but with very low flowrate), allows almost complete decoupling of the two effects, as concentration and flowrate can be manipulated independently of each other.

Alternatively, whole or partial uncoupling can often be achieved by appropriate control system choice. Figure 7.26 shows a block diagram to illustrate a coupled or interacting system. When the transfer functions G_A and G_B are small the degree of interaction is also small. When it is not possible to eliminate such interactions through engineering design it may nevertheless be possible to reduce the interaction or even eliminate it by appropriate design of cross controllers to 'cancel out' the effects of the interactions G_A and G_B.

7.8 Control system design for complete plants

Most modern processes involve a number of operations in series or which follow in sequence. The best procedure is to consider the process unit by unit, as dynamic considerations suggest that attempts to close the loop around the whole plant (strategy (a) in Fig. 7.27) will be less satisfactory than the alternative (b) of a sequence of separately controlled units.

Of course, the implications for successive units must be taken into account because, as we have seen, only a limited number of independent control schemes is possible for any given unit. Often it is convenient to engineer a degree of uncoupling between successive units by introducing

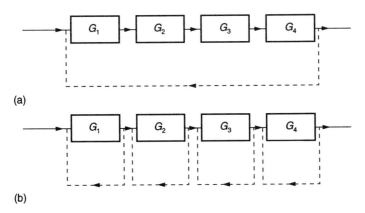

Fig. 7.27 Feedback control of a multi-unit process: (a) single closed loop; (b) sequence of separately controlled units.

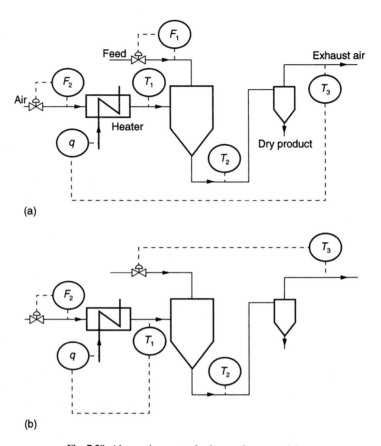

Fig. 7.28 Alternative control schemes for spray drier.

intermediate storage or buffer tanks. An important part of the system design is to ensure that material balance requirements can always be satisfied without process vessels overflowing or running dry, and that suitable alarms and overrides are incorporated into the control structure to cope with unforeseen problems such as failure in the supply of one of the services.

Some other aspects are illustrated by the control of a continuous spray drier (Fig. 7.28). The principle disadvantage of scheme (a) stems from the time delay between the output measured temperature and the control input; with large scale units this would be likely to give rise to poor system performance. Scheme (b) is much better from this point of view, since the time delays are reduced. It is important in any event to ensure that the final measuring element is as close to the feed as practicable. Thus if possible the temperature element would be sited between the drier and the cyclone (i.e. at T_2) rather than after the cyclone at T_3. In practice any system should incorporate an override on the exhaust temperature to shut down the plant or switch to a water feed if this temperature became too high.

Conclusions

Process control, which has been introduced in this chapter, is essentially concerned with making the best use of information in order to ensure that processes work efficiently, that product quality is maintained and that excursions from the desired operating conditions are minimized. Three types of information – all imperfect – might be available: measurements on some of the process inputs and their properties; measurements on some of the process conditions or 'outputs' in the language of control engineering (temperatures, pressures, product flowrates or quality measures such as colour, etc); and, finally, models of how the process is expected to behave. This chapter has introduced some of the methods and ideas underlying the theory and practice of control engineering, in putting these different types of information to best use.

Inevitably, control is concerned with transient behaviour, and this leads to mathematical complications; this chapter has tried as far as possible to avoid unnecessary mathematics, so as to stress the underlying principles. From the first part of the chapter you should have learned about the different types of control objective and their importance. You should also have seen how to represent processes in terms of block diagrams, in which the blocks or boxes represent operations and the directed lines connecting them represent the signal or information flows; later in the chapter the algebra of these diagrams was explained. You should also have seen how the dynamics of processes (even very complex ones) can be classified into a number of simple types or models. Two types of control system – feedforward and feedback – are discussed in some detail: you should understand the differences between them and their relative advantages and disadvantages. You should also understand the main types of controller action, and their significance. It is important to stress that these principles remain valid whether the controller itself is an old-fashioned pneumatic device, or a more up to date programmable logic controller or even a fully-fledged computer control system. Finally, you should also be aware of some of the questions that need to be asked about ways of controlling a complete plant.

Like other chapters, we have not tried to describe the hardware or the technology. Any further study of this field would need to include the rapidly developing technology of computer-based data gathering and process control and of sensor technology.

Further reading

From the large number of texts concerned with process control the following may be found useful:

Buckley, P.S. (1964) *Techniques of Process Control*, John Wiley, New York.

Douglas, J.M. (1972) *Process Dynamics and Control*, volumes 1 and 2, Prentice-Hall, Englewood Cliffs, NJ.

Coughanowr, D.R. and Koppel, L.B. (1965) *Process Systems Analysis and Control*, McGraw-Hill, New York.

Luyben, W.L. (1990) *Process Modelling, Simulation and Control for Chemical Engineers*, 2nd edn, McGraw-Hill, New York.

McFarlane, I. (1983) *Automatic Control of Food Manufacturing Processes*, Applied Science Publishers, London.

Newell, R.B. and Lee, P.L. (1989) *Applied Process Control: A Case Study*, Prentice-Hall, New York.

Seborg D.E., Edgar, T.F. and Mellichamp, D.A. (1989) *Process Dynamics and Control*, John Wiley, New York.

Shinskey, F.G. (1979) *Process Control Systems*, McGraw-Hill, New York.

Stephanopoulos, G. (1984) *Chemical Process Control: An Introduction to Theory and Practice*, Prentice-Hall, Englewood Cliffs, NJ.

8 Reactors and reactions in food processing

H.A. CHASE

Introduction

Chemical reactions are vital in food processing; for example, the development of flavour and the death of microbes during heating are all the result of reactions. To be able to design process plant efficiently, rather than by trial-and-error, it is necessary to be able to quantify the rates of reactions occurring in a food, and the ways in which they change with process variables such as temperature. The food industry tends to rely on different types of rate equation than the Arrhenius-type expressions developed by chemists; the two are, however, related, and this chapter describes both expressions and the relationship between them.

In processing, reactions are carried out in some type of vessel – the reactor. Frequently in food processing, reactions occur in process units which do other jobs, such as the sterilization reactions and changes in product taste and quality which occur within a heat exchanger. To design reactors, process engineers have developed simple mathematical models of idealized systems which will be described here. The idealized form of a tubular reactor is plug flow, where all the fluid travels at the same velocity, without any mixing, so that all parts of the flow stay in the reactor for the same amount of time. The other idealized vessel is the fully stirred vessel, in which total mixing occurs. In between lies the real world, in which some degree of intermixing and flow distribution is found in real reactors. These flows can be characterized using the residence time distribution (RTD) which measures the range of times which elements of fluid spend within the system. This concept is the basis, for example, of the design of practical sterilizers. The plant must be designed so that all the material leaving it is sterile: the RTD, once measured, allows the fastest moving part of the system to be identified. The concepts of this chapter will be used to analyse more food industry problems in Chapters 9 and 10.

Chemical Engineering for the Food Industry. Edited by P.J. Fryer, D.L. Pyle and C.D. Rielly. Published in 1997 by Blackie A & P, an imprint of Chapman & Hall, London. ISBN 0 412 49500 7

8.1   Reactor types

The word **reactor** in chemical engineering terms is the name given to a vessel in which some form of chemical reaction occurs. The use of the term in the food industry is somewhat more complicated, as reactions frequently occur in equipment primarily designed for heat exchange. Hence, in practice, reactor and heat exchanger design are inevitably going to be intimately associated. This chapter is restricted to a consideration of the gross design of a vessel based on the characteristics of the reactions occurring within it. The design of systems to achieve heat transfer is discussed in Chapters 3 and 9. Reactor types can be divided into two main categories, as follows.

- In **batch reactors**, a set amount of material is processed at a given time. Reactants (starting materials) are added, left to react and are then removed: this is not a continuous process.
- In **continuous** (or **flow**) **reactors**, material flows continuously through the reactor and is converted during its stay in the reactor. Hence there is a continuous and steady flow of reactants into and products out of the reactor. The use of continuous reactors can result in diminished labour costs and simplified automatic control, and the greater constancy in conditions allows better quality control.

8.1.1   Batch reactors

Most small- to medium-scale cooking procedures are essentially performed in a batch manner, and domestic cooking in a saucepan is a good example that illustrates the operational features. A simplified diagram of a typical batch reactor used for larger-scale operations is shown in Fig. 8.1.
    The main features are as follows.

- The reactor is essentially a simple vessel in which the reaction occurs.
- Contents are well mixed, normally by stirring, so the composition is (assumed to be) the same everywhere but changes with time. Reaction rates and the amounts of heat that may be added or removed from the reactor will also change with time.
- Batch reactors tend to be cheap and versatile and can be used for other conversions.
- Filling, emptying and cleaning may be expensive in labour.

8.1.2   Tubular reactors

The tubular reactor represents one extreme case of the design of a continuous reactor, the other being the continuous stirred tank reactor described in section 8.1.3. A diagram of a typical tubular reactor is shown in Fig. 8.2.
    The main features are as follows.

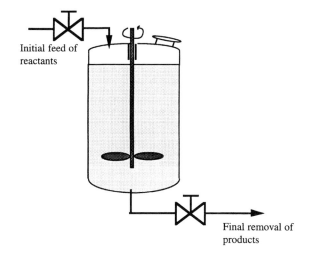

Initial feed of reactants

Final removal of products

Fig. 8.1 The batch reactor.

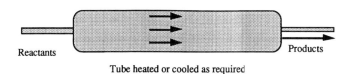

Reactants

Products

Tube heated or cooled as required

Fig. 8.2 The tubular reactor.

- The tube may be empty or packed with some form of catalyst pellets such as immobilized enzymes or immobilized metals for chemical modification of fats. If the tube contains a heterogeneous phase catalyst it is then called a **packed** (or **fixed**) **bed reactor**.
- The tube may be a single one of large diameter or a bundle of many small ones in parallel, which results in it appearing similar to a shell and tube heat exchanger, as described in Chapter 3.
- Flow through the reactor is often assumed to be plug or piston in nature: that is, there is no longitudinal (axial) mixing but there is perfect radial mixing. In this case the reactor is referred to as a **plug flow reactor** (PFR). In practice, flow may deviate significantly from idealized plug flow as a result of the design of the equipment or the properties of the material flowing through it. The nature of the actual flow through tubular reactors is described later in section 8.5.
- When the reactor is in the steady state, the local conditions (chemical composition, temperature etc.) at any point along the reactor do not vary with time, but these conditions do change along the reactor length.

- Flowrates and reactor sizes are chosen so that material resides in the reactor for an appropriate time for the reaction to proceed to the required extent. The resultant value of the Reynolds number for flow in the system will determine whether it is has a laminar or turbulent nature.
- Temperature control may be difficult, with temperature profiles building up across a radial section of the reactor if the only surface for heat transfer is the outside walls of the tube. It may be difficult to insert heating/cooling tubes within a tubular reactor.

8.1.3 Continuous stirred tank reactor (CSTR)

This type of continuous reactor is also known as a **back-mixed reactor** and represents the other extreme case of continuous reactor design. A typical diagram is shown in Fig. 8.3.

The main features are as follows.

- The tank needs to be very well mixed to prevent some material from passing too quickly through the reactor. The material emerging from the tank has the same composition as the bulk of material in the tank.
- Such reactors tend to be cheap and easy to run and a process may contain a sequence of CSTRs in series.
- Temperature control can be straightforward as cooling/steam coils can be inserted within the tank.
- The tanks are easier to clean than tubular reactors.

8.1.4 Choice of reactor type

When processing food materials, considerable attention must be given to the flow characteristics of the material in choosing the optimal reactor type.

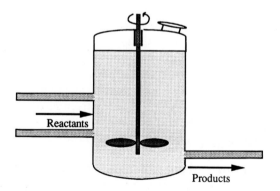

Fig. 8.3 The continuous stirred tank reactor.

The presence of complex rheologies, high viscosities and the presence of solids of different density from that of the surrounding liquid must be taken into account. For example, problems may arise if attempts are made to flow a liquid containing solids, such as a meat pie filling, through a tubular system without the chunks of meat settling out within the reactor. These problems can only be addressed for the food product of interest when its fluidic nature is known. As we shall see from what follows, a consideration of chemical reaction effects alone suggests that tubular reactors may be the preferred reactor configuration. However, such a criterion may be of minor importance compared with the problems arising from handling and pumping the material under consideration.

8.2 Physical chemistry of food reactions

In an ideal world, a prerequisite for the rational design of reactors is the availability of complete knowledge of the physical chemical characteristics of the reactions taking place. In the traditional chemical industry, this requires knowledge of the equilibrium, rate and enthalpy properties of the reactions taking place. However, reactions carried out in the food industry differ considerably from the types of reaction that form the backbone of the chemical industry, in which the identity and characteristics of the reactions are known and understood. In food processing it will almost always be necessary to make gross assumptions and simplifications about the nature of the reactions occurring in order to be able to attempt a rational design for food reactors. These simplifications are essential, as comparatively little is known about the precise physical chemical characteristics of most cooking reactions. Such studies are greatly complicated by the presence of complex reactions in which many different separate (bio)chemical reactions are taking place simultaneously, such as the multitude of reactions taking place during the heating of a food.

8.2.1 Types of reaction in the food industry

Reactions in the food industry can be segregated into a number of classes, but in many processes reactions belonging to different classes may be occurring simultaneously. Many of these reactions occur as a direct result of heating the material under consideration, but some are biologically catalysed. In addition, some reactions occur during hydration and mixing, such as the changes in structure that occur upon mixing flour with water during breadmaking. The classes of reaction include:

- sterilization reactions, in which living biological cells are killed;
- reactions in which carbohydrates, fats and proteins are modified in form as a result of thermal and other processes;

- destruction of nutrients, vitamins, enzymes and colouring compounds;
- microbial conversions (fermentations);
- enzyme-catalysed processes.

8.2.2   Enthalpies of reaction

In almost all reactions in the food industry it is common to assume that the amount of heat liberated or absorbed in the reaction is negligible compared with the amounts of heat needed to raise the reactants to the reaction temperature and to maintain that temperature in the presence of a variety of sources of heat loss. Such heat losses include losses from the vessel arising from conduction, convection and radiation together with the loss of water vapour during certain cooking operations and the consequent need to supply enthalpy of vaporization (latent heat) to keep liquids at their boiling point. The ability to ignore enthalpies of reaction greatly simplifies reactor analysis, but such an assumption is not possible when strongly exothermic or endothermic reactions are being considered. One example when it would be inappropriate to ignore enthalpies of reaction in food processes is in the design of biological fermentation systems. Fermenters operate at near-ambient temperatures, and heat removal has to be undertaken with only small temperature driving forces between the fermentation liquor and the cooling water. Another example occurs in breadmaking, in which the mechanical work done during the mixing process is converted into heat, which can start to cook the dough.

8.2.3   Reaction rates

The rates of food processes are not generally described in terms of conventional chemical kinetics, probably because the processes were first studied by biologists or biochemists rather than by chemists or engineers. A number of (rather confusing) alternative techniques have been developed instead. It is common practice in the food industry to describe the rate of a process involving some kind of reaction in terms of a parameter D, the **decimal reduction time**. Implied in this concept is the notion of some type of reaction of the form

$$\text{Reactants} \rightarrow \text{Products}$$

The decimal reduction time is the time needed for the amount of reactant to be reduced to one tenth of its original value. This time is assumed to be constant over the entire course of the reaction provided that the temperature is held constant (isothermal conditions). The value of D will, however, be a function of temperature, as described in the next section. However, it is common practice to quote D_{121}, the value of D at 121 °C, a temperature often used in canning processes. Table 8.1 contains the values of D_{121} for a

Table 8.1 Kinetic data for some reaction processes in the food industry

	D_{121} (min)	E_a (kJmol^{-1})	z (°C)
Killing of micro-organisms			
C. botulinum	0.1–0.3	265–340	8–12
B. subtilis	0.4–0.8	230–400	6.8–13
B. cereus	0.038–0.06	305	10
C. thermosaccharolyticum	3–22	1340–1780	2–10
C. sporogenes	0.15–2.6	230	9–13
Cooking value (overall quality estimation)			
Peas	12.5	80–95	17–28
Whole corn	2.4	65–80	36
Broccoli	4.4	55	44
Carrots	1.4	160	15
Green beans	1.4	90–170	14–29
Potatoes	1.2	115	21
Chemical changes			
Non-enzymatic browning	0.4–40	100–250	17–39
Hydrolysis	0.4	60–110	
Fat oxidation	–	40–100	
Denaturation of proteins	5	250–800	5–10
Vitamin destruction			
In general	100–1000	80–125	20–30
Thiamine	38–380	90–125	20–30
Ascorbic acid	245	65–160	51
Pantothenic acid	250–6400	84–160	31
Riboflavin	2800	100	28
Folic acid	2800	70	37
Enzyme inactivation			
In general	1–10	40–125	8
Peroxidase	2–3	67–85	26–37
Colour deterioration			
Chlorophyll (spinach)	14–350	30–90	38–80
Carotenoids (paprika)	0.038	140	19
Betamin (beetroot)	48	46	59

Source: adapted from Hallström et al. (1988)

number of different types of reaction of interest in the food industry. However, this approach to the description of reaction rates is based on empirical observation and is not necessarily consistent with a more rigorous chemical analysis of the underlying events.

The standard chemical approach to the description of reaction rates involves the concepts of **orders of reaction** and **rate constants**. The rate of reaction is expressed in terms of amount of reactant (j) converted (kilograms, moles, cell numbers etc.) per unit volume of the reactor per time, r_j. Hence for the reaction

$$a\mathrm{A} + b\mathrm{B} \rightarrow e\mathrm{E} + f\mathrm{F} \tag{8.1}$$

the rate of reaction per unit volume can be written as

$$\frac{1}{e}r_E = \frac{1}{f}r_F = -\frac{1}{a}r_A = -\frac{1}{b}r_B \qquad (8.2)$$

We shall use the convention that a positive rate of reaction implies that the amount of the particular substance is increasing. Hence if the rate of reaction is being described in terms of loss of the reactant, the sign of the reaction rate will be negative. Note that the rate of reaction has not been written as dc_j/dt, as only in a batch reactor of constant volume is this term equal to the rate of reaction per unit volume. In a continuous reactor, the addition and removal of material will also affect the rate of change in the concentration of component j in addition to changes occurring as a result of reaction. Indeed, in a continuous reactor in the steady state,

$$\frac{dc_j}{dt} = 0 \qquad \text{while} \qquad r_j \neq 0 \qquad (8.3)$$

as a result of the chemical reactions involving component j.

It is assumed that the rate of reaction is some function of the concentrations of the reactants (and sometimes the products). These have to be determined experimentally, but for the above reaction it may be found that

$$r_A = f\left(c_A, c_B, c_E, c_F, T, \text{pH etc.}\right) \qquad (8.4)$$

In simple cases, the reaction can be classified into orders. If it is found for example that

$$-r_A = k\left(T\right)c_A^\alpha c_B^\beta \qquad (8.5)$$

where $k(T)$ is a rate constant that is a function of temperature, and α and β are integers, then the reaction is said to be of $(\alpha + \beta)$th order. Hence

$-r_A = k_0$ would be a zeroth-order reaction
$-r_A = k_1 c_A$ would be a first-order reaction
$-r_A = k_2 c_A c_B$ would be a second-order reaction.

But if, say,

$$-r_A = \frac{k' c_A c_B^{1.4}}{1 + k'' c_A} \qquad (8.6)$$

the reaction would be said to be of complex order. Reactions of complex order are produced when the reaction is a result of a series of consecutive steps.

Implicit in the above consideration is that there is knowledge of the chemical events occurring in the reaction and the factors that influence the rate of reaction. Such detailed knowledge is extremely unlikely in the food industry. However, it is often possible to reconcile the different approaches

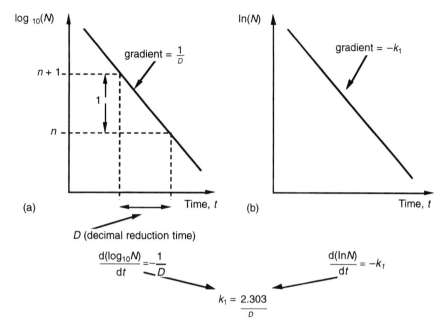

Fig. 8.4 Relationship between food and chemical approaches to reaction rates: (a) food industry reaction; (b) first-order chemical reaction.

to reaction rates used in the food and chemical industries in a straightforward manner. The ability to describe a food reaction in terms of a decimal reduction time implies, as is shown in Fig. 8.4, that the reaction is consistent with an irreversible first-order chemical reaction.

As is shown in Fig. 8.4, there is a simple relationship between D and the apparent first-order rate constant k_1, which can be obtained from a knowledge of D by using the expression

$$k_1 = \frac{2.303}{D} \tag{8.7}$$

The fact that reactions in the food industry are generally regarded as first-order leads to a conceptual problem, in that a first-order reaction implies that it is impossible to obtain complete sterilization. The time required for thermal sterilization of a food is calculated in terms of the most thermally resistant pathogen, commonly *C. botulinum*. If the concentration of this pathogen is reduced to the required level, all others will have been killed to a greater extent. Rather than total sterility, the concept of **commercial sterility** based on probabilities is used industrially; the aim of thermal processing is to reduce the number of organisms by a very large amount (commonly by a factor of 10^{12}: the **12D cook**). This mathematical treatment theoretically implies that, in the processing of cans or other batch containers, the vast majority of units are sterile, but that there will be a very small but finite probability that a can may still contain a live organism after treatment. In practice, the presence of contaminants in food can always be traced to incorrect processing, rather than to a statistical fluke rendering the process unsuccessful.

In addition to the use of the concept of decimal reduction time, the rate of death of bacteria is often described in terms of the **thermal death time (TDT)**: the time required at a certain temperature to kill a stated number of organisms. Thermal death times are difficult to measure; they can be most easily estimated by the growth–no-growth method described by Frazier and Westhoff (1988), in which the time needed to reduce the level of organisms so that they can no longer be detected in a standard growth test is taken as the appropriate thermal death time. Thermal death time is also a function of temperature, and as the temperature increases the rate of sterilization increases.

Another term that is used is the **F-value**, which is defined as the time needed to carry out the required sterilization procedure at the common canning temperature (T_{ref}) of 121 °C. An F-value of 3 min is taken as acceptable industrially, although process design values of at least 6 min are used in practice.

8.2.4   Variation of reaction rates with temperature

It is also a well-known fact that reaction rates increase with increasing temperature. It is found that plots of $\log_{10}(D)$ or $\log_{10}(TDT)$ against temperature are straight lines, and it is common to describe the variation of D (or the thermal death time) with temperature in terms of a parameter z, where z is the temperature increase that results in D being reduced to one tenth of its original value. z is also the increase in temperature necessary to achieve the same extent of reaction in one tenth of the time: that is, to reduce the TDT by a factor of 10. z is assumed to be constant over a range of temperatures close to that at which it was determined. Some values of z are shown in Table 8.1, and a value of 10 °C (that is, the value appropriate to the killing of *C. botulinum*) is often assumed for sterilization process.

The value of z can be used to estimate the effect of changing temperature on the processing time, using the equation

$$\left(\text{Time required at } T\right) = \frac{\left(\text{Time required at } T_{ref}\right)}{10^{(T-T_{ref})/z}} \tag{8.8}$$

Equation (8.8) can also be used to calculate the time at some different constant temperature that still results in the required F-value. For example, a 12D cook for *C. botulinum* ($z = 10\,°C$) requires 2.52 min at 121.1 °C: that is, it takes 2.52 min to reduce the concentration of spores to 1 in 10^{12}. This is the basis for an F-value of 3 min being commonly acceptable in industry. At 130 °C, the same F-value would be achieved by processing for

$$\frac{2.52}{10^{(130-121.1)/10}} = 0.324\,\text{min}$$

If a process is isothermal throughout its time course, equation (8.8) is adequate. However, some sterilization will occur while heating up and cooling down are occurring, and the whole temperature–time history of the food must be considered in calculating the actual degree of sterilization achieved. If the temperature–time curve for the food is known, a time known as the **integrated lethality**, defined as

$$F = \int_{\text{IN}}^{\text{OUT}} 10^{(T-T_{\text{ref}}^{\text{F}})/z_{\text{F}}}\,dt \tag{8.9}$$

can be calculated. For sterilization to be deemed successful, this time must be greater than or equal to the required F-value at temperature T_{ref}. This approach is widely used in the food industry but the major problems with it are that (a) it is algebraically complex, and (b) it is fundamentally wrong. It is argued below that sterilization probably follows Arrhenius kinetics, and the above equation is an approximation to true behaviour, but its use can underestimate the F-value achieved by up to 50% for predictions of high-temperature processes. The use of conventional chemical kinetics is easier and more accurate at high temperatures.

Analogous expressions have been written to express the degree of cooking (rather than sterilization) that a material has received. Cooking is a difficult quality to measure experimentally, but approaches that have been used as indicators of the quality of cooking include measurement of the deactivation of enzymes, the loss of vitamins and the change in the texture of the food. Thus it is possible to define the **C-value** of a process:

$$C = \int_{\text{IN}}^{\text{OUT}} 10^{(T-T_{\text{ref}})/z}\,dt \tag{8.10}$$

where again T_{ref} is the reference temperature at which the slope of the 'cooking' rate curve is z, and T is the temperature of the material being processed as a function of time t. Again, this approach approximates the true conditions.

The normal chemical approach to the variation of reaction rate constants with temperature based on kinetic theory involves the use of an **Arrhenius equation** of the form

$$k = Ae^{-E_a/RT} \tag{8.11}$$

where A is called a pre-exponential factor and E_a is the activation energy of the reaction. The temperature T must be given in kelvin, and R is the gas constant (use $R = 8.314\,\mathrm{J\,mol^{-1}\,K^{-1}}$ when E_a is measured in $\mathrm{J\,mol^{-1}}$). This expression, unlike that for the F-value, has a sound theoretical rather than empirical basis.

At temperatures close to the value of T_{ref} at which D and z are measured (T_{ref} is usually 121.1°C, 394.3 K in the food industry), it is possible to estimate a value of E_a from a knowledge of z using

$$E_a = \frac{2.303RT_{\mathrm{ref}}^2}{z} \tag{8.12}$$

However, as is shown in Fig. 8.5, the form of the Arrhenius expression is not entirely consistent with a description of the system with z being a parameter that is independent of temperature.

The fact that errors in the prediction of sterilization times may occur by

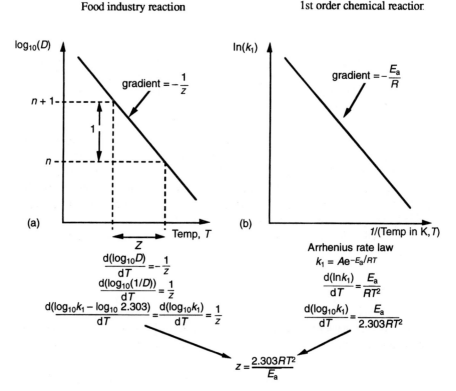

Fig. 8.5 Relationship between food and chemical approaches to the variation of reaction rates with temperature: (a) food industry reaction; (b) first-order chemical reaction.

using the z method to estimate reaction rates at temperatures far removed from T_{ref} has already been mentioned. It is suggested that the description of the variation of reaction rates with temperature by an Arrhenius expression is a more accurate approach. Table 8.1 shows a list of typical reactions occurring during food processing and values of the characteristic parameters D and z together with the derived 'chemical' rate parameter E_a. Values of k_1 appropriate to T_{ref} can be obtained from the values of D by using equation (8.7).

The design of food sterilization plant reduces, in an engineering sense, to an optimization problem: how to maximize sterilization with minimal loss in product quality. Temperature and time are the process variables, and activation energy values can be used for calculation. It can be seen from Table 8.1 that the activation energy for death of *C. botulinum* is about $300\,kJ\,mol^{-1}$ whereas that for the loss of quality in foods is in the region of $125\,kJ\,mol^{-1}$. Comparison of the rates of the two processes at 120°C and 140°C shows that sterilization reactions proceed about 15 times faster than loss of quality reactions at the higher temperature. This forms the basis for the design of new thermal processes, to sterilize at high temperatures and short times. This is discussed further in Chapter 9.

8.2.5   Other physical chemistry parameters

The types of reaction that occur in the food industry enable us to ignore certain other concepts that may have to be considered in the analysis of conventional chemical reactors. These factors include a consideration of equilibrium constants. Many reactions may only proceed part of the way to completion as a result of equilibrium effects. The equilibrium position of the reaction will also be a function of temperature. However, it appears that most reactions that occur in the food industry approach completion after a sufficient time and a consideration of equilibrium constants is thus inappropriate. An exception is a reaction such as carbonation, in which the solubility of carbon dioxide will depend on equilibrium effects. Certain enzyme-catalysed reactions (such as the isomerization of glucose to fructose) will also not proceed to completion, as a result of equilibrium effects.

8.2.6   Biological reactions

Rate expressions describing the reactions that occur during fermentation or enzymic processes are more complicated than those described to date, as they are not accurately described by quasi-first-order reaction rates.

Fermentations.   In the most simple analysis, the rate of increase r_x in cell mass x depends on the concentration c_S of a key (growth-limiting) nutrient S in the following manner:

$$r_x = \frac{\mu_m c_S}{K_S + c_S} x \qquad (8.13)$$

where K_S and μ_m are characteristic parameters for the growth of the organism on that substrate. This is the **Monod equation**. Similarly, the rate of utilization of that growth-limiting nutrient is given by

$$-r_S = \frac{\mu_m c_S}{(K_S + c_S)} \left(c_{S0} - c_S + \frac{x_0}{Y_{x/S}} \right) \qquad (8.14)$$

where $Y_{x/S}$ is the growth yield coefficient on that substrate, defined as the mass of cells formed per mass of the growth-limiting nutrient consumed, and c_{S0} and x_0 are the initial concentrations of cell mass and growth-limiting nutrient respectively. However, even in brewing and other microbial fermentations used in the food industry the relationship between 'product' formation and cell production or substrate utilization is often highly complex. In these circumstances, it is not possible to describe the rates of reaction by expressions as simple as those given above. A full analysis of more accurate expressions describing the rates of fermentation reactions is given in Bailey and Ollis (1986).

Enzyme-catalysed reactions.   For reactions carried out using enzymes, the simplest form of rate expression for the conversion of substrate S to product is given by

$$-r_S = \frac{V_m c_S}{K_m + c_S} \qquad (8.15)$$

where V_m and K_m are characteristic parameters for enzyme catalysis under the prevailing conditions. However, if an immobilized enzyme is used where the enzyme has been immobilized to a support material, additional considerations arising from decreased rates of mass transfer to the enzymic sites may also need to be included (Bailey and Ollis, 1986).

8.3   Analysis of isothermal 'ideal' reactor systems

Our initial approach to reactor analysis will involve the assumption that the temperature is constant throughout the reactor and does not vary with time in a batch reactor or with position in a continuous reactor. This 'isothermal' assumption permits us to ignore any variations of reaction rate that will occur as a result of temperature variations in the reactor, and hence the reaction rate-constant is indeed constant throughout the reaction. The assumption of isothermal operation will be inappropriate in a wide variety of cases as reactions will inevitably start to occur in heat exchangers as process streams are being heated to the final reaction temperature. In addition, a piece of process equipment may be specifically designed to ensure a varying temperature profile during passage of material through it (for example, a milk sterilizer/pasteurizer). However, the assumption of isothermal operation will allow the principles of reactor operation to be outlined without excessive mathematical complexity obscuring the basic concepts.

8.3.1   Concept of fractional conversion

Rather than describing extents of reaction in terms of the absolute amount of product formed or reactant utilized, it is common to use the dimensionless quantity **fractional conversion** X, defined for a component A by

$$X_A = \frac{n_{A0} - n_A}{n_{A0}} \tag{8.16}$$

where n_{A0} is the amount of reactant A at the start of the reaction and n_A is the amount left after an extent of reaction X_A has occurred. The amount of A can be expressed in any units (kilograms, moles etc.), but in this treatment the **mole** will be used as the basic unit of the amount of particular component to simplify the analysis. Obviously, the use of molar units is not well suited to most foodstuffs, where the molecular nature of the material is not well defined. Simple rearrangement of equation (8.16) yields

$$n_A = n_{A0}\left(1 - X_A\right) \tag{8.17}$$

In summary, therefore, $X_A = 0$ at the start of reaction and increases to a value of 1 when the reaction is complete.

8.3.2   Batch reactors

The following analysis of the conversion achieved in various types of reactor will be undertaken by performing a material balance on the reactor using the principles described in Chapter 2. Consider a situation in a batch reactor where a reactant A reacts irreversibly to yield products, and the reaction proceeds at a rate $-r_A$. In a batch reactor, the rates of reaction and the concentrations of reactants and products are functions of time. The simple batch reactor is shown in Fig. 8.6. A basic material balance over the system in a small time interval dt yields

Amount of component coming into the reactor
+ Amount of component made by reaction
= Amount leaving the reactor
+ Amount accumulated within the reactor

In the case of a batch reactor operating at constant volume V_r, there is no material entering or leaving the reactor. Hence:

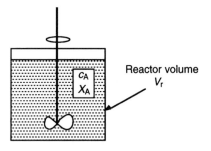

Fig. 8.6 Analysis of a batch reactor.

$$0 + V_r r_A dt = 0 + dn_A \tag{8.18}$$

The rate of conversion of reactant A to products is given by

$$r_A = \frac{1}{V_r} \frac{dn_A}{dt} = \frac{1}{V_r} \frac{d\left(n_{A0}\left(1 - X_A\right)\right)}{dt}$$

$$= -\frac{n_{A0}}{V_r} \frac{dX_A}{dt} = -c_{A0} \frac{dX_A}{dt} \tag{8.19}$$

and

$$\frac{dX_A}{dt} = \frac{-r_A}{c_{A0}} \tag{8.20}$$

This expression can then be integrated to yield the way that the extent of reaction varies with time once the rate expression r_A is known.

We have already stated that most reactions in food processing can be described in terms of pseudo-first-order chemical kinetics. Hence, for a first-order reaction where

$$r_A = -k_1 c_A = -k_1 c_{A0}\left(1 - X_A\right) \tag{8.21}$$

by combining equations (8.20) and (8.21) we find that

$$\frac{dX_A}{dt} = \frac{k_1 c_{A0}\left(1 - X_A\right)}{c_{A0}} = k_1\left(1 - X_A\right) \tag{8.22}$$

Integration of this expression (using boundary conditions that assume that $X_A = 0$ at the start of the reaction ($t = 0$) and rises to a value X_A at time t) gives

$$\int_0^{X_A} \frac{dX_A}{\left(1 - X_A\right)} = \int_0^t k_1 dt \tag{8.23}$$

$$\ln\left(1 - X_A\right) = -k_1 t \tag{8.24}$$

which on rearrangement yields

$$X_A = 1 - e^{-k_1 t} \tag{8.25}$$

Hence the fractional conversion achieved in a first-order batch reaction approaches the value of 1 asymptotically, as described by equation (8.25). The variation of extent of reaction with time as described by this expression can be seen in Fig. 8.7.

Integration of the basic equation (equation (8.20)) can be repeated in a similar manner for reactions of other orders.

EXAMPLE 8.1

A batch process is being used for cooking a food product, but the process also causes undesired breakdown of vitamin C. At present the process is carried out at 121 °C for 20 min in order to achieve satisfactory cooking. What percentage of vitamin C is destroyed in the current process, if the values of D$_{121}$ (min) for the cooking value and for vitamin C destruction are 12 min and 245 min respectively?

We shall work using a pseudo-first-order rate expression. Equation (8.4) gives:

$$k = \frac{2.303}{D}$$

Hence for cooking at 121 °C:

$$k_{c121} = \frac{2.303}{12 \times 60} = 3.2 \times 10^{-3} \, s^{-1}$$

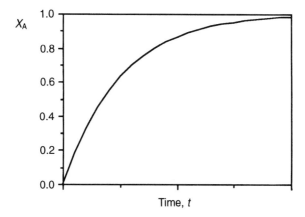

Fig. 8.7 Variation of extent of reaction with time in a first-order batch reaction.

and for vitamin C destruction at 121 °C:

$$k_{d121} = \frac{2.303}{245 \times 60} = 1.57 \times 10^{-4} \text{ s}^{-1}$$

Equation (8.19) gives:

$$(1 - X_{c121}) = e^{-k_{c121}t_{121}} = \exp(-3.2 \times 10^{-3} \times 20 \times 60) = 0.0215$$

and

$$(1 - X_{d121}) = e^{-k_{d121}t_{121}} = \exp(-1.57 \times 10^{-4} \times 20 \times 60) = 0.828$$

Hence percentage destruction of vitamin C

$$= 100 \times (1 - 0.828) = 17.2\%$$

EXAMPLE 8.2

A modification of the process described in Example 8.1 is being considered. It is proposed to improve the process with less destruction of vitamin C by reducing the cooking time as a result of increasing the temperature to 130 °C. It is known that the values of z for the cooking process and the destruction of vitamin C are 21 °C and 51 °C respectively. What is the new cooking time and what effect do the changes have on the percentage destruction of vitamin C?

We need to estimate the values of k_c and k_d at the new temperature of 130 °C. The Arrhenius equation tells us that $k_T = Ae^{-E_a/RT}$ and $k_{T_{ref}} = Ae^{-E_a/RT_{ref}}$. Dividing these two expressions by each other, we get:

$$k_T = k_{T_{ref}} \frac{e^{-E/RT}}{e^{-E/RT_{ref}}} = k_{T_{ref}} \frac{\exp(-2.303T_{ref}^2 / Tz)}{\exp(-2.303T_{ref}/z)}$$

because equation (8.6) gives:

$$\rightarrow E_a = \frac{2.303RT_{ref}^2}{z}$$

Hence

$$k_{c130} = 3.2 \times 10^{-3} \frac{\exp[(-2.303 \times 394^2)/(403 \times 21)]}{\exp(-2.303 \times 394/21)} = 8.4 \times 10^{-3} \text{ s}^{-1}$$

$$k_{d130} = 1.57 \times 10^{-4} \frac{\exp[(-2.303 \times 394^2)/(403 \times 51)]}{\exp(-2.303 \times 394/51)} = 2.34 \times 10^{-4} \text{ s}^{-1}$$

To calculate the new cooking time, equation (8.18) gives:

$$t_{c130} = \frac{-\ln(1 - X_{c130})}{k_{c130}}$$

Assuming that the same extent of cooking reaction is achieved in each case, then

$$(1 - X_{c130}) = (1 - X_{c121}) = 0.0215$$

i.e. the value in Example 3.1. Therefore

$$t_{c130} = \frac{-\ln(0.0215)}{8.4 \times 10^{-3}} = 457\,\text{s} \equiv 7.6\,\text{min}$$

that is, the cooking time significantly reduced from the previous value of 20 min at 121 °C.

To work out the extent of vitamin C reduction at the new temperature, equation (3.19) gives:

$$(1 - X_{c130}) = e^{-k_{d130}t_{130}} = \exp(-2.34 \times 10^{-4} \times 457) = 0.899$$

Therefore percentage destruction of vitamin C $= 100 \times (1 - 0.899) \approx 10\%$

Hence there is less destruction of vitamin C at the higher temperature.

8.3.3 Plug flow tubular reactors

In designing a tubular sterilizer, this type of reaction analysis allows the volume required to be estimated. We shall carry out an analysis of this type of flow reactor in the steady state: that is, we shall assume that local concentrations and extents of reaction have reached steady values and are not varying with time. In other words, no material accumulates or decreases within the reactor. In practice, the system will not be in a steady state during start-up (or shut-down), nor during changes in any of the operational parameters (such as flowrates and temperatures).

A balance on reactant A over the small volume element shown in Fig. 8.8 yields

$$\text{In} + \text{Made} = \text{Accumulation} + \text{Out}$$

That is,

$$F_A(1 - X_A) + r_A dV_r = 0 + F_A \left[1 - (X_A + dX_A) \right] \tag{8.26}$$

where F_A is the molar flow of reactant A entering the reactor. Integrating over the entire reactor (assuming no conversion at the reactor inlet) yields

$$\int_0^{X_A} F_A dX_A = \int_0^{V_r} -r_A dV_r \tag{8.27}$$

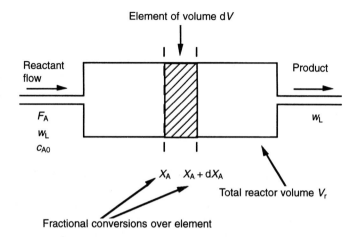

Fig. 8.8 Analysis of the plug flow reactor.

Equation (8.27) is the fundamental design equation for isothermal plug flow reactors in which reaction commences at the reactor inlet: that is, $X_A = 0$ at the inlet of the reactor.

For a flow of fluid at constant density through such a reactor at volumetric flowrate w_L:

$$F_A = w_L c_{A0} \tag{8.28}$$

That is,

$$V_r = w_L c_{A0} \int_0^{X_A} -\frac{dX_A}{r_A} \tag{8.29}$$

and for a simple first-order reaction in which $r_A = -k_1 c_A$:

$$V_r = w_L c_{A0} \int_0^{X_A} \frac{dX_A}{k_1 c_{A0}(1 - X_A)} \tag{8.30}$$

yielding

$$V_r = \frac{w_L}{k_1} \ln\left(\frac{1}{1 - X_A}\right) \tag{8.31}$$

It is convenient to introduce the concept of the **mean residence time** of material within a continuous reactor, which is simply the average length of time that material stays within the reactor as it passes through it. For a reactor devoid of catalyst particles, in which flow of material can be considered to be in plug flow, the residence time t for all material passing through the reactor is the same and is given simply by

$$t = \frac{V_r}{w_L} \tag{8.32}$$

Complications to the definition of residence time of fluid within a tubular reactor occur when the reactor contains catalyst particles. In such situations the appropriate quantity to use for the reactor volume V_r in the above expression is the void volume between the particles. Substitution of equation (8.32) into equation (8.31) followed by rearrangement yields

$$X_A = 1 - e^{-k_1 t} \tag{8.33}$$

which, on comparison with equation (8.25), shows that (as might have been anticipated intuitively) the conversion achieved in a plug flow reactor with a residence time t is the same as in a batch reactor after the reaction has proceeded for time t. Although this result has only been proved here for a first-order reaction, it is also true for any order of reaction carried out isothermally.

8.3.4 Continuous stirred tank reactors

A CSTR is a flow reactor in which a high extent of mixing of the reactor contents is achieved; this type is quite common in fermentation processes. In this analysis we shall assume 'perfect' mixing: that is, the mixing is so good that the conditions are uniform everywhere in the tank and the outlet stream also has the same properties as the contents of the tank. The situation is summarized in Fig. 8.9.

We shall again be conducting a steady-state analysis, under which circumstances the situation within the tank is not changing as a function of time. A material balance on reactant A conducted over the whole vessel requires that:

$$\text{In + Made = Out + Accumulation}$$

$$F_A + V_r r_A = F_A(1 - X_A) + 0 \tag{8.34}$$

where F_A is the molar flow of reactant A entering the stirred vessel of volume V_r. That is,

$$V_r = \frac{-X_A F_A}{r_A} \tag{8.35}$$

which is the basic design equation for a CSTR.

For our simple example involving the flow of fluid of constant density at volumetric flowrate w_L, $F_A = w_L c_{A0}$, and for a simple first-order reaction of the form $r_A = -k_1 c_A$ substitution into equation (8.35) yields

$$V_r = \frac{w_L X_A}{k_1(1 - X_A)} \tag{8.36}$$

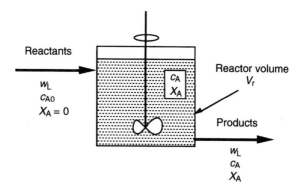

Fig. 8.9 Analysis of the continuous stirred tank reactor.

If the mean residence time of liquid in the tank is defined to be

$$t = \frac{V_r}{w_L} \tag{8.37}$$

then equation (8.36) can be rearranged to

$$X_A = \frac{k_1 t}{1 + k_1 t} \tag{8.38}$$

8.3.5 Comparison of conversions achieved in PFRs and CSTRs

Simple substitution in the above reactor conversion equations (equations (8.33) and (8.38)) enables conclusions to be drawn as to the influence of the type of continuous reactor on the conversion achieved for a given residence time. Qualitatively, the argument is based on the fact that the material within the CSTR has the same conditions as those in the outlet stream from the reactor. It can be said therefore that the CSTR 'operates at the outlet conditions from the reactor'. The concentration of reactant in the CSTR will be lower than or as low as that at any position along the length of a PFR that achieves the same overall fractional conversion. Hence the rates of reactions of simple order greater than zero will be lower in the CSTR than in the PFR, and hence longer residence times will be needed in the former to achieve the same degree of conversion. In practice this will mean that for a given volume of reactor the rate of flow through a CSTR configuration will have to be lower than for a PFR. Alternatively, to process a given stream at a constant flowrate, a larger CSTR reactor will be needed than if a PFR configuration is adopted.

The subsitution of some numbers into the design equations allows the differences between the two reactor types to be seen in a quantitative

Table 8.2 Comparison of conversions achieved in simple flow reactors

Reactor type	X_A		
	0.9	0.99	0.999
PFR	2.3	4.6	6.9
CSTR	9	99	999
Two CSTRs	4.32	18	61.2

Note: The table shows values of the dimensionless group k_1t for each circumstance.

manner. For a simple first-order reaction, equation (8.33) predicts values for the dimensionless group k_1t for a plug flow reactor for various degrees of fractional conversion. The corresponding values of this group for the same fractional conversions in a CSTR can be predicted from equation (8.38). The larger the value of this group for a given flowrate of reactant, the larger the volume of reactor needed to achieve the required conversion. Examination of Table 8.2 shows that the improvement in performance obtained by the use of a PFR rather than a CSTR gets substantially greater as the fractional conversion approaches unity: that is, as the reaction is taken to near-completion.

The following example shows that in sterilization processes, which are always characterized by the need to achieve very high extents of reaction in order to ensure sterility, the only sensible choice of continuous reactor would be one in which flow was close to plug flow. The use of reactors in which back-mixing was taking place would result in grossly impractical reactor volumes.

EXAMPLE 8.3

A continuous-flow sterilizer operating at 121 °C is being designed to treat a liquid flow of 1 l s⁻¹. Taking the value of D_{121} for C. botulinum to be 0.2 min, compare the reactor volumes needed for CSTR and PFR configurations if the level of C. botulinum has to be reduced by six orders of magnitude. How much larger does the sterilizer have to be if the sterilization criterion is raised to 12 orders of magnitude?

Equation (8.7) gives:

$$k = \frac{2.303}{D} = \frac{2.303}{0.2 \times 60} = 0.192\,\text{s}^{-1}$$

(a) For a 10^6 fold reduction in the level of *C. botulinum*:

$$X = 1 - 10^{-6}, \qquad \text{i.e. } (1 - X) = 10^{-6}$$

Calculation for the PFR: Equations (8.25) and (8.26) give:

$$t = \frac{1}{k} \ln\left(\frac{1}{1-X}\right) = \frac{1}{0.192} \ln(10^6) = 72\,\text{s}$$

Alternatively, we need 6 decimal reduction times and hence $t = D \times 6$ $= 12 \times 6 = 72\,\text{s}$. Hence the volume of the reactor, $V = w_L \times t = 10^{-3} \times 72$ $= 0.072\,\text{m}^3$.

Calculation for the CSTR: Equation (8.26) gives:

$$V = \frac{w_L X}{k(1-X)} = \frac{10^{-3} \times (1 - 10^{-6})}{0.192 \times 10^6} = 5208\,\text{m}^3!$$

(b) For a 10^{12} fold reduction in the level:

$$X = 1 - 10^{-12}, \qquad \text{i.e. } (1 - X) = 10^{-12}$$

For the PFR:

$$V = 10^{-3} \times \frac{\ln(10^{12})}{0.192} = 0.144\,\text{m}^3$$

i.e. twice as large as in part (a).

For the CSTR: $V = \dfrac{10^{-3} \times (1 - 10^{-12})}{0.192 \times 10^{-12}} = 5.2 \times 10^9\,\text{m}^3!!$

i.e. 10^6 times bigger than before.

Example 8.3 shows very clearly why flow sterilizers (which require very high degrees of conversion) are designed as tubular reactors in which plug flow is achieved as far as possible, and why any design based on a CSTR would be totally out of the question. The difference between the residence times needed to obtain a particular degree of conversion in each type of reactor gets yet more pronounced for reactions with orders higher than first order.

Remember that the above-stated preference for PFR-type continuous reactors is based entirely upon a consideration of the reaction kinetics. In practice, other factors associated with heat transfer, flow and mixing, together with process control and monitoring, may play important effects. In situations where a CSTR configuration has to be adopted as a result of these factors, it may be possible to achieve performance closer to that which would have been achieved by a plug flow reactor by using a sequence of CSTRs in series. For instance, a system of the same overall volume but containing two identical tanks in series can be analysed for a given fractional conversion. For a first-order reaction $k_1 t$, where t is based on the total volume of both tanks, is given by

$$k_1 t = 2\left(\sqrt{\frac{1}{1 - X_A}} - 1 \right) \tag{8.39}$$

The figures shown in Table 8.2 demonstrate that the dimensionless parameter characteristic of such a system would be less than for a single CSTR but is still higher than for a PFR. As the number of CSTRs is increased, the residence time gets closer to that of a PFR. In the limit, an infinite series of CSTRs would have the same residence time as a PFR.

8.4 Non-isothermal reactions

Considerable complications to the above isothermal analysis will occur when the temperature in the reactor is not constant with time or with position in the reactor. We have already stated that, in the food industry, it is likely that non-isothermal effects arise mainly from heat transfer processes rather than as a result of enthalpic processes associated with the reaction itself. However, in fermentations enthalpic processes may be significant, depending on the rate and scale of the biological reactions. To perform basic reactor analysis under non-isothermal conditions, knowledge is needed of the temperature as a function of time and position in the reactor so that a reaction rate constant appropriate to that temperature can be calculated from the Arrhenius equation (equation (8.11)). Values of the local temperature can be obtained by performing a heat balance on the system, and for reactions with negligible enthalpic effects such a heat balance with be independent of the extent of the reaction. When enthalpic effects are important, the heat balance itself will depend on the extent of reaction, leading to a coupling of the equations describing heat balance and extent of reaction.

We can discuss qualitatively an example for a simple heat exchanger in which a reaction occurs to material within the tubes. An expression showing the variation of temperature with position along a simple shell and tube heat exchanger can be derived, as has been shown in Chapter 3. This expression can be manipulated to yield the temperature at any point within the 'reactor', and an expression for the appropriate value of the local rate constant can be obtained from the Arrhenius equation (equation (8.11)) provided the activation energy of the reaction is known. Knowledge of the local rate constant enables an expression for the local value of the rate of reaction, r_A, to be constructed. Assuming that material within the tubes of the heat exchanger behaves as if it were in a plug flow reactor, equation (8.27) can now be used to describe the variation of extent of reaction with position in the heat exchanger. Integration of this expression along the length of the heat exchanger will yield the overall fractional conversion that will be achieved. In practice, integration of the basic design equations as functions of time or position may be complicated and may require the use of numerical methods. Under these circumstances it is not possible to derive simple analytical expressions showing the variation of the extent of reaction as a function of the residence time in the reactor.

In the non-steady state regime that occurs in a batch reactor, knowledge will be needed of the rates of heat transfer to the tank in order to predict the variation of the temperature of the contents with time. This then enables expressions to be constructed describing the variation of reaction rate constants with time, which can subsequently be substituted into the basic design equations.

8.5   Non-ideal flow and mixing in continuous reactors

Up to now, we have considered two extreme approaches to continuous flow reactors: the well-mixed CSTR and the plug flow tubular reactor. In practice, neither extreme may be achieved in a real reactor because of the presence of channelling, stagnant regions or short-circuiting. Some examples of flow maldistribution are shown in Fig. 8.10.

8.5.1   Residence time distributions

Flow maldistributions within a system result in variations in the time that liquid actually resides in the reactor, and the use of simple expressions (equations (8.32) and (8.37)) for the mean residence time may be wholly inappropriate. Elements of liquid taking different routes through the reactor may take different times to pass through the reactor and may experience different profiles of temperature. Hence the conversion achieved in material taking these different routes will also be different. When a reactor exhibits channelling or short-circuiting, the residence time of material within the reactor is not as long as anticipated, resulting perhaps in less-than-satisfactory degrees of sterilization and undercooking. Conversely, the presence of stagnant regions within the reactor results in material staying within the reactor for too long a period, which may result in overcooking with concomitant loss of product quality.

Flow abnormalities are described in a quantitative manner by measurements of the distribution of residence times for liquid leaving the reactor. This distribution is called the **residence time** (or **exit age**) **distribution**, $E(t)dt$. Because the distribution can be thought of as representing the probability that a given element of liquid is in the reactor for a certain length of time, it is convenient to normalize the distribution such that

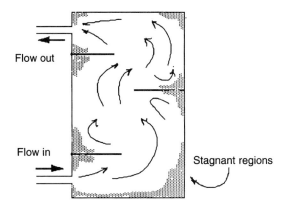

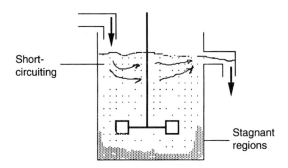

Fig. 8.10 Some examples of flow maldistribution in reactors.

$$\int_0^\infty E(t)\,dt = 1 \tag{8.40}$$

The fraction of the exit stream that has been in the reactor for a time between t and $t + dt$ (that is, of 'age' between t and $t + dt$) is $E(t)dt$. The normalization procedure ensures that these fractions sum up to unity. The fraction of material that is in the reactor for a time less than t_1 is

$$\int_0^{t_1} E(t)\,dt \tag{8.41}$$

and the fraction in the reactor for longer than a time t_1 is

$$\int_{t_1}^\infty E(t)\,dt = 1 - \int_0^{t_1} E(t)\,dt \tag{8.42}$$

These concepts are illustrated in Fig. 8.11.

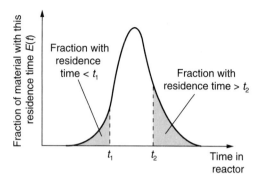

Fig. 8.11 A typical residence time distribution.

As discussed in Chapter 9, the presence of a broad residence time distribution in an item of cooking equipment can have serious consequences on the efficiency of the process. Material that emerges from the reactor with a short residence time may not have been in the reactor long enough for sterility to have been achieved, whereas material that remains in the reactor too long may be 'overcooked', with loss of quality of the product. Hence care must be taken to ensure a narrow residence time distribution, and it is important to measure the actual distribution that is achieved by a particular item of equipment (using the techniques outlined below in section 8.5.2) to confirm that such a distribution is indeed occurring.

8.5.2   *Experimental characterization of non-ideal flow*

Residence time distributions can be measured by the use of tracers in stimulus–response techniques. The requirements of the tracer are that it is distributed evenly in the bulk fluid flow and that its concentration can be measured conveniently in the reactor exit. The latter requires that the tracer has some physical property that can be simply measured, and such properties include radioactivity, colour and ionic strength. A discussion of the use of experimental residence time distributions to diagnose various types of poor flow in reactor systems is contained in Levenspiel (1972).

Measurement of the C-curve.   In this popular method, a very short pulse of tracer is added to the liquid entering the reactor, which initially contains no tracer. The concentration of tracer in the exit stream from the reactor, c_e, is then measured as a function of time. The method is illustrated in Fig. 8.12, in which the 'reactor' could be a vessel such as a milk pasteurizer.

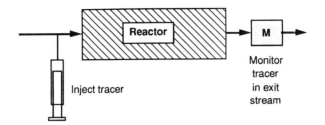

Fig. 8.12 Method for determining a C-curve.

Depending on the type of analytical equipment available, the tracer may be a coloured compound or a pulse of salt or acid/base. The concentration of tracer in the reactor exit stream can then measured by spectrophotometers, conductivity meters or pH meters fitted with flow-measuring cells. The data after normalization is called a **C-curve**. Normalization is performed by dividing the readings of c_e by A, the total area under the graph of c_e versus time. Thus

$$\int_0^\infty C(t)\,dt = \int_0^\infty \frac{c_e}{A}\,dt = 1 \tag{8.43}$$

where

$$A = \int_0^\infty c_e\,dt \tag{8.44}$$

The C-curve so obtained is identical in shape to the residence time distribution $E(t)$. Typical shapes for the residence time distributions shown by CSTRs and PFRs are shown in Fig. 8.13.

For a plug flow reactor (Fig. 8.13(a)), the outlet profile has the same sharp shape as the inlet pulse except that the appearance of this pulse is delayed by a time equal to the residence time of liquid within the reactor. The RTD for a CSTR is markedly different (Fig. 8.13(b)), with the highest concentration of tracer leaving the reactor immediately after injection. This is because the tracer is mixed instantly with the contents of the reactor after injection. A typical RTD for a real reactor is shown in Fig. 8.13(c). The measurement of RTDs in real systems in operation in the food industry is discussed by Sancho and Rao (1992).

Measurement of the F-curve. This is similar to the C-curve method described above, but instead of a pulse, a step input of tracer of concentration c_{in} is added to the fluid stream entering the reactor. The concentration of tracer in the exit stream, c_e, is monitored as a function of time, and c_e/c_{in} is

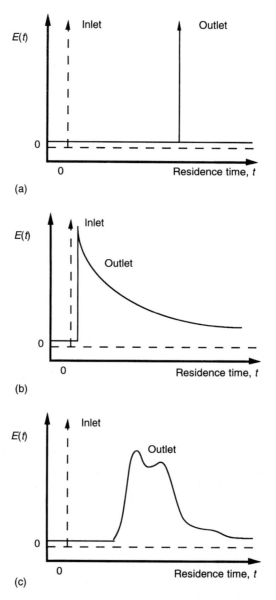

Fig. 8.13 Some residence time distributions measured with the C-curve method: (a) plug flow; (b) CSTR; (c) typical reactor.

plotted against time and is called the **F-curve**. A typical F-curve for a real reactor is shown in Fig. 8.14.

The value of F at time t_1 will be given by the fraction of tracer that has been in the reactor for a time less than t_1: that is,

$$F(t_1) = \int_0^{t_1} E(t)dt \quad \text{or} \quad \frac{dF}{dt} = E(t) \tag{8.45}$$

Hence the F-curve is often called the **cumulative residence time distribution**.

8.5.3 Analysis of residence time distributions

In order to characterize the experimentally determined distribution it is often convenient to calculate its mean and variance. The mean value of the distribution is given by

$$\bar{t} = \int_0^\infty t E(t)dt \tag{8.46}$$

and $\bar{t}$ is called the **mean residence time**. In many situations, it is convenient to show a residence time distribution as a function of dimensionless time ϑ such that

$$\vartheta = \frac{t}{\bar{t}} \tag{8.47}$$

and in such a situation the mean residence time occurs at the position where $\vartheta = 1$.

The spread of the distribution is commonly measured by the variance σ^2, defined as

$$\sigma^2 = \int_0^\infty t^2 E(t)dt - \bar{t}^2 \tag{8.48}$$

The quantities $\bar{t}$ and σ^2 can both be easily determined by analysis of the experimental residence time distribution, using a mathematical procedure. However, reduction of the data contained in a residence time distribution to

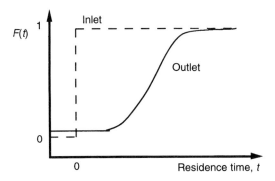

Fig. 8.14 A typical F-curve experiment.

yield the parameters $\bar{t}$ and σ^2 can result in the loss of important information contained in the distribution, particularly when the distribution is significantly asymmetrical or if it contains multiple peaks.

It is possible to characterize a non-ideal residence time distribution in certain simple situations where the distribution lies between the ideal limits of CTSR and PFR behaviour. These conditions imply that there exist no stagnant pockets and no gross by-passing or short-circuiting of liquid in the reactor. A typical shape of an RTD that can be analysed by these approaches would look like a Gaussian or Normal bell-shaped curve of the kind shown in Fig. 8.11.

Dispersion model. This model assumes that flow in the reactor is essentially plug flow on top of which is superimposed some degree of back-mixing (via either slippage or eddy formation) in the axial direction, the magnitude of which is independent of position within the vessel (see Fig. 8.15(a)). This mixing results in a radial velocity distribution, and this mechanism of dispersion is analogous to molecular diffusion but is described by a parameter D_a, the **axial** (or **longitudinal**) **diffusion coefficient**. The dispersion of material flowing at a velocity v_m in the x direction is described by

$$\frac{\partial c}{\partial t} = D_a \frac{\partial^2 c}{\partial x^2} \tag{8.49}$$

It is common to introduce a dimensionless group $D_a/v_m L$, called the **vessel dispersion number** (or **inverse Peclet number**), where v_m is the mean velocity of flow through the tubular reactor of length L. Thus as:

$$\frac{D_a}{v_m L} \to 0 \qquad \text{there is negligible dispersion, i.e. plug flow}$$

$$\frac{D_a}{v_m L} \to \infty \qquad \text{there is significant dispersion, i.e. mixed flow}$$

If an idealized pulse of tracer is applied to a reactor in which the dispersion is small, the resultant C-curve can be described by integrating equation (8.49) with appropriate boundary conditions. The result is a symmetical, Gaussian-shaped curve given by

$$C = \frac{1}{2\sqrt{\pi \left(\dfrac{D_a}{v_m L}\right)}} \exp\left[-\frac{\left(1 - \dfrac{t}{\bar{t}}\right)^2}{4\left(\dfrac{D_a}{v_m L}\right)} \right] \tag{8.50}$$

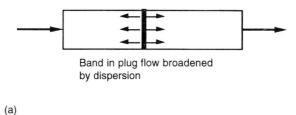

Band in plug flow broadened
by dispersion

(a)

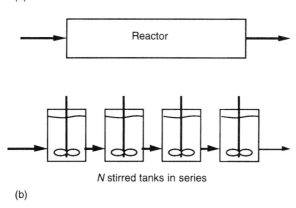

N stirred tanks in series

(b)

Fig. 8.15 Models for the analysis of residence time distributions: (a) the dispersion model and (b) the tanks-in-series model.

There are a number of ways of determining $D_a/v_m L$ from an experimental residence time distribution curve. Perhaps the easiest is to measure the maximum height of the normalized C-curve, which is equal to

$$\frac{1}{2\sqrt{\pi \dfrac{D_a}{v_m L}}} \qquad (8.51)$$

Other methods involve calculating the variance of the experimental curve, or its width at the points of inflection, and are described in Levenspiel (1972).

The tanks-in-series model. The other main theoretical approach to a description of residence time distribution curves is the use of a tanks-in-series model. In this model, the reactor is assumed to behave as if it consisted of a number of equal-sized CSTRs placed in series one after the other (Fig. 8.15(b)). Flow through the reactor system is characterized by the parameter N, the number of tanks in the system. Again, N can be determined from the experimental data in a number of ways. The easiest is from the maximum height of the normalized curve, which is approximately equal to

$$\frac{N}{\sqrt{2\pi(N-1)}} \qquad (8.52)$$

The value of N will approach infinity for an ideal plug flow system with no dispersion. Conversely, N will approach unity in a system where there is almost perfect mixing.

8.5.4 Use of RTDs to predict actual reactor conversion

As has been stated above, when a reactor has first-order reactions, a knowledge of the apparent residence time distribution of liquid within the reactor can be used to estimate unequivocally the average conversion that will be achieved in that reactor. Consider the first-order process

$$A \rightarrow \text{products} \qquad \text{with } r_A = -k_1 c_A$$

The liquid in the reactor can be considered as consisting of a large number of individual elements. Each element of liquid will have a residence time t within the reactor, and if each of these elements is considered to be a small batch reactor then the conversion achieved in that element after time t is given by equation (8.25):

$$X_A = 1 - e^{-k_1 t}$$

The average fractional conversion in the exit stream can then be determined from

$$\overline{X}_A = \int_0^\infty X_A(t) E(t) \, dt \qquad (8.53)$$

This integration can be performed graphically in cases where the experimental RTD has a complex form that cannot conveniently be described by an algebraic expression. A point $(E(t), t)$ on the E curve is taken and the product

$$E(t)\left(1 - e^{-k_1 t}\right)$$

is calculated and plotted on a second graph versus the value of t. The process is repeated for a series of points over the entire range of residence times until the second graph has been built up. The integral that gives the required average fractional conversion is then simply the area under this second curve evaluated over the whole range of residence times, as shown in Fig. 8.16.

A simple computer routine can be written which performs the necessary manipulations on digitized points from the experimentally determined E-curve. This method provides therefore a useful way to predict the average conversion that will be achieved in a real reactor system.

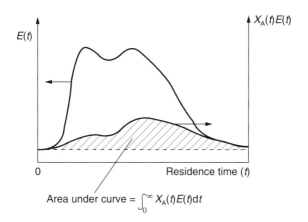

Fig. 8.16 Graphical method for estimating mean conversions for first-order reactions using residence time distributions.

Conclusions

Most food processing operations involve reactions of one type or another, most of which are thermally driven. This chapter has demonstrated how some of the techniques of chemical reaction engineering can, with profit, be used to analyse and design food processes where reactions are important. It has concentrated on a few key ideas.

You should understand how the classical descriptions of reaction kinetics can be related to food and biological operations. In particular you should understand how the physical chemist's use of reaction rate constants is related to the methods used in the food industry to describe sterilization and quality changes, that is in terms of D- and z-values, lethality measures, etc. Both methods of analysis have their merits, but it is important to know how they are related to each other.

Another theme of the chapter is to explain how the processing environment can dramatically affect process operation when reactions are involved. In particular, you should appreciate the difference between batch and continuous operations, and the significance of the mixing characteristics of the process for process efficiency and product quality. You should, then, understand the difference between a tubular or plug flow device and one which is perfectly mixed, and the significance of these ideal systems for process efficiency. Few processes are ideal in this sense, and some of the ways in which the mixing characteristics of real operations can be measured and modelled are also outlined.

References and further reading

Bailey, J.E. and Ollis, D.F. (1986) *Biochemical Engineering Fundamentals*, 2nd edn, McGraw-Hill, New York.

Denbigh, K. and Turner, J.C.R. (1972) *Chemical Reactor Theory*, Cambridge University Press, Cambridge.
Frazier, W.C. and Westhoff, D.C. (1988) *Food Microbiology*, McGraw-Hill, New York.
Hallström, B., Skjöldebrand, C. and Trägårdh, C. (1988) *Heat Transfer and Food Products*, Elsevier Applied Science, Barking.
Levenspiel, O. (1972) *Chemical Reaction Engineering*, John Wiley & Sons, New York.
Sancho, M.F. and Rao, M.A. (1992) *Journal of Food Engineering*, **15**(1), 1–20.

9 Thermal treatment of foods
P.J. FRYER

Introduction

Many processes in the food industry use heat transfer. Rather than describing these processes in detail, and thus becoming rapidly out of date whenever a new process is introduced or a modification developed, this book seeks to explain the principles underlying them. The concepts introduced in previous chapters, such as the ideas of heat transfer as a set of sequential steps, of residence time distributions, and of fluid flows, will be applied here to the study of real systems.

Thermal sterilization is taken as an example where a process engineering approach has led to a redesign of real plant. Although the canning process is efficient in a mechanical sense, it does not produce high quality product. The type of analysis developed in the previous chapters can be used to explain why this happens, along with ways of designing processes to enhance product quality. Higher quality product can be produced in continuous sterilizers which use the principles developed in Chapter 3; for example it is necessary to know the range of product residence times to ensure that the process is safe. To design plant that processes food in continuous flow requires an understanding of the flow properties of the fluid and of the rates of heat and mass transfer which will result from that processing.

It is difficult to heat or cool solid foods quickly because of the slowness of thermal conduction through solid materials. Alternative methods, in which heat is generated within a food by the action either of electric current or microwaves, allow rapid heating of the food. These processes require different skills of the food process engineer, and the rates of heating are often difficult to predict. Although the equations which govern electrical and microwave heating are difficult to solve in practice, they are introduced here to show how processes could be designed and controlled. The problems of continuous sterilization clearly demonstrate the importance of the ideas developed elsewhere in the book.

Finally, this chapter considers one of the key processing problems, that of the fouling of heat exchanger plant and the consequent need to clean the equipment. Fouling problems are very rapid and severe in food processing;

Chemical Engineering for the Food Industry. Edited by P.J. Fryer, D.L. Pyle and C.D. Rielly. Published in 1997 by Blackie A & P, an imprint of Chapman & Hall, London. ISBN 0 412 49500 7

frequently, daily cleaning of process plant is required. The operation of food plant undergoing fouling is very difficult to predict. However, simple models for fouling can be developed, and guidelines for minimizing fouling in practice produced. This book has shown frequently that processes must be designed as a unit rather than as a series of individual steps; the length of operating cycles must be set to ensure that the plant is not difficult to clean when processing is stopped.

Engineering in food preservation

Historically, food preservation techniques were developed to enable locally grown food to be eaten all year round. The increased separation of the producer and consumer in an industrial society added another reason: food must be safe and palatable as it reaches the consumer. Many ways of preserving foods are used industrially, among which are:

- **drying**, which aims to reduce the water activity within the food to prevent bacterial and enzyme action, typically to a water content less than c.5%;
- adding **preservatives**, such as salt, which retard bacterial action;
- **low-temperature storage** – freezing, which effectively prevents microbial growth, and refrigeration, which slows it to acceptable levels;
- **high temperatures**, in which microbes and microbial spores are killed by heat;
- **asepsis**, in which food is kept sterile throughout processing;
- the **removal of organisms**, such as by filtration;
- **irradiation**, in which high-energy radiation is used to destroy contaminants.

The demands of the consumer determine which products are successful. Making food processes produce safe and acceptable products is extremely difficult. A variety of engineering skills are required. Equipment and materials for the process plant are designed by mechanical engineers, while electrical engineers design and install the systems that enable the plant to be operated and controlled. The role of the chemical engineer is less immediately obvious; the chemical engineer is concerned within the design and specification of the process itself. The aim of this book is to demonstrate the ways in which chemical engineering techniques can be applied to food processing. This chapter uses the principles outlined elsewhere in this book and applies them to the problems of thermally processing foods. This is an area of active research in which process engineering techniques are being increasingly applied.

Chemical engineering evolved to meet the challenges of the oil industry. In petrochemical and plastics processing, heat transfer and chemical reactions generally occur separately; reactants are heated to the required temperature, the reaction occurs, and then heat is removed from the products. Many petrochemical fluids can also be heated up and cooled down without the properties of the fluid changing; if reactions do occur, they may well be reversible. This rarely, if ever, happens in the food industry. In food processing, the rates of reaction are commonly so swift that heat transfer and reaction cannot be separated; whenever a food material is heated, changes occur within the food that cannot be reversed by subsequent cooling. Food-heating processes must thus be considered in terms of both heat transfer and reaction.

Heating and cooling in the food industry

Heating is carried out both to preserve the food product and to add palatability – and digestibility – to the material. Foods are so thermally unstable that reactions occur very rapidly at low temperatures and pressures, below 150°C and at 1 bar, whereas in the petrochemical industry much higher temperatures and pressures are common. The chemical processes that occur on heating foods are complex, but have been thoroughly studied by food scientists. When a food is heated, reactions occur that result in increased sterility and in the development of the taste and texture of the food material. Thermal processing results in protein denaturation and aggregation reactions, which cause enzyme deactivation and consequent bacterial death.

A number of types of heating process are found in the food industry. They include:

- **blanching** or **pasteurization**, which are designed to extend the shelf-life of a product by destroying enzymes that might subsequently reduce product quality, by perhaps allowing volatile components to escape and reducing the content of bacteria (these do not result in substantial changes to the structure or properties of the material);
- **baking**, **roasting** and **frying** – 'cooking' processes in which significant changes are made to the food, which can then be eaten directly;
- **sterilization** processes, in which the amount of bacterial contamination in a food is reduced to a statistically insignificant level, enabling the food to be stored for a considerable length of time. Once a product has been made sterile, it must be kept sterile. Aseptic packaging processes, which allow sterile material to be packed and sealed without contamination, have been developed for liquids and then solid–liquid mixtures, making the commercial development of continuous sterilization processes possible.

A number of cooling processes are also common:

- **refrigeration** to slow bacterial action – for example, 'cook-chill' meals, which have been cooked as in the home and which are then chilled prior to distribution, rely on this slowed bacterial growth to prevent damage to the food;

• **freezing** to prevent bacterial and enzyme-induced decay, allowing food to be stored for a considerable time. Chapter 3 has discussed simple models for freezing which allow an approximate estimate of the freezing time to be made. However, the structural damage caused by the expansion of water on freezing can impair product quality. The selection of optimal freezing conditions requires an understanding of material properties as well as information on the design of the freezer.

Sociological factors, such as the increase in the number of women employed outside the home, have increased the market for food that requires minimal home cooking, and thus for 'ready-meal' products. Neither canning nor bottling, which contain material that has been extensively processed, are well suited to this type of product. The range of storable food products available has grown enormously over the last 20 years, beginning with dried foods, which involve significant home preparation before they can be eaten, and then frozen foods, which, although convenient, require a freezer. More recently, cook-chill meals, bought from the cold cabinet and then kept in the refrigerator, and ambient shelf-stable products, which can be stored at room temperature, have been introduced.

The production of sterile food of high quality is an area that still presents many engineering challenges. This chapter will concentrate on sterilization as an example of the ways in which chemical and process engineering techniques can be applied to a food industry problem. Effectively, two sorts of reaction are taking place when food is cooked: those that lead to a sterile product, and those that result in a loss in product quality. The basic problem of sterilization is in many cases to maximize the first set of reactions whilst minimizing the second; this sort of optimization is common in the petrochemical industry, and can be examined with chemical engineering principles.

The kinetics of cooking

Thermal processes involve chemical reactions that can be quantified if they are to be optimized. As discussed in Chapter 8, the rates of chemical reactions can be expressed as a chemical rate law, a function of concentration, with a temperature dependence characterized by an activation energy:

$$\text{Rate} = k_r c^n = A \exp\left[\frac{-E_a}{R_g T}\right] c^n \tag{9.1}$$

but the rates of food processes are not generally described in terms of conventional chemical kinetics. The F-value (in minutes) is used to define the amount of sterilization that the food has received. If the temperature T

of the food is known as a function of time t the **integrated lethality**, defined as

$$F = \int_{t_{START}}^{t_{END}} 10^{\left(\frac{T - T_{ref}^F}{z_F} \right)} dt \qquad (9.2)$$

can be calculated. As described in Chapter 8, this is widely used within the industry.

It is much more difficult to quantify quality, which is a more non-mathematical concept, than to measure sterility. Some attempts have been made to relate quality in similar terms to the F-value, using data for enzyme loss. Thus it is possible to define the **C-value** of a process:

$$C = \int_{t_{START}}^{t_{END}} 10^{\left(\frac{T - T_{ref}^C}{z_C} \right)} dt \qquad (9.3)$$

where T_{Ref}^C is the reference temperature (now generally $100\,^\circ C$) of the process at which the slope of the 'cooking' rate curve is z_c. This approximates the true kinetics in the same way as does the F-value, but has the added complication that it is attempting to measure a much more diffuse quantity. Some work has been done relating the C-value to quality; a value of 100 min is generally taken as corresponding to 'satisfactory' for z_c in the range 20–$35\,^\circ C$.

To see how to design process plant, activation energies are more immediately useful than z values. A table of activation energies has already been given (Table 8.1 in Chapter 8), and can be used with equation (9.1) to investigate the effects of temperature on the two rates.

EXAMPLE 9.1

Compare the ratios of the rates of the sterilization and quality loss at $120\,^\circ C$ and $140\,^\circ C$, assuming: (a) the activation energy for C. botulinum death is $300\,kJ\,mol^{-1}$; (b) the activation energy for the loss of quality in foods is $125\,kJ\,mol^{-1}$.

If sterilization is an nth-order reaction while quality loss is an mth-order reaction, the ratio of the rates of the two at any temperature T is

$$\frac{\text{Rate of sterilization}}{\text{Rate of quality loss}} = \frac{A_s \exp\left[\frac{-E_{a(s)}}{R_g T} \right] c^n}{A_q \exp\left[\frac{-E_{a(q)}}{R_g T} \right] c^m} \qquad (9.4)$$

When the ratios are compared for the same concentration but different temperatures, the pre-exponential factors and concentration dependences cancel. R_g is $8.314\,\mathrm{J\,mol^{-1}\,K^{-1}}$, so $E_{a(s)}/R_g = 300\,000/8.314 = 36\,083\,\mathrm{K}$. The ratio is thus

$$\frac{\text{Rate at }140\,^\circ\text{C }(313\text{K})}{\text{Rate at }120\,^\circ\text{C }(293\text{K})} = \frac{\exp\left[\dfrac{-E_{a(s)}}{R_g 313}\right]\exp\left[\dfrac{-E_{a(q)}}{R_g 293}\right]}{\exp\left[\dfrac{-E_{a(q)}}{R_g 313}\right]\exp\left[\dfrac{-E_{a(s)}}{R_g 293}\right]}$$

$$= \frac{\exp[-115.28]}{\exp[-48.04]}\frac{\exp[-51.313]}{\exp[-123.152]} = 98.7 \quad (9.5)$$

The calculation in Example 9.1 shows that sterilization reactions proceed about 100 times faster than loss-of-quality reactions at the higher temperature. However, it says nothing about the absolute rates of the reactions. As a result of the temperature change, the time required for a given process will also change, as shown in the next example.

EXAMPLE 9.2

Compare the time required to carry out a sterilization at 120 and 140 °C, for the same data as Example 9.1.

Here only a single ratio is required since the ratio of the rates is the inverse of the times:

$$\frac{\text{Rate at }140\,^\circ\text{C }(313\text{K})}{\text{Rate at }120\,^\circ\text{C }(293\text{K})} = \frac{\exp\left[\dfrac{-E_{a(s)}}{R_g 313}\right]}{\exp\left[\dfrac{-E_{a(s)}}{R_g 293}\right]} = \frac{\exp[-115.28]}{\exp[-123.15]} = 2600 \quad (9.6)$$

Example 9.2 shows that, if sterilization is carried out at high temperature, both the time needed for sterilization and the amount of quality loss are reduced. There are thus good reasons for sterilizing at high temperatures and for short times. Before studying this further, it is important to understand why classical sterilization processes, such as canning, may be unsatisfactory.

9.1 Engineering principles

9.1.1 *Heat transfer and sterilization: convection and conduction*

Canning is the classical sterilization process, invented by Appert in the 19th century, and still the basis of a very large industry. A typical process, based on a series of pressurized steam cookers containing many cans, is shown schematically in Fig. 9.1. The key step in ensuring sterility is the mechanical engineering process of putting the lid on the can. The lidding process is in general not aseptic; usually, cans must be sterilized after the lid has been applied and sealed.

The two governing processes of heat transfer to the sealed can are convection and conduction, discussed in Chapter 3. Enough heat must be given to the system to sterilize the centre of the can. Heat is generally applied by condensing steam. The heat transfer coefficient from the steam to the outside of the can is very high. It might be thought that this would lead to rapid heating. However, Chapter 3 has shown that an overall heat transfer process is governed by the rate of the slowest, 'rate-controlling' step. This can be seen by the construction of the overall heat transfer coefficient in equation (3.21). The Biot number of the can defines the relative roles of internal and external heat transfer in a system.

EXAMPLE 9.3. ESTIMATE THE BIOT NUMBER OF A CAN

The standard size of a UK can is a cylinder about 100 mm high and 66 mm in diameter. An appropriate Biot number would be hr/λ, where h is the external heat transfer coefficient, r the radius of the cylinder and λ the thermal conductivity. Here $r = 0.033$ m, and assuming the filling has the properties of water at 20 °C the thermal conductivity is 0.7 W mK^{-1}. A lower estimate for the heat transfer coefficient for condensing steam is 1000 W m^{-2}K^{-1}, so the Biot number will be $1000 \times 0.033/0.7 = 47$. This is a very high Biot number.

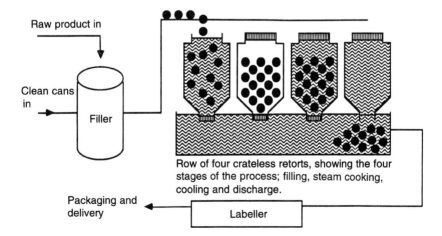

Fig. 9.1 Schematic diagram of a semi-continuous canning process, showing a row of four crateless retorts. Use of the four retorts enables the process to run continuously.

The Biot number in Example 9.3 is so large that heat transfer within the can will be the slowest step. The temperature at the centre of a can will lag behind the outside by an amount dependent on (a) the size of the container and (b) the mode of heat transfer. If the food is a liquid, it will heat by natural convection, setting up a circulating flow within the can that acts to stir it; this ensures that it heats quite quickly. If the food behaves as a solid (in practice, is a solid or a very viscous liquid) however, it will only heat by conduction: a slower process as shown in section 3.3.5. A lower limit can be placed on the possible sterilization time if it is assumed that the liquid within the can is fully stirred: that is, at a uniform temperature.

EXAMPLE 9.4

Assuming (a) that the fluid in the can is fully stirred and (b) that the heat transfer coefficient between the outside of the can and the condensing steam is infinite, find an equation from which the required heating time can be calculated.

Let the volume of the can be V and its surface area A_c, the temperature of the steam and the can be T_s and T_c and the density and specific heat of the food be ρ and c_P respectively. Then a heat balance can be written to describe the change in temperature with time. The heat transferred to the food increases its temperature according to

$$UA_c(T_s - T_c) = V\rho c_P \frac{dT_c}{dt} \qquad (9.7)$$

where U is the overall heat transfer coefficient. If the steam temperature is constant, this equation can be integrated as

$$\frac{T_s - T_c(t)}{T_s - T_c(0)} = \exp\left(-\frac{A_c U t}{V\rho c_P}\right) \qquad (9.8)$$

That is,

$$t = -\frac{V\rho c_P}{A_c U} \ln\left(\frac{T_s - T_c(t)}{T_s - T_c(0)}\right) \qquad (9.9)$$

The heating time thus depends on both the ratio of the can volume to the surface area and the heat transfer coefficient U between the steam and the food. This will be governed by natural convection between the fluid and the inside and the can.

In Example 9.4, if the steam temperature $T_s = 125\,°C$, the initial and final can temperatures are $60\,°C$ and $123\,°C$, ρ and c_P are for water, and the can dimensions are 66 mm in diameter and 102 mm deep, then substituting into equation (9.9) gives $t = 180000/U$ s. The internal heat transfer coefficient could well be low, say $U = 300\,\mathrm{W\,m^{-2}\,K^{-1}}$, giving a heating time of 600 s: about 10 min. The reader may wish to calculate the process time for a catering product in a can where the linear dimensions are doubled.

In practice, longer cook times are needed, because it is not economically sensible to sterilize single cans. Cans are processed either in batch retorts (pressure cookers in which several thousand cans are sterilized simultaneously) or in continuous systems, in which cans are conveyed through regions of varying temperature. Not all the cans will be exposed to the steam at the same time. This creates a problem: the process time must be set to ensure that the centre of the coldest can in the retort is sterilized.

The net result is to ensure that the vast majority of food in cans has a higher F-value that that specified for the process. In many cases this heat is so great that the food is significantly overprocessed. C-values of 400–500 min can be found in canning or retort pack foods, giving tinned vegetables and fruit that may bear little relation to the fresh product. In some cases canned food may be acceptable, such as in baked beans and mushy peas, but for some foods, such as strawberries, the reduced quality of the canned product is less acceptable.

One approach would be to sterilize using higher steam temperatures, in an attempt to process for a shorter time. However, the size of the can means that thermal lag will always be present, so the outside of the can will always be overcooked.

EXAMPLE 9.5

Estimate the increase in quality damage if the process of Example 9.4 is carried out using steam at 140 °C rather than 125 °C.

Equation (9.9) can be used to estimate the change in the process time:

$$\frac{\text{Time at }140°C}{\text{Time at }125°C} = \frac{\ln\left(\dfrac{140-123}{140-60}\right)}{\ln\left(\dfrac{125-123}{125-60}\right)} = 0.44 \qquad (9.10)$$

but the ratio of the accumulation of C-value will also change. For $T^{C}_{\text{ref}} = 100\,°C$ and $z_{c} = 20\,°C$, then

$$\frac{\text{Rate of quality loss at }140°C}{\text{Rate of quality loss at }125°C} = \frac{10^{\left(\frac{140-100}{20}\right)}}{10^{\left(\frac{125-100}{20}\right)}} = 5.62 \qquad (9.11)$$

So the increased quality loss as a result of moving to the higher temperature is $0.44 \times 5.62 = 2.47$.

The slowness of heat transfer, and the resulting quality losses, thus limit the use of higher temperatures in canning. In addition, the cost of pressure vessels is also limiting; if too high a steam temperature is used the vessel will be too expensive. Canning temperatures are limited to about 120–125 °C.

The advantages of the canning process are considerable, however. The process is basically cheap and straightforward and gives a robust and safe product. More than 100 years of operating experience in canning mean that the process and the factors that result in a safe product are well understood, and the product is also accepted by the consumer. Any alternative process must offer significant improvements if it is to be adopted by the industry.

9.1.2   The ideal food sterilization process

Kinetic data suggest that the higher the process temperature is, the better is the quality of the food when it is sterilized. The analysis of the canning process carried out above indicates that even if a high temperature is used, all parts of the food should be processed simultaneously, or else portions of the food will be overcooked. The requirements for an ideal process are thus:

- instantaneous heat transfer to the food, ensuring that all parts reach the same temperature at the same time, and follow the same time–temperature path;
- high temperatures, allowing sterilization reactions to predominate over the reactions that reduce quality.

Partial solutions are found if the distance over which heat has to be transferred is reduced, lowering the Biot number and decreasing the cooking time. A number of retortable pouches and trays are now available that combine a marketing advantage of a novel and convenient package (from which the food can often be eaten) with the better quality of food that results from faster heat transfer and thus a shorter process. Although these packs improve final product quality, they do not solve the problem; a new approach is needed.

The two 'ideal' concepts form the design philosophy behind **HTST** (high-temperature short time) or **UHT** (ultra-high temperature) processes. These processes are commonly considered to consist of three heat transfer stages, as follows.

1. Food is **heated** rapidly to temperatures around 130–140 °C.
2. It is **held** at high temperature in a holding section for the few seconds necessary to ensure sterilization.
3. It is then rapidly **cooled** before significant product degradation occurs.

This simple picture ignores preheating of ingredients and any packing step. Comparison of typical temperature–time curves for canning and HTST processes shows that much shorter processing times are possible.

9.1.3   Engineering implications of HTST

HTST process plant requires flowsheets that are significantly different from those for canning. Equipment is necessary to provide:

- high rates of heat transfer;
- aseptic packaging;
- uniform residence time distributions.

High rates of heat transfer.   The rate of heating required by HTST processes is much faster than in canning. Forced convective heat transfer coefficients are significantly greater than those possible in conduction. Forced convection is also faster than free convection, which is driven by the density difference between hot and cold fluid: within a heated can, for example. It is thus possible to heat flowing food much faster than static food. HTST processes are thus ideally suited to continuous rather than batch operation. Processing is carried out by heating food before packaging through heat exchangers, which give high heat transfer coefficients, rather than after packaging, as in canning.

EXAMPLE 9.6

Calculate the heating rate possible when a food fluid with the thermal properties of water flows at $1\,ms^{-1}$ down a $1\,cm$ pipe, assuming (a) a $5\,°C$ temperature difference between the inside and outside, and (b) that heat transfer coefficients are equal on both sides and that

$$Nu = 0.023Re^{0.8}Pr^{0.4} \qquad (9.12)$$

applies on the inside.

For water at $1\,ms^{-1}$ in a $1\,cm$ pipe

$$Re = 10^6 \times 1 \times 0.01 = 10\,000$$

and

$$Pr = 5.8$$

so

$$Nu = 0.023 \times 10\,000^{0.8} \times 5.8^{0.4} = 74.3$$

so

$$h = 74.3\lambda/d = 74.3 \times 0.61/0.01 = 4535\,W\,m^{-2}\,K^{-1}$$

So the overall heat transfer coefficient can be found from

$$\frac{1}{U} = \frac{1}{4535} + \frac{1}{4535} = 2268W\,m^{-2}\,K^{-1}$$

Then the heat balance on an element of length dx is

$$h.\pi d\,dx\Delta T = \rho c_p v \frac{\pi d^2}{4}\,dT \qquad (9.13)$$

and, as dx = v dt, then

$$\frac{dT}{dt} = \frac{4h\Delta T}{\rho c_p d} = \frac{4 \times 2268 \times 5}{1000 \times 4200 \times 0.01} = 1.08\,^{\circ}C\,s^{-1} \qquad (9.14)$$

Example 9.6 demonstrates that very rapid heating rates can be obtained for liquid foods using forced convection. However, the need for rapid convective heat transfer limits the applicability of HTST techniques to foods that contain particles. Particles heat by thermal conduction. If large particles are processed by conduction, the time required to raise their temperature to the required level is such that, as with Example 9.5, by the time particle centres are sterile the liquid in which they were immersed is unacceptably overcooked. In practice, therefore, conventional heating techniques can only process very small particles, of the order of a couple of millimetres in diameter. Section 9.2 discusses some possible solutions to this problem.

Aseptic packaging.   HTST processes involve the sterilization of food materials prior to packaging. Packaging process must therefore be sterile (aseptic): that is, no contamination of the already sterile product can be allowed to occur during filling. Until such processes were developed, HTST techniques could not be commercially used. A number of companies produce aseptic packaging equipment. Common features are:

- a prefill step, in which the unfilled pack or laminate is presterilized using (for example) steam, ultraviolet light or hydrogen peroxide;
- a filling step, in which measured amounts of material are passed to the carton (in a batch fill the nozzle is then flushed out, with steam for example, to ensure sterility);
- a sealing stage.

The requirement for sterility means that aseptic packaging plant requires a lot of complex and expensive mechanical engineering. It is more difficult to pack foods that contain particles than liquids, because of problems in ensuring that the particles do not block the filler head or make the seal imperfect. Such problems have not been completely solved, but effective commercial solutions are available.

Uniform food residence time distributions. At UHT temperatures, degradation reactions are rapid. The need for product safety implies that the process must be designed to sterilize the material that travels at the fastest speed through the plant. However, if a significant fraction of the food is unacceptably overprocessed, then the equipment is a failure.

The concept of the **residence time distribution** (RTD), introduced and discussed in Chapter 8, is critical in the quality of continuously processed food. In food processing, it is important that all parts of the material are sterilized, and the food produced must reach a required quality standard. Two criteria, for **sterility** and **product quality**, must be met by any process plant. For example, the process objectives may be an F-value of at least 6 min in the whole medium. This process requirement can be termed the F_p value. In achieving this aim, quality changes must take place: beyond a certain C-value, C_{max}, the product will no longer be commercially acceptable. The acceptability of a food product can thus be expressed in terms of sterility and quality ratios, ϕ_F and ϕ_C, defined by

$$\phi_F = \frac{F}{F_P} \qquad \phi C = \frac{C}{C_{max}} \tag{9.15}$$

These two ratios can be used to decide whether the process is producing an acceptable product as, at each point,

- if $\phi_F < 1$, the food is insufficiently sterile;
- if $\phi_C > 1$, it is overcooked.

Figure 9.2 shows schematically the changes in ϕ_F and ϕ_C that take place during processing. Each point in the food must be processed for a time longer than t_{min}, the time at which $\phi_F = 1$, but for no longer than t_{max}, the time at which $\phi_C = 1$, to ensure that the food is of satisfactory quality. The task of the food engineer in designing a process is thus to ensure that residence times of food in the equipment lie between these two values. A possible problem resulting from velocity distributions in a process plant is shown by the next example.

EXAMPLE 9.7

Estimate the distribution in F-value that results when a fluid with the properties of water flows at 130 °C at a mean velocity of 0.02 m s⁻¹ through a 5 cm diameter tube 2 m long. Take $T_F^{ref} = 121.6 °C$ and z = 10 °C.

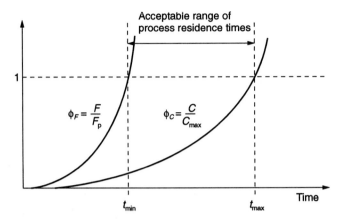

Fig. 9.2 The acceptable process RTD lies between the point where the food is sterile ($\phi_F = 1$) and where it is overcooked ($\phi_C = 1$).

The Reynolds number of the flow is ca. $1000 \times 0.02 \times 0.05/0.001 = 1000$: that is, the flow is laminar. As described in Chapter 2, the velocity profile of such a flow is parabolic:

$$v = 2v_m\left[1-\left(\frac{r}{R}\right)^2\right] \qquad (9.16)$$

The residence time for fluid at the wall of the pipe is thus much longer than that for fluid along the axis. The RTD function for such a system is

$$E(t)dt = 2\frac{t_o^2}{t^3}dt \qquad (9.17)$$

where t_o is the residence time along the axis. At 130 °C, the change in F with time is given by:

$$\frac{dF}{dt} = 10^{(T-T_{ref})/z} = 10^{(130-121.6)/10} = 6.918\,\text{min}^{-1}$$

The velocity profile is such that for $r = R/2$, the velocity is only 75% of that at the axis; fluid at that radius thus spends 33% longer in the tube than fluid on the axis. Nearer the wall the residence time increases further until the layer at the wall is theoretically stationary. Along the centreline, the velocity is $0.04\,\text{m s}^{-1}$, the residence time is $2/0.04 = 0.833\,\text{min}$, so that F is 5.76 min. At a radius of 4 cm, however, the velocity is $0.04 \times (1 - 0.8 \times 0.8) = 0.0144\,\text{m s}^{-1}$, so that the F accumulated along the tube is 16.0 min. The process must be designed to sterilize the fluid flowing along the centreline; material in the wall region will be significantly overcooked.

Developed parabolic flow gives the worst case; in many cases, hold tubes for particle–liquid mixtures are designed as if the flow were parabolic: that is, it is possible for material to pass through the system at twice the mean velocity. This is a conservative estimate. A well-designed process plant should have as small a difference between minimum and maximum residence times as possible. It is important that RTD be measured using real process fluids; even for fluids such as milk and water, differences in RTD have been found in plate heat exchangers.

Similar analyses can be carried out on other food processing equipment. For example, the spray drier is widely used to produce powdered products. Here a food is sprayed through a nozzle that produces a dispersion of small particles (much less than 0.25 mm) into a countercurrent flow of heated air. This offers very rapid drying rates because of the high surface area available for mass transfer, and gives minimal heat damage to the food material. Flow patterns are extremely complex, however, and the design of the nozzle is critical. If droplets are too small they produce particles that can be entrained by the air. These drops will stay in the drier for too long or be carried out with the airstream. If droplets are too large they will not dry. If too wide a droplet size distribution is produced, therefore, problems will result with unevenly dried product, owing to a wide product RTD.

The idea of the RTD is a powerful one, which can be widely used in the analysis of process equipment.

9.1.4 Problems in HTST processing

The logic behind HTST processing is, as outlined above, straightforward, and the technical problems discussed above appear easy to solve. In practice, they are not.

Many of the **mechanical engineering design** problems of food processing are highly complex. Hygienic design of equipment is crucial; it is vital to ensure that it is impossible to contaminate the food stream from outside and that process plant is as simple to clean and sterilize as possible. This requires that plant be carefully designed, and made from materials that do not contaminate the food. The design of hygienic valves and the need for sterile cleaning-in-place (CIP) makes food plant very complex. This type of plant is essentially similar to a petrochemical plant; for safety, the status of each valve must be known and the system must be continuously monitored.

In addition, there are a number of problems with **flow and heat transfer**, owing to the nature of food fluids. Data are widespread on petrochemical fluids, which have fairly stable properties, and largely Newtonian viscosities. In contrast, food fluids are complex and thermally unstable, with non-Newtonian rheology, as discussed in Chapter 5. Rheology can also be strongly temperature-dependent as a result of reactions on heating, such as starch gelatinization or protein aggregation within the fluid. During cooling, the viscosity of the product will also change. It is very difficult to predict the flow and heat transfer properties of food fluids. In addition, the thermal instability of foods makes process plant prone to the formation of fouling deposit: solidified material on the inside surfaces of processing plant, which must be frequently cleaned.

Control of continuous plant is much more important than in conventional batch canning. In canning, the process is well defined; provided a given temperature (or steam pressure) is maintained inside a retort for a given length of time, then all the food material will be sterile. In continuous plant, flowrate, pressure and temperature should be monitored throughout the plant to ensure that each stage of the process is operating correctly. This is especially important when dealing with complex fluids. For control and process validation, the development of **models** for the process is necessary; this requires an understanding of the process and of food physical and engineering properties.

The rest of this chapter will discuss some of these difficulties and their possible solutions.

9.2 Continuous processing: problems and solutions

9.2.1 Design principles for heat transfer equipment

The previous section has developed the arguments that led to the adoption of HTST processing. Continuous rather than batch processing is necessary, and it has been pointed out that the nature of food fluids makes them very prone to fouling and cleaning problems. The food industry uses a very wide range of heat transfer equipment. This section indicates the chemical engineering principles on which process equipment operates, rather than provide a guide to the best available.

Continuous heat exchange is commonplace in the chemical industry. Most of the petrochemical industry uses shell and tube exchangers of the type discussed in Chapter 3, which are fairly simple to design and fabricate and have high heat transfer coefficients. Food fluids are generally of high and non-Newtonian viscosity, and may contain particles. Flow of such a material through a tubular exchanger would give a poor RTD, poor heat transfer coefficients, and probably severe fouling. When selecting a heat exchanger, a number of questions must be answered, as follows.

- Is the RTD narrow enough to give uniform **final product quality**? Does the exchanger give unacceptable product damage (for example, food particles damaged by scraped surface units)?
- Is the **pressure drop** through the unit acceptable? If the food fluid is of high viscosity, very high pressure drops can result.
- Does the **extra value** given to the product by the unit make it cost-effective? For example, if an expensive scraped-surface exchanger is used

to increase product quality, does the increased price of the product generate enough extra revenue to offset the capital expenditure on the plant?
- Is it possible to **recover the energy** used in heating, by (for example) cooling the food down using material that is required at high temperatures?

The types of exchanger used in the industry will now be reviewed briefly.

Direct contact.   One simple way of getting efficient heat transfer and minimizing fouling is to inject steam directly into or over the food material, eliminating the heat transfer surface. This principle is used in direct steam injection or infusion sterilizers. In the latter process, steam at a pressure higher than that of the product is injected into the product stream via a suitable nozzle, and its condensation releases latent heat, which increases the product temperature and causes sterilization. The food is then sprayed into a vacuum chamber to reduce its temperature by evaporation of added water, which requires latent heat to be absorbed. These systems offer efficient sterilization, but are highly energy-inefficient and expensive to operate.

Plate heat exchangers.   These are the main type used in the food industry. Plate exchangers consist of a series of vertical shaped steel plates, separated by gaskets and held in a metal press, which form parallel corrugated channels through which liquid food and heating media can be passed in various configurations. High film heat transfer coefficients are possible even for viscous liquids, as thermal boundary layers are very thin and the plates are designed to enhance fluid mixing. Unlike tubular exchangers, few design correlations of the type described in the heat transfer section are available in the literature. The precise form of the correlations are particular to each manufacturer's design. One published equation for a heat exchanger is (Rene *et al.*, 1991)

$$Nu = 0.352Re^{0.639}Pr^{1/3} \qquad \text{for } Re > 5$$

where the hydraulic diameter (defined in equation (2.77)) is used as the length term in the Nusselt and Reynolds numbers. The form of this equation is similar to those given in the section on heat transfer and can be compared with the other equation for plate exchangers (p. 131). Care should be taken when calculating heat transfer coefficients in plate exchangers unless manufacturer's data are available for the particular case.

Plate exchangers are compact and are well suited to energy recovery. In pasteurizers, it is common for hot product to be cooled against inlet liquid; this makes them inherently more efficient than injection systems. They are, however, commonly limited by the pressure at which the gaskets burst (at about 750 kPa) which means that only low flowrates are possible. Welded units are now available that can operate at higher pressures.

Scraped-surface exchangers.   Many food materials are highly viscous and foul heavily; they are thus difficult to process in more conventional plant. The principle of the scraped surface exchanger is simple: food is passed through a heated chamber, which contains a rotating blade. This prevents deposition on the heat transfer surface and also stirs the food. Scraped-surface units are widely used for very viscous solid–liquid mixtures and for materials such as ice-cream and spreads. However, if they are incorrectly operated they can damage the food. Owing to the complexity of the flow patterns, it is difficult to design and model scraped-surface systems. A wide range of residence times may also be encountered in operating plant.

Tubular exchangers.   Simple shell-and-tube exchangers are used to a small extent for food processing, but are limited to low-viscosity foods (up to about $2\,N\,s\,m^{-2}$). However, most food plant will contain such exchangers, for example in boiler or evaporator plant. Their design is straightforward and is discussed in Chapter 3. A number of companies offer modifications of the conventional design, such as corrugated tubes, which give better heat trans-fer than a straight tube while not involving excessive turbulence. This sort of system may be better for fragile foods. Enhanced heat transfer can be obtained by using mixing elements inside the tube, but these significantly increase the pressure drop through the unit.

Evaporators.   All the above units operate on liquids or liquid–solid mix-tures. Different designs are required where vapour is produced, as in evapo-ration. Evaporation can be conducted in multitube heat exchangers in which liquid travels either up or down tubes heated by condensing steam on the outside, or inside plate exchangers.

The operation of an evaporator is limited by the temperature difference that is possible between the hot surface and the liquid: if the wall tempera-ture is too high, heavy fouling will result. The increase in viscosity as the solid concentration increases will also lower the heat transfer coefficient. The energy efficiency of evaporators can be increased by using the vapour evaporated in one device as the material that condenses in the next; such multiple-effect systems have a much higher steam efficiency. Two possible configurations of multiple-effect evaporator are shown in Fig. 9.3. In for-ward feed the hottest steam contacts the least concentrated solution, whereas in backward feed the hottest steam contacts the most concentrated solution. If the product is thermally stable, backward feed has an advantage. The viscosity of the most concentrated fluid will reduce on heating; the heat

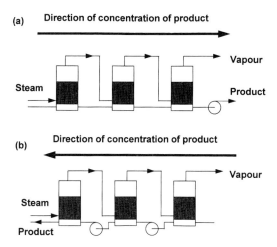

Fig. 9.3 Multiple-effect evaporators: (a) forward feed; (b) backward feed.

transfer coefficient in the final effect will thus be higher than for a cold fluid. For food fluids, however, forward feed is usual, as concentrated fluids will foul heavily at high temperatures.

9.2.2 The processing of solid–liquid food mixtures

The techniques discussed in section 9.1.1 all use conventional heat transfer. The slowness of conduction has already been noted; because of the time taken for conduction, it is impossible for particles greater than about 4 mm to be sterilized in the same time as liquids. The possible commercial advantage offered by the HTST processing of foods containing larger particles, up to the 25 mm commonly used in the home, has stimulated a number of innovations.

Separate processing of solids and liquids. The time required to process large solids and liquids by conductive and convective heat transfer will always be different. One ingenious solution is to treat solids and liquids separately, as in the Jupiter technology developed by APV Baker. Liquid is sterilized in conventional plate exchangers, while solids are processed more slowly in a rotating vessel, which has both steam-heated walls and provision for steam injection. The governing heat transfer processes are thus convection for the liquid phase and conduction for the solid phase. The two sterile phases can then be mixed prior to aseptic packaging. The technique, although elegant, is not an ideal solution, as it requires a large amount of complex pipework.

Heat generation processes. Rather than use conventional heat transfer, a number of techniques exist that exploit heat generation rather than heat transfer. Here, the heat required for sterilization is generated within the food rather than using thermal conduction. Heat generation has the advantage that, if the process is correctly designed, solid and liquid can be heated at the same rates. The heating process is thus much faster than conventional processes, although cooling still depends on heat conduction. Heat generation processes depend on the passage either of an electric field or an electric current through the food material. Heating occurs as a result of friction during molecular rotation, in microwave processing, or by the electrical resistance of the food, in ohmic heating. Unlike conventional processing, where the highest possible temperature is the temperature of the heating medium, there is no theoretical upper limit to the temperature that can be reached by this sort of heating. Long residence times are thus more damaging to product quality than in conventional cooking.

Microwave processing is widespread both in the home and in industry. When high-frequency electric fields are applied to foods, the electric dipoles of water molecules are excited into rapid oscillation. Some of this energy is converted into heat. The heat generation rate per unit volume for heat generation alone is given by

$$Q_G = 0.556E^2\omega\varepsilon' \tan\delta \times 10^{-19} \qquad (9.18)$$

where ω is the frequency, E is the electric field strength, ε' is a measure of the number and strength of the dipoles and $\tan\delta$ is the loss tangent. The latter two parameters are functions of the material being heated, and will vary with temperature. Ice has an entirely different response from that of liquid water; as a material thaws the liquid will absorb much more strongly than the ice, causing rapid heating of the liquid portion. Microwave thawing processes must thus be controlled carefully.

The practical efficiency of microwave heating depends on the depth to which the microwaves penetrate into the material. This is a strong function of frequency: as shown by the equation:

$$d = \frac{\lambda}{2\pi\sqrt{\varepsilon_r} \tan\delta} \qquad (9.19)$$

where d is the depth where the intensity decays to $1/e$ of its surface value, λ is the wavelength of the microwave radiation and ε_r the relative permittivity. This equation applies strictly only to the case where microwave energy decays exponentially; more complex behaviour is generally found because of the shape of foods, but the equation is a good guide.

The expression suggests that greater penetration and thus more uniform heating is obtained by low-frequency (high-wavelength) systems. Commercial microwave heating thus uses frequencies in the region of 900 MHz. It is arguable that the main influence of microwave processing on the food industry is home microwaving, and the introduction of meals that can be cooked in the microwave. However, for safety reasons, domestic microwaves use higher frequencies than industrial systems, commonly 2450 MHz, at which the penetration depth is low (commonly of the order of 10 mm). Domestic microwaves thus do not give very uniform heating. In addition, rapid heating to 100 °C is unlikely to sterilize the food. The way in which the consumer uses microwave processing is thus not as safe as conduction cooking; microbial contamination that would be destroyed by half an hour in the oven may survive reheating in the microwave. Microwave ovens have added to the safety problems of the food industry.

Electrical heating is conceptually simple. A schematic diagram of a process is given in Fig. 9.4. A continuous stream of flowing fluid is passed vertically through a tube, which contains a series of electrodes. A voltage is applied between the electrodes; the fluid is rapidly sterilized by heat generated within it due to its electrical resistance. Once sterilized, the material is

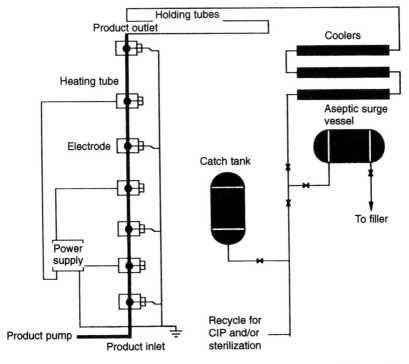

Fig. 9.4 APV Baker 'ohmic heater' unit. Liquid flows through a tube containing a series of electrodes connected to three-phase supply.

cooled and passed to an aseptic packaging system. Such an 'ohmic heating' process has been commercially developed by APV Baker and plants are now operational in the UK.

The process has a greater energy efficiency than microwave heating, as almost all of the electrical power supplied is transformed directly into heat, and it uses low-frequency a.c. (50 or 60 Hz) to eliminate electrolysis. As heat generation rather than heat transfer governs sterilization, irrespective of the particle size, if solid and liquid have identical electrical conductivities, both phases will generate heat at the same rate. In practice, as shown in Fig. 9.5, solids can often heat faster than liquids. This is not possible using conventional techniques.

Electrical heating is unfamiliar by comparison with conventional sterilization processes, and requires new skills of the food technologist and chemical engineer. The controlling factor in the process is the electrical conductivity: both the overall conductivity, which controls the power consumption of the process, and the variation of local conductivity, which affects the local temperature. As with any process, it is necessary to develop operating procedures that assure product safety. The process can be confirmed, in terms both of safety and product quality, by a four-step procedure, as follows.

1. Find the electrical conductivity of all the components as a function of temperature, and measure their heating rates under static conditions as a function of the orientation to the electric field.
2. Thus identify the 'worst-case' particle: the one that heats slowest. The process parameters should be set to sterilize the worst-case particle in the worst orientation.

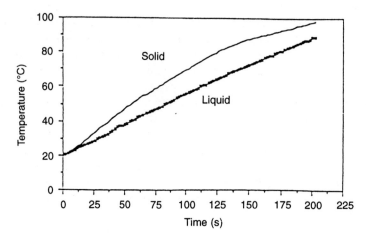

Fig. 9.5 Electrical heating of a potato piece, 3 cm × 4 cm × 0.75 cm, showing particle heating faster than the liquid.

3. Once the process parameters have been determined, perform tests to determine the effect of the process on the fastest-heating component, to check that no unwanted degradation occurs.
4. Also, perform calculations and tests on any component that is known to be thermally fragile.

Once the fastest and slowest cases have been checked and found satisfactory, and provided no intermediate case suffers unacceptable damage, the process can be considered satisfactory. Similar approaches must be adopted for other techniques, such as microwaving, where the dielectric properties of the material, rather than the electrical conductivity alone, control the heating rate.

9.2.3   Flow of food materials

Ideally, all the food material should remain within the process plant for the same time. It is vital to be able to predict the flow properties of foods, but there are two major problems:

• the non-Newtonian rheology, both of food fluids and mixtures;
• the possibility of different behaviour of solid and liquid foods in mixtures.

Although a range of complex flow effects can occur, the techniques used to analyse the flows are straightforward, and are based on the principles outlined in Chapters 2 and 5 on Newtonian and non-Newtonian flows. Turbulent flow, in which the velocity profile is described by the one-seventh power law, offers the nearest approach to ideal plug flow. However, to minimize product damage, solid–liquid mixtures are usually processed in laminar flow, in which a strong velocity profile exists that is dependent on the liquid viscosity. A range of velocities will therefore be expected in commercial plant, giving rise to a range of product qualities and sterilities; this will be especially true in volumetric heating processes, in which the temperature of the food is directly dependent on the time spent in the heater.

The addition of solids to a viscous fluid tends to flatten the velocity profile. In addition, the strong temperature-dependence of viscosity may help the flow of solid–liquid mixtures, as the hot region near the wall may have the lowest viscosity, in which case the central region could move as more of a plug. For efficient operation, however, solids and liquids should flow together, without separation. In practice, particles may be conveyed in plugs (**capsule flow**) or in layers (**heterogeneous** or **saltation flows**). Figure 9.6 shows photographs of flows of carrot particles in water at different solids concentrations, showing the sedimented bed; as the solids fraction increases, the flow becomes more uniform. Processes must be designed to minimize sedimentation: that is, for high-volume solids fractions and vis-

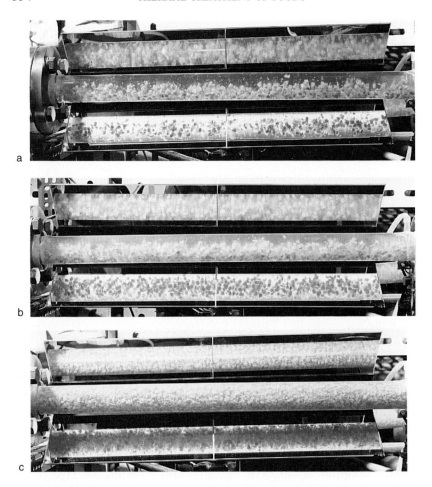

Fig. 9.6 Flow of carrot particles in water at different concentrations of solids: (a) 8%; (b) 14%; (c) 35% (Liu, 1993, PhD thesis, Cambridge University.)

cous carrier fluids. The pressure drop characteristics of such flows are unknown, making it difficult to predict the pressure required to allow the food to flow.

To ensure the microbiological safety of the process, the speed of the fastest-moving particle relative to the average particle velocity must be known. Any process must be designed to sterilize the fastest-moving part of the system while minimizing the cooking of the slowest-moving part. The fastest-moving particle, with the shortest residence time, thus determines the process time, while the particle residence time distribution determines the quality of the final product. Some estimate of the variation in velocity is needed. Applying the technique of dimensional analysis (discussed in section 2.4) to the flow of a single particle suggests that eight parameters are involved: particle and mean fluid flow velocities v_p and v_m, particle and pipe diameters d and D, particle and fluid densities ρ_p and ρ_f, the fluid viscosity μ, and the acceleration due to gravity, g:

$$v_p = f(d, D, \rho_p, \rho_f, \mu, v_m, g) \qquad (9.20)$$

which, as these involve the three dimensions of mass, length and time, can be rewritten in terms of five dimensionless groups:

$$v_r = f\left(Fr_p, Re, \frac{d}{D}, \rho_r\right) \qquad (9.21)$$

Here v_r is the velocity ratio $= v_p/v_m$ (that is, the ratio of particle velocity to mean fluid velocity), Re is the Reynolds number based on pipe diameter, ρ_r is the ratio of particle to fluid density, and Fr_p is the particle **Froude number**, defined as:

$$Fr_p = \frac{v_m}{\sqrt{gd(\rho_r - 1)}} \qquad (9.22)$$

To demonstrate the use of dimensional analysis, Fig. 9.7 shows results for the flow of single particles of different shapes in water, expressed as the variation of v_r as a function both of the particle Froude number defined in equation (9.22) and of the pipe Reynolds number. It can be seen that the Reynolds number is a poor fitting parameter, but when the particle Froude number is used a single curve results. For $Fr_p > 5$ the particle velocity is comparable to that to the fluid, values of v_r between 0.9 and 1.2 being found. For $Fr_p < 5$, however, the mean particle velocity decreases rapidly, until for $Fr_p < 2$ the flow is insufficient to move the particle, leading to a velocity ratio of zero. The empirical equation

$$v_r = 1.16 - \frac{0.7234}{Fr_p} \qquad (9.23)$$

gave a good fit to the data. Similar equations can be found for other sizes of particle and fluids, but the same physical principles apply. In non-Newtonian flow the process is more complex. The velocity profile of a laminar flow is such that the centreline velocity is significantly greater than the mean. If a particle is suspended in the centre of a pipe in a laminar flow it might be expected to travel at a higher v_r than if it were centred in a turbulent flow. The lighter the particle is, therefore, the more likely it is to be suspended at the velocity of the bulk fluid.

The range of velocities possible in a flow can be estimated by following the lightest and heaviest particles. The variation of carrot densities in the flows shown in Fig. 9.6 is between 1010 and 1080 kg m^{-3}. Figure 9.8 shows data for the velocity of two tracer particles of density 1010 and 1040 kg m^{-3}

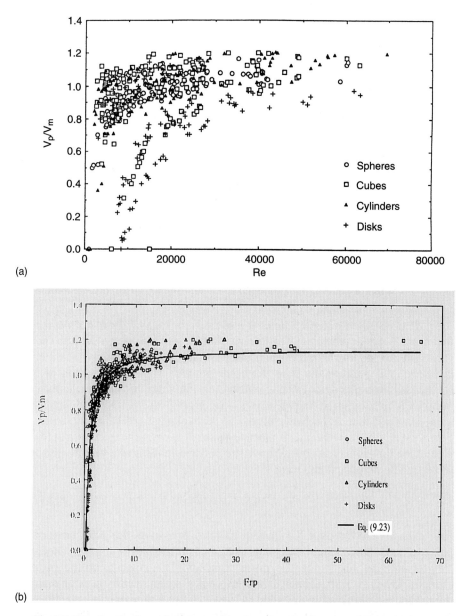

Fig. 9.7 Data for the flow of single particles in water as a function of: (a) tube Reynolds number; (b) particle Froude number.

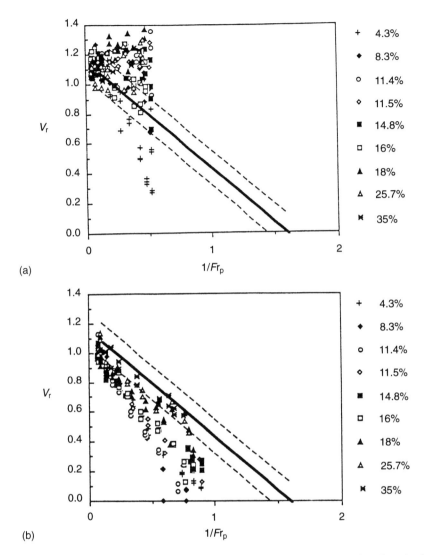

Fig. 9.8 Data for the flow of tracer particles in carrot–water mixtures as a function of solids fraction: (a) tracer specific gravity 1.01; (b) tracer specific gravity 1.04. Black line is equation (9.23); dotted lines are ±10%.

in flows of carrots of various solids fractions in water, together with equation (9.23) for comparison. The lightest particle spent most of the time in the region of low solids fraction at the top of the pipe, and the heaviest spent most time in the sedimented bed. To maintain continuity, if the sedimented bed is travelling at less than the mean velocity then the flow of the liquid above the bed must be faster than the mean velocity; any particles suspended or saltated by the liquid will thus travel significantly faster than the bed. For the heavier particle, at all solids fractions, the particle velocity is less than that of a single particle, and the data are not widely scattered. Much greater scatter is seen for the lighter particle. The particle can travel up to about 1.5 times the mean flow velocity, well above that of single particles. The highest velocities are found for solids fractions between 10 and 20%. At low solids fraction the effect of the particles is minimal, so that the velocity of the particles can be modelled by the single-particle correlation. However, the depth of the sedimented bed becomes significant for solids fractions greater than about 10%, increasing the liquid phase velocity. At solids fractions above about 20%, the whole pipe is filled by the high solids fraction phase. There is thus no room for a fast-moving stream, and the flow can again be predicted by the single-particle equation. The top of the bed continues to move at higher velocities than the base, but the difference decreases at higher solids fractions. In practice, care must be taken in designing any system that contains a two-phase mixture.

9.2.4 Control and modelling of heat transfer equipment

Food plant must be operated safely, and produce a safe product. To do that, it is necessary to ensure that every part of the food has been sterilized, which requires a model for the heat transfer process that can be used to calculate F and C values. The principles used to develop equations for these systems are those of thermal balance and heat transfer, described in earlier sections.

Modelling conduction and convention. Chapter 3 has discussed the basic principles of heat conduction, both steady and unsteady state. The unsteady-state heat conduction equation has been derived in Section 3.1.4. In general, modelling the conduction heating of a three-dimensional body requires the solution of the three-dimensional version of the equation:

$$\rho c_P \frac{\partial T}{\partial t} = k \nabla^2 T = k \left(\frac{\partial^2 T}{\partial x^2} + \frac{\partial^2 T}{\partial y^2} + \frac{\partial^2 T}{\partial z^2} \right) \tag{9.24}$$

at each point in the material, where T is temperature, k is the thermal conductivity, and ρ and c_P are the density and specific heat of the solid, with the requisite boundary conditions, such as

$$q = h \left(T_{liq} - T_{surf} \right) = \left(k \nabla T \right)_{surf} \tag{9.25}$$

that is, external heat transfer to the surface is the same as internal conduction from the surface. At high Biot number, conduction dominates. The rate of heating does not depend on the magnitude of the heat transfer coefficient, and the boundary condition becomes simpler:

$$T_{surf} = T_{liq} \tag{9.26}$$

In practice in the food industry, Biot numbers are often so high that this latter condition applies (Example 9.3), and so it is not possible to increase the heating or cooling rate by increasing the external heat transfer coefficient, for example by increasing the flowrate over the surface.

Equation (9.24), with whichever boundary condition, is difficult to solve. Analytical solutions are rare, and simple ones rarer still; the charts given in Chapter 3 apply to the very limited situation of constant heating temperature and for constant physical properties and simple shapes. It is much more likely that the heating temperature is a function of time, that the physical properties are not constant and that the shape is complex. The simplifications that are necessary to produce a simple equation can be demonstrated by deriving the Plank equation for the freezing time of a solid, already used in Chapter 3.

EXAMPLE 9.8

To derive the equation, it is necessary to assume: (a) the specific heat of the water can be neglected with respect to latent heat, i.e. all the heat supplied goes to freeze water; (b) heat transfer is one-dimensional, through a layer of thickness x from a medium of cooling temperature T_b *to a freezing front at* T_f*, where* $\Delta T = T_f - T_b$*; (c) the physical properties are constant. The rate of convective heat transfer from the solid will equal that due to conduction from the freezing front:*

$$q = h(T_i - T_b) = \frac{\lambda}{x}(T_f - T_i) \tag{9.27}$$

where T_i is the solid–coolant interface temperature and the interfacial heat transfer coefficient is h. This heat is evolved by latent heat due to freezing:

$$q = \theta_w h_{fg} \frac{dx}{dt} \tag{9.28}$$

where h_{fg} is the latent heat of water and θ_w is the fraction of water in the material. Eliminating the unknown temperature gives

$$q = \theta_w h_{fg} \frac{dx}{dt} = \Delta T \left(\frac{1}{h} + \frac{x}{\lambda} \right)^{-1} \tag{9.29}$$

which, when integrated, gives

$$t = \frac{h_{fg} \theta_w}{\Delta T} \left[\frac{x}{h} + \frac{x^2}{2\lambda} \right] \tag{9.30}$$

from which the freezing time can be estimated, as in Chapter 3.

The equation derived in Example 9.8 is useful only for a first estimate. Solutions for heat transfer where changes in temperature occur throughout the material have been discussed in Chapter 3, and are best expressed graphically. More accurate models are needed to cope with different shapes and the complex variation of physical properties with temperature found in real systems. Numerical models are thus used, in which the differential equation (9.24) is approximated at a series of points or regions. The numerical accuracy of the techniques depends on the spacing of these points: the more points, the more accurate the calculation, but the more the computing power that is needed. It is also vital to be able to predict the physical properties of the system. Thermal properties (density, specific heat, thermal conductivity) of most common foods are now reasonably well documented.

For the control of retort processes, much work has gone into the development of mathematical models of heat penetration into a can or retortable pouch. Such models solve the conduction equation to calculate the temperature, and hence the F-value, at the centre of the package, using the monitored temperature–time profile in the retort. Problems arise in modelling the effect of the headspace, for example between the food and the lid in retortable trays; here, the interfacial heat transfer coefficient is more important than it is in slow-moving liquid–liquid flows. These models enable the plant operator to determine when the cans in a retort are sterile, and minimize process losses.

Modelling and control of HTST processes.   Control of a continuous aseptic HTST process requires a different approach from the above. Canning effectively requires the measurement of one temperature as a function of time. In continuous HTST processes, a number of temperatures must be measured continuously to ensure that every part of the plant maintains sterility and that cooling is effective; at the very least, the start and finish of the heating, holding, and cooling sections should be monitored. In addition, the flowrate and the pressure in the system must be monitored: if pressure falls too low in the heating section, the product may begin to boil, and if it falls too low at the filler, insufficient pressure will be available to enable filling.

The sterilizing effect of the heating regime on the food must be calculated. For a single-phase fluid the heat balances are as given in Chapter 3, but a two-phase fluid requires the use of an enthalpy balance on both solid and liquid phases. For each particle in a fluid, the interchange between the particle and the fluid is given by equation (9.25). The balance on the liquid side is more complex, as there could be i particles exchanging heat with the liquid, each with its own physical properties and velocities. Assuming (a) a heat transfer coefficient of h_w between wall and fluid, (b) a fully stirred liquid, and (c) a constant velocity v_L for the whole fluid, then the liquid phase heat balance on a length dx of tube of diameter D becomes

Heat transfer from wall + Heat transfer from i particles = Heat change in fluid

$$\pi D dx . h_w \left(T_w - T_L \right) + \sum_i h_i a_i \frac{\pi D^2}{4} dx \left(T_{si}^0 - T_L \right)$$

$$= \left(1 - \phi \right) \frac{\pi D^2}{4} dx \left(\rho c_P \right)_L \frac{dT_L}{dt} \tag{9.31}$$

where a_i is the surface area of the ith particle per unit volume and ϕ is the total solid fraction occupied by the particles. The accuracy of the assumption that the liquid is well stirred is not known; it is likely to be true for turbulent fluids. The length of the holding tube must be calculated using a model that calculates the temperature distribution in the particle as a function of the bulk temperature, and determines when it is sterile.

Once the holding time is known, the velocity of the food through the hold tube must be calculated. This requires an understanding of the material RTD. If the RTD is not known, very conservative estimates must be used, such as the assumption of fully developed Newtonian flow. One ingenious technique for determining the sterilization given to foods by a process has been developed by Campden Food RA. Particles of sodium alginate containing spores of *B. stereothermophilus* are passed through the heater, and their activity before and after heating is compared, allowing the F-value of the process to be calculated directly. This allows direct confirmation of the effects of the process.

Modelling heat generation.   Heat transfer processes require knowledge of physical properties such as the thermal conductivity of the solid and liquid phases, specific heats, densities, and (in some cases, although conduction normally dominates in liquid–solid processing) interphase heat transfer coefficients. Other factors control heat generation: in electrical heating it is vital to know electrical conductivity; in microwave heating the dielectric properties of foods.

To illustrate the difficulties of measuring physical properties, the following was found during an investigation of food electrical conductivity.

• It can be a strong function of frequency. As commercial conductivity meters work at much higher frequencies than the 50 Hz used in ohmic heating, errors can result unless measurements are made at 50 Hz.
• It can be anisotropic, presumably reflecting the structure of the material. For example, the conductivity of carrot at 25 °C is 0.25 mS cm^{-1} across the axis and 0.42 mS cm^{-1} parallel to the axis.
• Conductivity–temperature profiles for some foods can differ significantly between ohmic and conventional heating.

In electrical processing, the heat generation rate at any point is given by $Q_G = \kappa E^2$, where E is the local field strength and κ is the local electrical conductivity. In microwave heating, the heat generation rate is given by equation (9.19). The heat generation term must be combined with the conduction equation to give

$$\rho c_P \frac{\mathrm{d}T}{\mathrm{d}t} = Q_G + k\nabla^2 T = \kappa E^2 + k\nabla^2 T \tag{9.32}$$

For electrical heating, if the local electric field strength and the physical properties of the material are known, the heating rate can be predicted. The field distribution must be calculated to find E. This requires the solution of Laplace's equation for voltage V:

$$\nabla(\kappa \nabla V) = 0$$

which reduces to

$$\nabla^2 V = 0 \tag{9.33}$$

if electrical conductivity is constant. Maxwell's equations must be solved for microwave heating; this will not be dealt with here. The voltage distribution in electrical heating will depend on the distribution of electrical conductivities within the fluid, and thus on particle shape and its orientation.

If the physical properties of the medium are not uniform, temperature differences can result. This is clearly demonstrated in Fig. 9.9, which shows

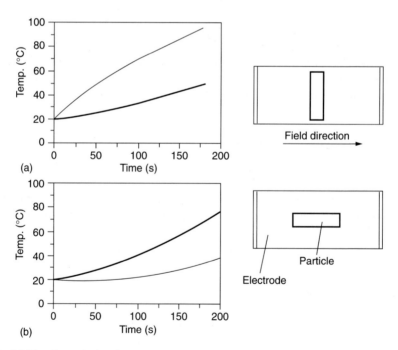

Fig. 9.9 The change in heating rate with particle orientation for potato particles undergoing electrical heating: (a) perpendicular, (b) parallel to the field. Heavy line shows the liquid temperature.

the heating of two identically shaped potato slices in brine, one perpendicular and one parallel to the field. The difference in heating rate between the
two is readily seen; when the particle is perpendicular to the field it heats
faster than the liquid, but when parallel it heats slower. In practice, this will
not matter if the process is designed so that (a) a particle that travels
through the heater in the slowest-heating configuration is sterile, and (b) a
particle that travels through in the fastest-heating configuration is not unacceptably overcooked: that is, that the system operates between the limits of
Fig. 9.3. It is vital to calculate the heating rate to determine the differences
that may result.

Calculation of the electrical heat generation rate is difficult and requires
either experiment or complex numerical modelling. If it is assumed that the
heat generation rate in the liquid and solid phases is uniform and equal to
Q_L and Q_S, however, a simple model is possible. As heat generation is much
faster than heat transfer it is possible to assume that the particle temperatures are uniform. For a solid particle of temperature T_S moving at velocity
v_S in a fully developed flow of temperature T_L the heat balance can be
written as

$$-ha\left(T_S - T_L\right) + Q_S = v_S\left(\rho c_P\right)_S \frac{dT_S}{dx} \tag{9.34}$$

where h is the convective heat transfer coefficient, and a is the area of the
particle per unit volume ($6/d_p$ for a sphere of diameter d_p). The balance on
the liquid side is more complex, as there could be i particles exchanging
heat with the liquid, each with its own physical properties and velocities. In
the holding section, the liquid phase heat balance becomes

$$\frac{\sum_i \phi_i h_i a_i\left(T_{Si} - T_L\right)}{\left(1 - \sum_i \phi_i\right)} + Q_L = v_L\left(\rho c_P\right)_L \frac{dT_L}{dx} \tag{9.35}$$

where ϕ_i is the fraction of the volume of the system occupied by solid i. If all
the particles are travelling with the same velocity, this can be rewritten

$$\frac{\phi ha\left(T_S - T_L\right)}{\left(1 - \phi\right)} + Q_L = v_L\left(\rho c_P\right)_L \frac{dT_L}{dx} \tag{9.36}$$

Manipulation gives

$$-H_S\left(T_S - T_L\right) + G_S = v_S \frac{dT_S}{dx}$$

$$H_L\left(T_S - T_L\right) + G_L = v_L \frac{dT_L}{dx} \tag{9.37}$$

The equations can thus be written in terms of G, the inherent heat generation in each phase together with two modified heat transfer terms, $H_S = ha/(\rho c_P)_S$ and $H_L = [\phi/(1 - \phi)][ha/(\rho c_P)_L]$ and the phase velocities.

Equation (9.37) can be solved numerically, but an analytical solution is available if all the factors in the equation are constants. The difference between the two phase temperatures is then found to be

$$\Delta T = T_S - T_L = \Delta T_\infty + \left(\Delta T_0 - \Delta T_\infty\right)\exp\left(-\beta x\right) \tag{9.38}$$

where

$$\alpha = \frac{G_S}{v_S} - \frac{G_L}{v_L}$$

$$\beta = \frac{H_L}{v_L} + \frac{H_S}{v_S}$$

$$\Delta T_0 = T_S^0 - T_L^0 \tag{9.39}$$

and the final temperature difference between the two phases, ΔT_∞, is α/β. Individual phase temperatures can then be calculated using the following equations:

$$T_S = T_S^0 + \frac{H_S}{\beta v_S}\left(\Delta T_0 - \Delta T_\infty\right)\left(\exp\left(-\beta x\right) - 1\right) + \left(\frac{G_S}{v_S} - \Delta T_\infty \frac{H_S}{v_S}\right)x \tag{9.40}$$

and

$$T_L = T_S - \left(\Delta T_\infty + \left(\Delta T_0 - \Delta T_\infty\right)\exp\left(-\beta x\right)\right) \tag{9.41}$$

Using these equations to find temperatures, F and C for each phase can then be found by integrating equations (9.2) and (9.3) numerically. Figure 9.10 shows the type of temperature data which can be produced by the model; here the solid first underheats and then overheats the liquid (Zhang and Fryer, 1994).

As with all analytical solutions, the applicability of the equations is limited; however, they can be used to see how a real system could behave. The equations show that the thermal response of the two phases is in two parts; a term that is linear in distance along the heater, and is governed largely by the rate of heat generation; and an exponential heat transfer term that includes β, and thus takes account of the magnitude of h. The rate at which ΔT_∞ is approached depends on the heat transfer coefficient.

Heat transfer models of this sort are essential for process design and control; although the equation can be difficult to solve numerically, the physical principles are straightforward.

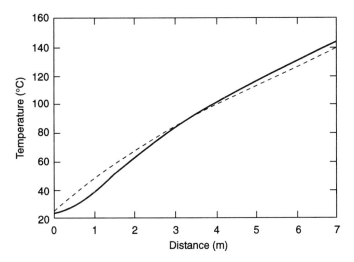

Fig. 9.10 Variation in temperature of a solid (—) and a liquid (---) using the model of (9.34)–(9.41).

9.3   Fouling and cleaning in food process plant

9.3.1   Introduction: the fouling problem

The operation of food processing plant is complicated by the thermal instability of food material. During operation, the inner surfaces of food plant gradually become covered with a solid fouling deposit. Deposition is most rapid in heating equipment such as heat exchangers and evaporators, but can occur elsewhere, for example in high-temperature holding tubes. Fouling causes a number of problems, as follows.

- By adding an insulating solid layer to the heat transfer surface, it creates a barrier to heat transfer.
- By decreasing the area available to flow and changing the roughness of the surface, it increases pressure drop.
- By providing areas in which microbes can adhere and survive, it threatens plant sterility.

Fouling is common in the process industries, but food fouling is especially severe: for example, it is possible to operate an oil refinery for several months between cleanings, but food plant commonly has to be cleaned daily. Food fouling has been solved empirically by the food industry. Many of the types of heat exchanger used by the food industry, such as the scraped-surface exchanger, have an antifouling action that allows run times to be extended before excessive deposit build-up is reached. In addition, it is necessary to clean process plant regularly, and cleaning-in-place (CIP) equipment is widely used to ensure that this is done efficiently. The aim of this section is to describe fouling and cleaning problems and how they can be reduced.

The effect of fouling is included in the basic heat transfer equation by the inclusion of the **fouling resistance** (or **fouling factor**) R_F:

$$\frac{1}{U} = \frac{1}{U^0} + R_F \tag{9.42}$$

where U and U^0 are the overall heat transfer coefficients in the presence and absence of fouling respectively. Although U^0 may be calculated fairly accurately from correlations, such as those described in Chapter 3, R_F cannot; this makes heat transfer equipment difficult to design.

In addition, fouling is a transient process; the surface starts clean and ends up fouled in a number of ways, as shown in Fig. 9.11. Before fouling there may be an induction period during which heat transfer and pressure drop change only slightly; indeed, the extra roughness given to the surface by the first layer of fouling can increase the heat transfer coefficient for a short time. At the end of this period the surface fouls rapidly; the fouling rate may slow to produce a final equilibrium deposit, but this will probably occur at too high a value to be acceptable in industrial plant. The transient nature of fouling causes problems, because equipment oversized to cope with a high fouling resistance may overprocess food when it is clean; control systems must cope with the changes that occur during a process run.

Mathematically, the rate of fouling is commonly expressed as a balance between deposition and removal processes:

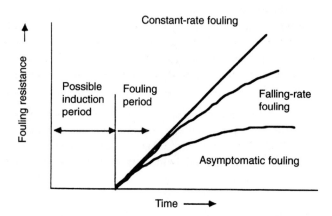

Fig. 9.11 The types of fouling curve found in practice.

$$\frac{dR_f}{dt} = \phi_d - \phi_r \tag{9.43}$$

To operate process plant it is obviously important to be able to predict the rate and severity of fouling in a given environment: that is, the deposition and removal rates ϕ_d and ϕ_r in the above equation. Most research in the food area has been done on milk, a model system of relevance to many areas of food processing; much less information is available on other systems of industrial importance. Even for milk, results are sometimes contradictory, and milk fouling has been found to vary with the time of the year, the age and pH of the milk and the lactation stage of the cow, as well as with the pretreatment that the milk has received.

Some basic characteristics of the fouling process can be inferred from observation of industrial plant. That fouling is **temperature-** and **concentration-dependent** is demonstrated by multiple-effect evaporators: fouling is concentrated in the first effect, where the temperature is highest, and in the last, where the liquid is most concentrated. **Velocity dependence** is shown by individual tubes in multitube evaporators, which can clog solid with deposit. If small amounts of deposit form in an individual tube, the flow through that tube will be reduced, resulting in increased deposition and eventually in total blockage. Multitube evaporators thus foul by having most of the tubes clean and a few blocked solid.

The study of fouling has a number of aims: to interpret experimental data in terms of basic mechanisms; to develop operating procedures that minimize fouling; and to develop new types of heat exchanger. Some model for the reactions that give rise to fouling is required. It is common in process engineering to consider the sequence of steps that give rise to a final effect, such as in the construction of an overall heat transfer coefficient from individual film coefficients. The end result of fouling is the deposition of solids on the heat transfer surface. Fouling from foods may result from a combination of diffusion and reaction steps. The material that becomes fouling deposit will either be generated in the bulk and then transferred to the surface, or its precursor will be transported from the bulk to the surface, where reactions that produce the deposit will take place. The process will be at least a two-stage one: diffusion to the surface followed by reaction on it, as shown in Fig. 9.12. The flux of foulant N will be given both by

$$N = k(c_b - c_i) \tag{9.44}$$

where k is a mass transfer coefficient and c_b and c_i are the bulk and interfacial concentrations of foulant respectively, and by the surface reaction rate

$$N = k_r c_i \tag{9.45}$$

if the reaction is first order, where k_r is a reaction rate constant (a strong Arrhenius function of temperature, not a function of flow conditions). The

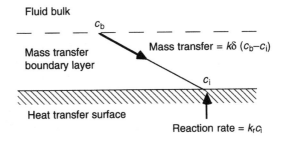

Fig. 9.12 Schematic diagram of consecutive mass transfer and reaction steps in fouling.

overall rate can be found by combination of the two equations to eliminate the unknown interfacial concentration:

$$N = \frac{c_b}{1/k_r + 1/k} \tag{9.46}$$

Depending on the relative magnitude of the mass transfer and reaction coefficients, fouling can be controlled either by mass transfer or by surface reaction. The mass transfer coefficient will be a strong function of the flow conditions, but is less affected by temperature, while the rate of any reaction will be an Arrhenius function of temperature but not a function of the flowrate. Although this analysis is a simple one, it shows how the net rate of fouling may thus depend on either or both of the temperature or flowrate.

9.3.2 The chemistry of fouling

The fouling from milk can be used as an example of food fouling processes. Reflecting its industrial importance, fouling from milk fluids has been studied by a number of workers. Two types of deposit from milk fluids are found, as follows.

- **Type A** or **milk film**: found at temperatures below 110°C, this deposit is creamy and white, and consists of 50–60% protein and 30–35% minerals.
- **Type B** or **milk stone**: found at temperatures above 110°C, this consists of 15–20% protein and up to 70% minerals.

Deposition results from the degradation of thermally unstable components of the fluid, milk proteins and calcium phosphate. Calcium phosphate becomes less soluble with increasing temperature and thus will precipitate out onto heated surfaces to form a mineral scale. On heating whey proteins, denaturation and aggregation reactions can occur. Denaturation describes the unfolding of the complex three-dimensional shape of the protein chain, which thus loses the activity that it normally possesses as a result of its shape. This process may be reversible; however, if reactive groups are exposed in denaturation, individual strands can polymerize in an irreversible reaction to give insoluble aggregates. Figure 9.13 shows an electron micrograph of a section of deposit, which is composed of a mixture of deposited mineral salts and aggregated proteins. The most thermally labile milk protein, β-lactoglobulin, makes up only 10% of raw milk protein but up to half of the protein content of type A deposit. At higher temperatures, a similar process occurs. In type B deposit, the amount of calcium phosphate in the deposit is higher because the saturation concentration is lower, and different proteins deposit, including some casein fragments.

The thermal behaviour of β-lactoglobulin is complex; it is shown schematically in Fig. 9.14. On heating to about 70 °C, the protein structure partially unfolds in molecular denaturation. This exposes reactive

Fig. 9.13 SEM image of a fouling deposit. (Reproduced from Belmar-Beiny and Fryer, 1993.)

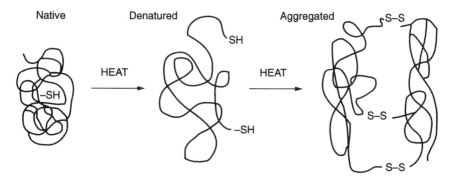

Fig. 9.14 The thermal behaviour of β-lactoglobulin.

sulphydryl groups, which are normally concealed within the core of the protein. Groups in different denatured molecules can then react to form large polymerized and eventually insoluble protein aggregates; this process happens rapidly above about 74 °C. The link between protein denaturation and aggregation and fouling is well established; addition of a sulphydryl oxidizing agent, which makes it impossible for aggregates to form, reduces the amount of deposit formed.

The change in fouling with pH suggests that protein aggregation, rather than denaturation, is the controlling process in type A fouling. Denaturation of β-lactoglobulin increases above pH 6.25, but fouling in pasteurization and UHT plants increases rapidly below pH 6.6. If β-lactoglobulin denaturation were the limiting step, fouling should increase at higher pH, but the reverse is true. However, β-lactoglobulin aggregation increases significantly below pH 6.0, reflecting increased molecular unfolding during denaturation at this pH, resulting in increased disulphide exchange reactions. Although the **rate** of β-lactoglobulin denaturation increases above pH 6.5, the amount of molecular unfolding associated with denaturation is reduced, decreasing the concentration of free sulphydryl groups. This prevents intermolecular disulphide exchange reactions, and thus aggregation. Below pH 6.5, although the denaturation rate is slow, it results in a high concentration of sulphydryl groups, and rapid aggregation. Although denaturation is necessary for fouling to occur, the stage which directly leads to the formation of deposit thus appears to be the formation of insoluble aggregates.

Protein aggregates will be formed wherever the temperature is hot enough, and yet induction periods of several hours can be found in industrial plant before the effect of fouling is noticed. Some of this is due to the fact that the fouling resistance will be initially small and will make little change in the overall heat transfer coefficient, but it is likely that some conditioning of the surface must occur before heavy fouling can take place.

Experimental results thus imply that the fouling process is two-stage.

1. The **induction period**, during which little change in heat transfer coefficient takes place, corresponds to the time taken to condition the surface or a region of it so that formation of heavy deposit can begin.
2. The **fouling period** starts when the surface is conditioned so that rapid fouling can begin.

This model reflects the types of deposit formed in commercial milk processing. Different deposits will be found in different situations. When faced with a fouling problem, analysis of the deposit should first be conducted, to determine which components of the food material are causing the problem. The next step is to determine where the processes which result in fouling are taking place.

9.3.3 Fouling as a problem in reaction engineering

Section 9.3.2 has shown that the chemistry of the fouling process is fairly well understood. To the process engineer, an understanding of the chemistry of the process is insufficient; it is necessary to know where the controlling reaction takes place, and what can be done to reduce its effects. It is not easy to determine basic mechanisms from experiments on industrial plant. Practical equipment such as plate heat exchangers contains a range of different temperatures and surface shear stresses, which will give different local fouling rates: so the fouling resistance measured in such plant will be a composite of these different rates. This section describes some laboratory experiments to elucidate fouling mechanisms.

Induction period. If the processes that control the first layer of deposition are known, it might be possible to modify the surface to resist fouling. When the final deposit, of the type of Fig. 9.13, is analysed, a thin film of calcium phosphate (less than 20 μm) can be seen next to the heat transfer surface. On top of this layer is a much thicker layer of protein aggregates, sometimes clustered around crystalline protrusions from the mineral layer. This might suggest that minerals are the first species to be deposited. However, if experiments are carried out over much shorter periods, it can be seen that proteins are the first layer to be absorbed. Figure 9.15 shows the XPS spectra obtained for unfouled and fouled stainless steel with a contact time of 40 s. XPS (X-ray photoelection spectroscopy) is a technique that measures the presence of particular atoms. Figure 9.15(a) gives the basic spectrum of the steel; after contact with fluid for only 40 s, no stainless steel peaks remain, showing that the surface has become covered. No peaks corresponding to calcium or phosphorus can be found; the surface becomes covered with a smooth layer of protein. Electron micrographs of the surface show that protein aggregates are not seen until after a longer period, as in Fig. 9.16. It seems likely that the layer of calcium phosphate found on the surface after extended periods of time is caused by diffusion of the material through the deposit after it has formed, i.e. that ageing of the deposit changes its local composition.

Fouling period. From the two-stage model above it is clear that the rate of fouling could be controlled by diffusion or wall processes. If it is assumed that deposition results from a combination of mass transfer and chemical reactions, in any situation one of these processes – the slowest – will be the rate-controlling step. Using the simple ideas developed in earlier chapters, we can develop a possible mechanism for fouling.

Fouling may be **mass-transfer controlled**: that is, the transfer of reacted protein to the wall may be the slowest step. Here, deposit formation will not be a strong function of temperature. However, if the process is **reaction-**

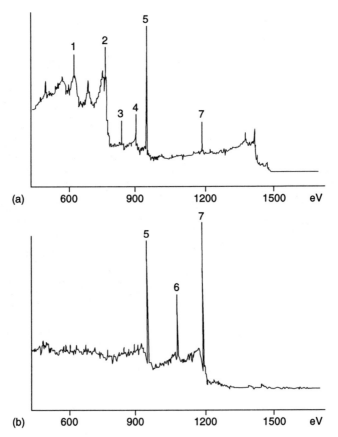

Fig. 9.15 XPS spectra on stainless steel surfaces (AISI 321): (a) clean surface; (b) surface fouled with whey protein concentrate for 4s. Temperatures: inlet, 73 °C; outlet, 75 °C; wall 96 °C. Main characteristic peaks: 1, Fe_{Auger}; 2, Fe_{2P}; 3, Ni_{Auger}; 4, Cr_{2P}; 5, O_{1s}; 6, N_{1s}; 7, C_{1s}; 8, S_{2p}. (Reproduced from Belmar-Beiny and Fryer, 1993.)

controlled, deposition will be a function of wall or bulk temperature, depending on where the controlling reaction takes place. Chapter 3 has described the film model of a turbulent flow, in which the rate of heat transfer is modelled by conduction through a fluid thermal boundary layer that is near the wall temperature. Any reaction controlling it could take place in two possible places and in three different ways, as follows.

1. **Surface reaction**. If fouling is controlled only by surface processes, deposition will occur wherever the surface temperature is high enough for protein denaturation and aggregation to occur. The fouling rate will be a function of surface rather than bulk temperature.
2. **Bulk reaction**. If the controlling reaction for fouling takes place in the fluid bulk, then two cases can be envisaged.

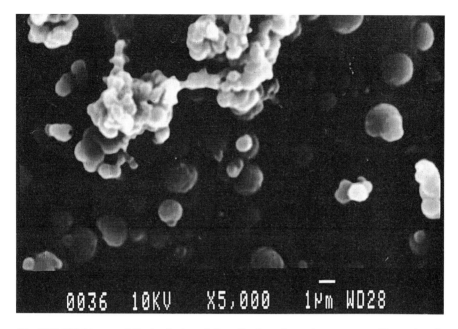

Fig. 9.16 SEM image of the beginning of the adhesion of protein aggregates. (Reproduced from Belmar-Beiny and Fryer, 1993.)

(a) If the wall and bulk temperatures are such that protein denaturation and aggregation will occur at the wall but not in the bulk, fouling will only result from deposition of protein that has denatured and aggregated in the **thermal boundary layer** adjacent to the wall.

(b) If both the boundary layer and the **turbulent core** are hot enough for protein denaturation and aggregation, protein denatured and aggregated in both regions will contribute to deposit formation.

If a surface reaction is responsible for fouling, the amount should depend only on the wall temperature. If bulk processes contribute, then the amount of fouling should increase when the fluid bulk becomes hot enough to produce denatured and aggregated protein.

Figure 9.17 shows the result of experiments showing the initial rate of fouling for a system corresponding to case 2(a). The rate of fouling is temperature-dependent, showing an activation energy of about 90 kJ mol^{-1}, but decreases with increasing Re. The rate law for the initial rate of fouling was correlated as

$$\frac{dR_F}{dt} = \frac{k}{Re} \exp\left(\frac{-E}{RT_w}\right) \qquad (9.47)$$

where Re is the fluid Reynolds number and T_w is the wall temperature. An equation of this form can be obtained if the variation of the thickness of the

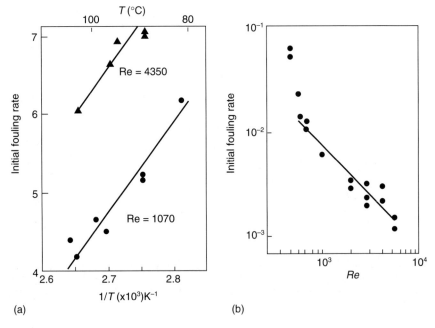

Fig. 9.17 (a) Temperature and (b) flow dependence of the initial rate of fouling for a wall temperature of about 90 °C and bulk temperature constantly below 65 °C. Fouling rate is dBi/dt; dimensionless.

thermal boundary layer of the fluid is considered as a reactor at the temperature of the heat transfer surface. Further evidence for the involvement of bulk processes comes from experiments such as that shown in Fig. 9.18, where the wall temperature is constant and above the aggregation temperature, and the bulk fluid is below the temperature at inlet and above it at outlet. When the bulk temperature exceeds the point where aggregation occurs significantly, an increase in deposition results.

Although the final step in the fouling process is the adhesion of aggregates to the wall, the fouling rate is critically influenced by the generation of denatured and aggregated protein in the bulk of the fluid: that is, c_b in equation (9.46) is the concentration of reacted rather than native protein. In many industrial situations the temperature difference between the wall and the bulk is small and this effect might be obscured.

9.3.4   Implications of the fouling model

The above experiments have demonstrated the controlling mechanisms. Fouling results from a series of processes:

1. deposition of proteins on the clean surface to give an initial layer; when nucleation sites are available,

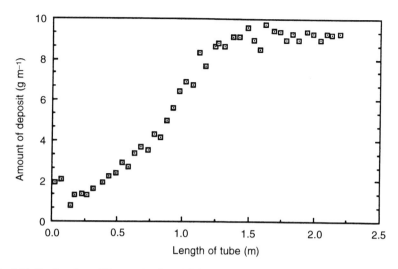

Fig. 9.18 Fouling from 1% protein: $Re = 7500$; protein inlet $73\,°C$ and outlet $83\,°C$; oil inlet $97\,°C$ and outlet $95\,°C$. Fluid enters below the temperature at which β-lactoglobulin thermal instability is significant, and leaves above that temperature.

2. deposition of proteins that have reacted in the hot region of the fluid, either the bulk of the fluid or the wall layer, can occur.

The mechanistic model can be used to examine industrial heat exchangers. Equipment should be designed to reduce adhesion, avoid high temperatures, and minimize surface fluid residence times.

- **Reduce adhesion.** Fouling is reduced by high surface shear stresses and smooth surfaces, which do not contain crevices in which deposition can start. Good hygienic design (that is, providing no points where microbial contamination can occur) will thus reduce fouling. Once the heat transfer surface is covered with a layer of protein, fouling on different types of surfaces will be the same; this is found in practice.
- **Avoid high temperatures.** The formation of denatured and aggregated protein depends only on the fluid temperature, but salt deposition depends on the difference between wall and bulk temperatures: that is, on the amount by which the salt is supersaturated at the surface. Fouling thus depends on both T_w and T_b: low temperature differences between bulk and wall will reduce salt formation, and low temperatures will reduce protein aggregation.
- **Minimize surface fluid residence times.** Surface bonding of proteins to the wall will take a finite time. If the residence time of fluid at the wall is kept low, by high turbulence or good mixing, the chance of adhesion will be reduced. However, if the surface reaction is rapid, and mass transfer controls deposition, increasing mixing may enhance fouling by increasing k_m in equation (9.46). Some plate heat exchangers contain points of

contact between plates; these will be low-shear regions, and are generally the points at which fouling begins.

Fouling models can also be used in the design of process plant. To do this, a computer model of the flow and temperature profiles in the heat exchanger is needed, together with a model for the kinetics of fouling as a function of process variables. Such models are not available as yet. Under these circumstance it might be possible to model fouling using an equation of the type

$$\frac{dR_f}{dt} = k_d \exp\left(-E/RT_w\right) - k_r \tau R_f \tag{9.48}$$

where both constants k_d and k_r are functions of process variables such as surface shear stress. The direct dependence of the removal rate on the surface shear stress has been noted in a number of fouling experiments.

9.3.5 Cleaning fouled surfaces

In commercial practice, fouling must be lived with. Once a deposit has formed it must be removed, and this requires frequent and expensive cleaning. Cleaning involves several types of cost, of which the actual cost of cleaning chemical may not be the most severe; the production time lost both during cleaning and in preparing for it may be the most expensive loss in a plant designed for continuous operation.

Current cleaning techniques are largely empirical. This is largely due to the poorly understood nature of fouling; before cleaning can be optimized, it is necessary to understand both the nature of the deposit that is to be removed and the processes that give rise to it. Cleaning is necessary both to remove fouled deposit and to control possible contamination from microorganisms. The limit on the operation of a plant is generally the pressure drop through the system due to deposition; a plant is operated until fouling is so severe that it is no longer possible to maintain full flowrate through the equipment. If the plant is operated until the pressure drop is too great for the pumping capacity of the unit, the resulting fouling deposit is very difficult to remove. It may be that operation for a shorter period, producing a deposit that takes a shorter time to remove, would give higher overall production. Such calculations are difficult to do, and are rarely if ever done in practice; cleaning cycles either arise through trial and error or, more frequently, are arranged to fit in with existing shift patterns.

Industrial cleaning-in-place systems are highly developed and automated. Two types of chemical treatment are used.

- **Two-stage acid and alkali cleaners**: typically sodium hydroxide and nitric acid are used. Their use reflects the structure of the fouled deposit described in section 9.3.2; the alkali is added first to remove the protein deposit and expose the thin mineral layer, which is then dissolved by the acid.

- **Single-stage commercial cleaners**, usually detergent based, and which contain surface-active agents to increase the wetting properties of the solution, decrease its surface tension and emulsify and disperse soil. Chelating agents may also be used to maintain removed material in solution.

Two-stage cleaners are more complex to use in practice, requiring extra dosage equipment and more rinsing steps, which are not needed by single-stage cleaners. Although two-stage alkali and acid sequences are designed to cope with organic and inorganic soils, caustic and acid alone have been shown to be insufficient to achieve a completely physically and chemically clean surface. It is, of course, difficult to define 'clean': in an engineering sense, a surface is clean if its subsequent fouling behaviour is indistinguishable from a surface that has never been used before. If material is left on a surface after cleaning it may provide nucleation sites for future deposition of protein aggregates.

Single-stage cleaners have been developed to produce a clean surface in a short time. Although they are more expensive than base chemicals, they are more efficient under most circumstances. A cleaner surface than is possible using caustic and acid alone can be obtained, together with savings in time, wash water, and energy. Comparisons of single- and double-stage cleaners do not, however, agree on which is most economic.

9.3.6 Stages and kinetics of cleaning

Cleaning is a multistage process. A soiled system consists of three phases: the **heat transfer surface**, the **deposit** and the **cleaning solution** (Fig. 9.19). Cleaning agent:

1. contacts the surface of the material to be removed;
2. wets and penetrates the deposit;
3. reacts and breaks down the deposited material; and
4. disperses the material into the cleaning solution.

Cleaning thus involves processes that are governed by mass transfer (stages 1 and 4) diffusion (stage 2) and reaction (stage 3), any of which could control the overall rate of the process. Problems with any step will result in a deposit which is difficult to clean, as follows.

- Mass transfer from the cleaning solution in low-shear areas – such as points of contact between exchanger plates – will be slow. This will limit both contact and dispersal.
- Non-wetting deposit surfaces will resist the cleaning solution.
- Cleaning material will diffuse only slowly through hard non-porous

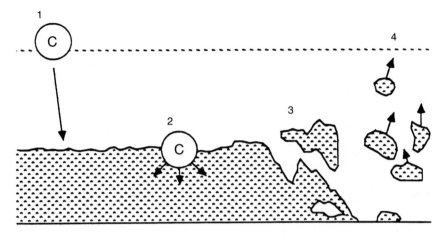

Fig. 9.19 Stages of cleaning: (1) mass transfer to the deposit; (2) penetration and wetting; (3) reaction to loosen deposit; (4) dispersal into fluid bulk.

deposit, such as the largely carbonized deposit that forms by overcooking.

• Some forms of deposit, again perhaps produced by overcooking, may be resistant to chemical attack; the reaction step will be slow.

The fouling model predicts that severe fouling will be found in low-shear areas; it is thus doubly important to ensure their absence.

Various kinetic models have been proposed for cleaning, but they have largely been produced by experiments on the cleaning of large systems, which contain a range of deposit types and thicknesses. These results are difficult to interpret kinetically. Figure 9.20 shows an electron micrograph of the cleaning, by sodium hydroxide, of a surface that has been fouled by whey protein concentrate; by comparison with the deposit seen in Fig. 9.13, a much more open structure can be seen. Deposit behaviour during cleaning from sodium hydroxide has also been observed visually. At time $t = 0$, sodium hydroxide contacts the deposit and weakly bound material is removed immediately. Over the next 5–20s the surface of the deposit swells and becomes translucent. Over the next 10min, the thickness of the translucent layer increases and the surface gradually breaks up, with aggregates about 0.1–0.2mm detaching from the surface and being swept away. This suggests that removal of protein deposit by hydroxyl ions takes place in several stages:

1. contact between hydroxyl and deposit;
2. diffusion of hydroxyl through sponge to unreacted deposit;
3. reaction of hydroxyl ions with deposit to create an expanded deposit;

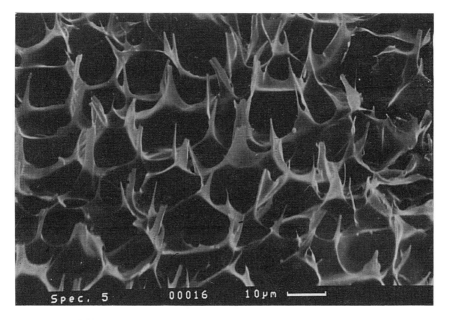

Fig. 9.20 Fouled surface that has been contacted with sodium hydroxide.

4. removal of this expanded deposit by fluid shear and by chemical reaction.

Figure 9.21 shows a typical cleaning curve for a whey protein deposit cleaned by sodium hydroxide. There is a delay before cleaning begins, presumably due to the time required for hydroxyl to diffuse into the deposit. The cleaning rate then builds up steeply, before falling to zero as deposit is removed. Cleaning rates vary as a function of temperature, flowrate and cleaning chemical concentration. Removal rate increase substantially at temperatures above 50 °C, suggesting that chemical reactions are taking place. Removal rate also increases as the flowrate increases. The effect of concentration is the most interesting result. Figure 9.22 shows a plot of the cleaning time for the same deposit as a function of the cleaning chemical concentration. An optimal concentration of cleaning chemical can be seen; the rate of removal of deposit for both 0% and 2% sodium hydroxide is much less than for 0.5% hydroxide. It appears that too high a concentration of cleaning chemical can seal the surface and prevent removal. This effect has been found for both whey protein concentrates and whole milk deposits. Industrially it suggests that the addition of extra cleaning chemical to cope with difficult deposit may increase the cleaning time rather than having the desired effect; increasing the temperature at which cleaning is carried out may prove more effective.

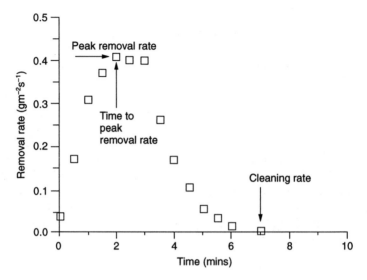

Fig. 9.21 Typical plot of protein removal as a function of time.

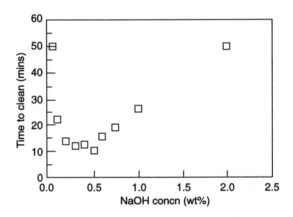

Fig. 9.22 The variation of cleaning time with cleaning agent concentration.

9.3.7 Control: monitoring fouling and cleaning

The above sections have described fouling and cleaning mechanisms. Both processes are complex and involve several stages. Unlike the sterilization and quality processes described earlier in this chapter, mathematical models are not available; this limits the optimization of process designs.

Until accurate kinetic data are available, the best way to ensure that plant is operated at peak efficiency is to monitor the plant and control it correctly. Very few plants are instrumented well enough to detect fouling until it is large enough to affect outlet temperature or pressure drop to a significant extent. Any monitor developed should be cheap and small enough to be easily serviced and replaced but, above all, reliable and relevant enough for the information it provides to be acted on by plant operators.

Two types of measurement are required. In the latter stages of fouling it is sufficient to measure heat transfer and pressure drop across the whole plant. However, more subtle measurements are required in the early stages of fouling and the last stages of cleaning. Detecting fouling directly is difficult, especially in its early stages. Pressure sensors are least sensitive to the very small initial and final amounts of deposit. It is important to remove all deposit during cleaning or it will act as nucleation sites for fresh deposition when the plant is restarted. At this stage, it is not possible to propose a general approach to ensuring that optimal operating cycles are chosen; process plant must be monitored closely and operated in accordance with the principles described above.

Conclusions

Thermal processing is at the heart of the food industry, and this chapter returned to the subject, following our earlier incursions into energy balances, the analysis and design of heat exchangers and heat integration. As well as drawing on those chapters the discussion here also built on some of the elements discussed in the chapters on mass transfer and reaction engineering.

Several topics which are specific to the food industry and which are not covered in existing texts were touched on. The first section was mainly concerned with how to design batch thermal processes so as to simultaneously achieve the desired level of sterilization and an acceptable level of product quality. The discussion then moved on to some specific engineering problems in the design and operation of continuous processes; this included a discussion of the importance of the residence time distribution (described in the previous chapter) for process operation and a number of other important issues in the selection and heat transfer equipment.

Another section was concerned with the important operations involving mixtures of fluids and solids, where the classical chemical engineering texts have little that is directly relevant to offer: the discussion here touched on aspects of flow and heat transfer behaviour and of modelling of these systems, including microwave and ohmic heating processes.

The final section was concerned with fouling in thermal food processes, and outlined some recent results on the mechanisms of fouling together with a discussion of the significance of fouling for quantitative process design. The results presented here apply only to one particular case, but, as throughout this book, the principles are of general use.

References and further reading

Bird, M.R. and Fryer, P.J. (1991) An experimental study of the cleaning of surfaces fouled by whey proteins. *Transactions of the Institution of Chemical Engineers C*, **69**, 13–21.

Belmar-Beiny, M.T. and Fryer, P.J. (1993) A study of the sequence of events in milk thermal fouling. *Journal of Dairy Research*, **60**, 467–483.

Burton, H. (1988) *Ultra-High-Temperature Processing of Milk and Milk Products*, Elsevier.

Corrieu, G., Lalande, M. and Ferret, F. (1988) Online measurement of fouling and cleaning of industrial plant, in *Fouling Science and Technology* (eds L.F. Melo, T.R. Bott and C.A. Bernardo), NATO ASI E 145, Kluwer, pp. 575–590.

de Alwis, A.A.P., Halden, K. and Fryer, P.J. (1989) Shape and conductivity effects in the ohmic heating of foods. *Chemical Engineering Research and Design*, **67**(3), 159–168.

Fellows, P. (1988) *Food Processing Technology*, Ellis Horwood, Chichester.

Frazier, W.C. and Westhoff, D.C. (1988) *Food Microbiology*, McGraw-Hill.

Fryer P.J., Belmar-Beiny, M.T. and Schreier, P.J.R. (1995) Fouling and Cleaning in Milk Processing, in *Heat-Induced Changes in Milk*, 2nd edn (ed. P.F. Fox), IDF, Brussels.

Gould, G.W. (1995) *New Methods of Food Preservation*, Blackie, Glasgow.

Hallström, B., Skjölderbrand, C. and Trägårdh, C. (1988) *Heat Transfer and Food Products*, Elsevier.

Holdsworth, S.D. (1993) *Aseptic Processing and Packaging of Food Products*, Elsevier, London.

Knudsen, J.G. and Somerscales, E.F.C. (1981) *Fouling of Heat Exchangers*, McGraw-Hill.

Melo, L.F., Bott, T.R. and Bernardo, C.A. (1988) *Fouling Science and Technology*, NATO ASI E 145, Kluwer, Amsterdam.

Rene, F., Leuliet, J.C. and Lalande, M. (1991) Heat transfer to Newtonian and non-Newtonian fluids in plate heat exchangers: Experimental and numerical approaches. *Transactions of the Institution of Chemical Engineers C*, **69**, 115–126.

Zhang, L. and Fryer, P.J. (1994) Food sterilization by electrical heating: sensitivity to process parameters. *American Institution of Chemical Engineers Journal*, **40**, 888–898.

10   Mixing in food processing
C.D. RIELLY

Introduction

Mixing is fundamental to food processing operations, such as in the preparation of ingredients, the addition of solids to liquids and the development of structure and incorporation of air in the dough mixing process. Chapters 2 and 5 have described the basics of fluid mechanics and of food rheology. Rheology is crucial in mixing; it is obviously more straightforward to mix a fluid such as water than it is to ensure the homogeneity of a highly viscous and non-Newtonian fluid such as a starch solution.

This chapter describes the types of equipment used to carry out a number of different types of mixing process and the principles used to define the extent of mixing. Different types of system are required for the different requirements of the food industry, for example:

- **gas–liquid mixing:** ensuring that enough air is mixed into a fermenter liquid to ensure microbial growth is not oxygen-limited;
- **liquid–liquid mixing:** the creation of liquid–liquid emulsions is central to the manufacture of margarines and spreads;
- **solid–liquid mixing:** the addition of solids to liquids is involved in the reconstitution of fluids, such as when tea or coffee solids are added to hot water. The addition of liquids to solids is key to the production of many food batters, pastes and doughs.

The ideas of dynamic similarity developed in Chapter 2 are critical here in attempting to scale up mixers; it is important to select the right criteria by which mixers are scaled in practice, otherwise large scale systems may not perform as effectively as would be predicted from small-scale tests.

10.1   Fundamentals of mixing

10.1.1   Mixing processes

Mixing operations occur widely throughout the food processing industries. Mixing is used to bring about a physical or chemical change in the materials

Chemical Engineering for the Food Industry. Edited by P.J. Fryer, D.L. Pyle and C.D. Rielly. Published in 1997 by Blackie A & P, an imprint of Chapman & Hall, London. ISBN 0 412 49500 7

being processed: rates of heat and mass transfer are much improved by agitation; the energy input through mixing may be used to blend materials, giving new physical and rheological properties; agitation may be used to disperse multiphase or multicomponent mixtures, prior to further process-ing or packaging; and chemical reaction rates may be increased by ensuring that the reactants are well mixed and in intimate contact. An application that is peculiar to the food industry is the development of structure by the action of mixing: for example, in dough making, shear and extensional forces generated by the mixer may be used to develop the flour and water into a viscoelastic protein matrix that is capable of retaining the gas pro-duced during proving and baking. Other examples of structured fluids produced by mixing are creams, butters and margarines; in each of these materials the flow field generated by the mixer is used to disperse one liquid phase in another and so form a stable emulsion, which has the required physical, rheological and organoleptic properties.

This chapter follows the conventional chemical engineering approach of identifying similar physical processes and studying them in a unified man-ner: the processes described here are liquid blending, gas–liquid dispersion, emulsification, solids suspension and dissolution. Qualitative descriptions of mixing mechanisms are presented, along with a discussion of design methods; in many operations the design methods are only approximate and caution should always be exercised in applying these techniques. The dis-cussion in 10.1.2 is equally applicable to either fluid or solids mixtures. The discussion in subsequent sections concentrates on fluid-mixing processes, although solid–solid mixers are described in section 10.10.

10.1.2   The importance of the scale of scrutiny

Assessment of the quality of any mixture depends on how closely the mixture is scrutinized. Consider Fig. 10.1, which shows a mixture of black and white particles, regularly arranged. The first grey square appears well mixed and homogeneous, but as it is increasingly magnified, distinct regions of black and white appear. At each magnification stage a smaller volume of the mixture is scrutinized, until the mixture appears completely segregated. In the last square, at the highest magnification (the smallest scale of scrutiny is of the order of the particle size) the mixture appears to be completely segregated: the composition varies from point to point, but not in a smooth manner. Clearly, any definition of 'mixedness' needs to include a statement about the scale on which the mixture is examined and this in turn must depend on the end use for that mixture.

Danckwerts (1953) defined the scale of scrutiny of a mixture as 'the maximum size of regions of segregation which would cause it to be regarded as unmixed'. For instance, in production of home cake mixes, the propor-tion of ingredients should be the same in each packet: that is, the important

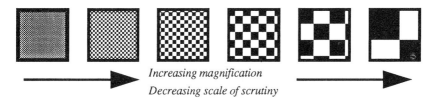

Increasing magnification
Decreasing scale of scrutiny

Fig. 10.1 The effect on the mixture appearance of changing the scale of scrutiny.

scale of scrutiny is the size of one packet, and there is no need to ensure homogeneity at a smaller scale. However, when the customer bakes a cake from such a packet, the contents must be mixed on a much finer scale, so that differences in texture or composition cannot be detected by the palate. The scale of scrutiny in the latter case is of the order of one mouthful, but probably less since chemical reactions during baking depend on the homogeneity of the mixture.

The cake mix is an example of a coarse-grained mixture, which consists of a randomization of particles, each of which may be distinguished by the eye. In fine-grain mixtures (such as smoke in air, or a mixture of miscible liquids, such as sugar syrups in water) the composition appears to vary smoothly from point to point. Here, two quantities are required to describe the mixture: the scale of segregation and the intensity of segregation. The **scale of segregation** is a measure of the size of 'clumps' of unmixed components in an imperfect mixture, while the **intensity of segregation** is a measure of the difference in composition from the mean, averaged over all points in the mixture. The latter does not depend on the size of the 'clumps' but rather on the extent to which interdiffusion between components of the mixture has taken place. Figure 10.2 shows schematically the effect of changing the scale and intensity of segregation. As the scale of segregation decreases, the size of the dark regions is reduced; however, as the intensity of segregation decreases, the mixture becomes increasingly diffuse. As the perfectly mixed state is approached both of these quantities tend towards zero. The degree to which these two parameters must be reduced depends on the required scale of scrutiny of the mixture, which in turn depends on the end use for that mixture. It will be seen in the following sections that where diffusional processes are slow or do not exist, then the mixer should be designed to reduce the length scale of segregation to an acceptably small level (for example, in laminar mixing or with coarse solids). In this case the mixture remains segregated at a scale of scrutiny less than the length scale of segregation.

Danckwerts (1953) formally defined the scale and intensity of segregation for a mixture of components A and B in terms of their average and root mean square fluctuating concentrations and correlation functions. In prac-

Decreasing scale of segregation

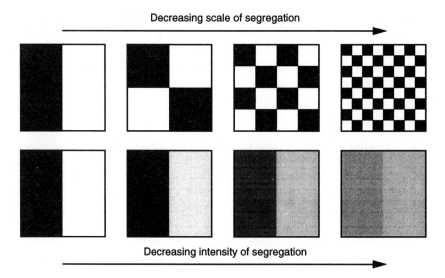

Decreasing intensity of segregation

Fig. 10.2 The effects of scale and intensity of segregation on mixedness (adapted from Poux *et al.*, 1991).

tice these quantities are not easy to measure as they require concentration data from a large number of points within the mixture. However, they do provide a sound basis for describing the quality of a mixture and are useful concepts for understanding the way in which fluid or solid mixtures approach a state of homogeneity.

10.1.3   *Flow regimes for fluid mixer operations*

The flow regimes for fluid mixing may be divided into **laminar** and **turbulent** regions. In a stirred tank, this depends on the impeller Reynolds number, defined as

$$Re = \frac{\rho_L N D^2}{\mu_L} \tag{10.1}$$

In equation (10.1), N is the impeller speed (revolutions per second), D is the impeller diameter, ρ_L is the liquid density and μ_L is the viscosity. In both of these regimes mixing takes place by convective transport of material throughout the mixer and by high shear dispersion in local regions of the mixer close to the moving blades. In the turbulent regime, mixing rates are much enhanced by turbulent diffusion. Molecular diffusion also operates in both regimes and is ultimately responsible for molecular scale homogeneity: that is, at a length scale very much smaller than the typical scale of scrutiny. Molecular diffusion is a slow process, even in low-viscosity systems, and is only effective over very long times, or at very short length scales. In studies of macro-mixing phenomena (mixing at length scales very much larger than the molecular scale) it is often legitimate to ignore the effects of molecular diffusion, except close to the point of 'perfect' homogeneity.

10.1.4   Laminar mixing mechanisms

The fully laminar flow regime is usually restricted to impeller Reynolds numbers, $Re < 10$. Under typical operating conditions this can only be achieved using liquids with viscosities greater than about 10 Pa s.

In low Reynolds number flows, viscous effects dominate over inertial effects so, to provide adequate agitation, the impeller should sweep through as much of the vessel volume as possible. The regions close to the moving blade have large velocity gradients and high shear rates, where stretching and elongation of fluid elements takes place (see Figs 10.3 and 10.4). Con-

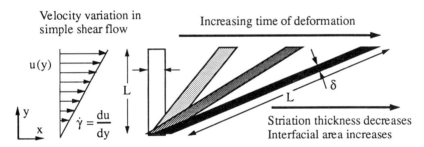

Fig. 10.3 Thinning of fluid elements in a simple laminar shear flow. The initial element is shown in white; the deformed element, at later times, is shown with an increasing depth of grey. The thickness of the element is progressively reduced, whereas its interfacial area (or length) increases with increasing time.

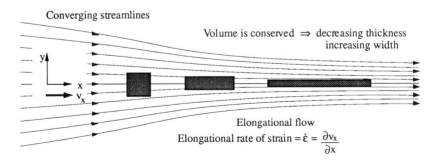

Fig. 10.4 Thinning of fluid elements in an extensional (accelerating) flow.

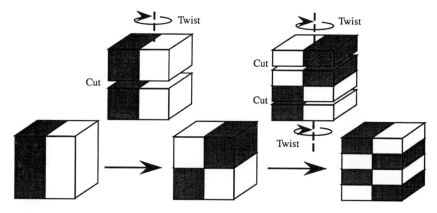

Fig. 10.5 Distributive mixing by repeated cutting and twisting operations.

sider the deformation of a shaded fluid element in these simple flow fields. With increasing duration within the shear or elongational flow the thickness of the element decreases and the material becomes better mixed. If the effects of molecular diffusion are ignored, then the 'interface' between the shaded fluid and the bulk remains sharp. The change in this interfacial area or in the thickness of the element (the striation thickness) may be used as a measure of the degree of mixing that has been achieved.

These effects are most intense near the blades of the mixer. The distorted fluid elements are convected into the bulk flow, where they are reoriented before passing once more through the region of high shear or accelerated flow. The continual process of stretching and thinning, followed by convective mixing and reorientation in the bulk, gradually reduces the striation thickness of fluid elements and increases the homogeneity of the tank contents. Molecular diffusion is required to bring about homogeneity on a molecular scale, but this is a very slow process in viscous liquids and typically the criterion for mixer design is to reduce average striation thickness until inhomogeneities are not visible at the required scale of scrutiny.

In some laminar mixers (such as static mixers, discussed more fully in section 10.9), the mixer blades or elements physically cut and twist the fluid elements and reorientate them in the flow. Figure 10.5 shows the effect of a series of repetitions of these processes: each cutting and rotating operation reduces the striation thickness or scale of segregation, until the required degree of homogeneity is achieved.

10.1.5 Turbulent mixing mechanisms

At high impeller Reynolds numbers, typically $Re > 10^4$, the flow is fully turbulent. Under these conditions inertial effects predominate over viscous effects and the fluid can be pumped by a small diameter impeller to all regions of the tank. A feature of turbulent flow is that transport processes are much enhanced by turbulent eddy diffusion: that is, turbulent velocity fluctuations give much larger mass, heat and momentum transfer rates than for molecular diffusion alone.

Turbulence is not distributed uniformly throughout the vessel; regions close to the impeller have high turbulent energy dissipation rates and hence high values of the turbulent eddy diffusivity. Thus rapid mixing takes place close to the impeller, while less intense mixing occurs in the bulk flow owing to the combined effects of convection, steady shear and turbulent and molecular diffusion. Effective mixers must provide a rapid turnover of the tank contents, so that fluid elements frequently spend time in the regions of intense agitation, where their scale and intensity of segregation are rapidly reduced. The smallest turbulent motions in a stirred tank have length scales (typically of the order of $10\mu m$) much larger than the molecular scale and thus molecular diffusion is still necessary for ultimate homogeneity. In reacting systems the interaction between turbulent mixing and molecular diffusion is important, as molecules of the reacting species must be intimately mixed for significant reaction rates to be achieved. Furthermore, the relative rates of mixing near the molecular scale and chemical kinetics can affect the selectivity of certain reactions.

In both laminar and turbulent regimes there is an input of energy to the liquid that generates flow and mixing and is eventually dissipated as heat by the action of viscosity. The next section describes design methods for estimating the power requirements for mixing.

10.2 Fluid-mixing equipment

10.2.1 Standard geometry stirred tanks

Low-viscosity applications. In chemical processing and particularly in the food industry there is no such thing as a **standard geometry stirred tank**; however, most design information, from experimental studies and plant-scale measurements, exists for the range of geometries given in Table 10.1. Figure 10.6 shows the geometry of stirred tanks and defines the important dimensions. Much research has been carried out on flat-bottomed tanks, despite the fact that the majority of industrial vessels have dished ends (ellipsoidal or torispherical) for ease of fabrication, cleaning and operation at elevated pressures.

Any design engineer would be well advised to work within these ranges, unless there is a specific process requirement that demands a change from the standard design.

Table 10.1 Standard geometric ratios for stirred tanks (low viscosity applications)

Geometric ratio	Typical range of values	Standard geometry
$\dfrac{H}{T}$	1–3	1
$\dfrac{D}{T}$	$\frac{1}{4} - \frac{2}{3}$	$\frac{1}{3}$
$\dfrac{C}{T}$	$\frac{1}{4} - \frac{1}{2}$	$\frac{1}{3}$
$\dfrac{C}{D}$	~1	1
$\dfrac{B}{T}$	$\frac{1}{12} - \frac{1}{10}$	$\frac{1}{10}$

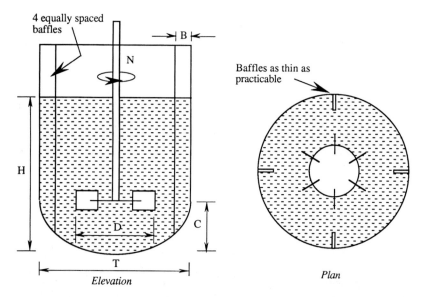

Fig. 10.6 Standard geometry stirred tank (low-viscosity applications).

The tanks may be baffled or unbaffled. More effective mixing is obtained by placing baffles on the tank wall, which generate large axial and radial velocities rather than a purely swirling flow. Full baffling may be achieved using four vertical baffles mounted radially, 90° apart; the baffles should extend to at least the free surface but often have a small clearance from the base of the vessel. For fluid mixing with dispersed solid particles, the baffles may be supported off the wall, leaving a gap of $\sim T/14$. This is designed to prevent build-up of particles in the crevice between the baffles and the wall and to facilitate cleaning. In the food industry, prismatic baffles (with triangular cross-section) with flush welds are often used to eliminated build-up of residues in corners and for ease of cleaning and sterilization.

In low-viscosity liquids, small-diameter impellers (small D/T ratios) are able to generate flow in all parts of the tank at moderate power inputs. The common impeller types are shown in Fig. 10.7; they can be classed according to the type of discharge flow produced (see section 10.2.2 for further details).

Impeller flow type	**Examples**
Radial	flat paddle, disc turbine
Axial	marine propeller
Axial and radial mixed flow	pitched blade turbine, hydrofoil

With aspect ratios (H/T) greater than about 1.5 it is usual to have multiple impellers on the same shaft (each a distance of $\sim 1\text{--}2D$ apart) to give

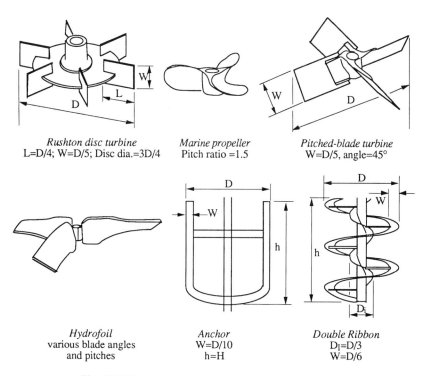

Rushton disc turbine
L=D/4; W=D/5; Disc dia.=3D/4

Marine propeller
Pitch ratio =1.5

Pitched-blade turbine
W=D/5, angle=45°

Hydrofoil
various blade angles
and pitches

Anchor
W=D/10
h=H

Double Ribbon
D$_I$=D/3
W=D/6

Fig. 10.7 Standard geometries for common impeller types.

effective agitation throughout the tank volume. These impellers also have standard geometry designs: for example, a typical width to diameter ratio, W/D, of 1/5 for Rushton disc turbines and mixed-flow pitched-bladed turbines. The standard geometries for a number of common impeller types are shown in Fig. 10.7. A large number of literature measurements have been made on the standard Rushton disc turbine (six-bladed). Formerly this design was regarded as one of the best multipurpose agitators; however, recent research has shown that hydrofoil or pitched-bladed impellers have certain advantages for specific low-viscosity operations (see section 10.2.2). Marine propellers (three-bladed) are also much used, operating at high rotational speeds with low D/T ratios. No 'standard' propeller design has emerged, because of the variety of blade shapes, blade sections and pitch ratios available. For all these designs the typical impeller tip speed would be about $3\,\mathrm{m\,s^{-1}}$ and certainly no more than 4–$5\,\mathrm{m\,s^{-1}}$. High tip speeds cause shear damage to sensitive particulates, cells and structured fluids.

High-viscosity applications.   A great variety of tank and impeller designs are available to suit specific requirements for agitating high-viscosity liquids. Small-diameter impellers, described in the previous section, are only suitable for liquids with viscosities up to $2\,\mathrm{Pa\,s}$ for propellers and $50\,\mathrm{Pa\,s}$ for turbines (Edwards, 1985).

At high viscosities, small impellers only generate significant flows in the vicinity of the blades and are wasteful in their use of power compared with large-diameter paddles. Anchors and helical ribbon impellers are used, which have close clearances between the blades and the wall, and sweep through a large volume of the tank. These features are designed to prevent

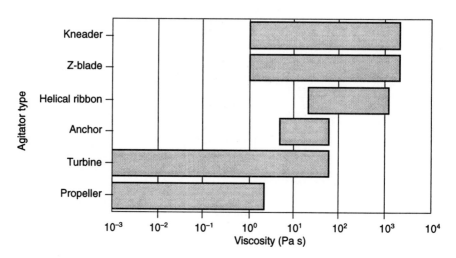

Fig. 10.8 Mixer selection chart for fluid processing.

the formation of stagnant zones within the fluid. Some typical geometries for anchor impellers and helical ribbons are also shown in Fig. 10.7. With viscous liquids these tanks are often unbaffled, as gross vortexing is not a problem. For very high-viscosity mixing applications ($\mu > 1000\,\text{Pa}\,\text{s}$) ribbons are unsuitable and kneaders, Z or sigma blade mixers are used (see section 10.9). Figure 10.8 summarizes this information in a selection chart for mixer types as a function of the viscosity of the fluid to be agitated.

10.2.2 Flow patterns

All small-diameter impellers, rotating at high speed in low-viscosity liquids, in **unbaffled** tanks produce a predominantly tangential swirling flow, with weaker, secondary vertical circulations. Nagata (1975, Ch. 3) presents velocity profiles for a variety of impellers in unbaffled tanks and (Ch. 1) describes a theoretical model for the flow, consisting of a central solid body (forced vortex) region with an outer free vortex. For a full description of forced and free vortex motion see Kay and Nedderman (1985, Ch. 3) Clearly, in the central, solid-body rotation (see Fig. 10.9) there is no relative movement of fluid elements and hence no mixing; in the outer region mixing is only achieved in the tangential direction (secondary vertical circulations, which are not included in the analysis, do not contribute significantly to mixing). At higher impeller speeds the surface vortex extends to the impeller blades and air is entrained. Consequently, unbaffled tanks are not efficient for blending operations. Use of an eccentric impeller improves blending efficiency by preventing the formation of the forced vortex, but

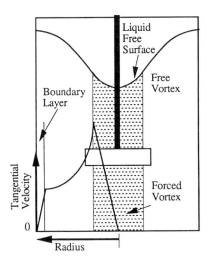

Fig. 10.9 Forced/free vortex rotation in an unbaffled tank.

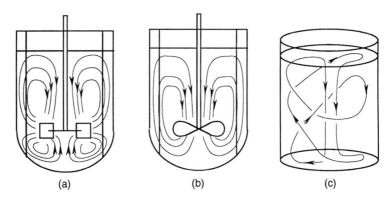

Fig. 10.10 Flow patterns for common impeller types: (a) radial flow pattern (low-viscosity liquids); (b) axial flow pattern by marine impeller (low-viscosity liquids); (c) flow pattern by ribbon mixer (high-viscosity liquids).

also introduces an additional problem that air is entrained from the free surface at low impeller speeds. In some food processes air entrainment is undesirable, as oxidation of vitamins and spoilage may occur during product storage.

Baffling redirects the tangential and radial flow in the impeller discharge stream, generating strong vertical circulations. In baffled tanks, two distinct types of flow may be identified: (a) **radial flow**, as produced by the Rushton disc turbine; and (b) **axial flow**, as produced by the marine propeller. Pitched-bladed turbines generate a **mixed** flow with both axial and radial components in the discharge stream. These common flow patterns are illustrated in Fig. 10.10 (note that there is an additional tangential velocity superimposed on these flows). In addition, these flows exhibit a pseudo-periodicity due to shedding of trailing vortices from the impeller blades; that is, there is an element of unsteadiness in the flows. Clearly these extremely complex, three-dimensional flows are difficult to model theoretically, and so many results are based on experimental observations and simplified physical models.

More modern impeller designs (such as the hydrofoil impeller shown in Fig. 10.7) give various combinations of axial and radial flow, depending on blade shape and pitch. In applications such as blending or particle suspension, the impeller should produce a strong circulating flow, but consume only a small amount of power. In contrast, in gas–liquid or liquid–liquid dispersions high rates of energy dissipation are required to break up droplets or bubbles (see sections 10.5 and 10.6). Recent interest has focused on the distribution of energy dissipation within the tank: the energy input through the shaft is not dissipated uniformly throughout the tank. For example, the radial disc turbine has a high power input and also has high rates of energy dissipation in the vicinity of the impeller and low dissipation rates in the bulk flow. It will be seen in the following sections that this implies intense mixing in the impeller regions but more gentle mixing elsewhere. By comparison, modern hydrofoil impellers produce strong liquid circulations, yet have a low overall power input and dissipate this energy more uniformly throughout the tank volume. Therefore these types of impeller show some advantages for solids suspension and liquid blending.

When anchor impellers or helical ribbons are used in high-viscosity liquids, the fluid flow patterns are very different from those for small diameter impellers: compare the diagrams in Fig. 10.10. Large-diameter impellers attempt to generate flow throughout the whole tank and eliminate stagnant zones. Anchors are often used for heat transfer applications or to scrape sticky materials off the wall, but are not recommended for liquid blending (see section 10.4.3) as they produce only weak vertical circulations. Ribbon mixers (see Figs 10.7 and 10.10) give strong flows in the radial and axial directions, and are preferred for mixing of miscible liquids.

Mixing in low-viscosity systems is determined by the amount of turbulence and rate of circulation generated by the impeller. The intensity of turbulence within the flow depends on the power input of the impeller (discussed in the next section). The circulation rate depends on the pumping capacity of the impeller. Many authors have calculated impeller discharge flowrates, Q_L, from velocity measurements in the vicinity of the blades (e.g. Nagata, 1975, Ch. 3). Their results are presented in dimensionless form as a flow coefficient N_Q (analogous to the discharge coefficient for a centrifugal pump) versus the impeller Reynolds number (defined in equation (10.1)):

$$N_Q = \frac{Q_L}{ND^3} = f(Re) \tag{10.2}$$

For low-viscosity fluids the flow is usually turbulent ($Re > 10^4$) and the flow coefficient is a constant, independent of impeller speed and diameter, so that the discharge flow rate is directly proportional to ND^3. Revill (1982) recommends that for standard geometry disc turbines

$$N_Q = \frac{Q_L}{ND^3} = 0.75 \qquad \text{for} \qquad 0.2 < \frac{D}{T} < 0.5 \tag{10.3}$$

Uhl and Gray (1966, Vol. 1, Ch. 4) also present a large number of flow coefficients, N_Q, for various impellers in baffled and unbaffled vessels. The concept of the discharge flow gives a good qualitative indication of the impeller's ability to generate fluid motion, but is not particularly useful in the design of mixing systems, unless it can be directly linked to blend times or solids suspension criteria (examples of this are provided by Joshi et al., 1982). Moreover, as the discharge stream leaving the impeller entrains other fluid from the bulk flow, Q_L is **not** the same as the circulation flow within the vessel.

10.3   Power consumption in stirred tanks

10.3.1   Single Newtonian liquid phase: dimensional analysis

Calculation of the power input by agitation is of fundamental importance to both the process and mechanical design of stirred tanks. As described in section 10.2, the fluid dynamics of stirred tanks is so complex as to preclude an a priori calculation of power input for a given impeller speed. In such cases, dimensional analysis may be used to indicate the form of the relationship between power and impeller rotational speed.

The power input P_o through a rotating impeller is a function of impeller speed N, impeller diameter D, liquid density ρ_L and viscosity μ_L, gravitational acceleration g, and the tank geometry (see Fig. 10.6). The subscript 'o' is used to indicate the power input in the absence of gas sparging: that is, for a single liquid phase. By convention the impeller speed is measured in revolutions per second (rps) rather than radian s^{-1}.

$$P_o = f_1\left(N, D, \rho_L, \mu_L, g, T, H, C, B, \ldots, \right.$$
$$\left. \text{impeller type and geometry}\right) \tag{10.4}$$

Forming dimensionless groups using Buckingham's theorem:

$$\frac{P_o}{\rho_L N^3 D^5} = f_2\left(\frac{\rho_L N D^2}{\mu_L}, \frac{N^2 D}{g}, \frac{D}{T}, \frac{H}{T}, \frac{C}{D}, \frac{B}{T}\right) \tag{10.5}$$

Define

$$N_{po} = \frac{P_o}{\rho_L N^3 D^5} = \text{ungassed power number} \tag{10.6}$$

$$Re = \frac{\rho_L N D^2}{\mu_L} = \text{Reynolds number} \tag{10.1}$$

$$Fr = \frac{N^2 D}{g} = \text{Froude number} \tag{10.7}$$

Note that the Reynolds and Froude numbers reduce to their familiar forms (Chapter 2)

$$Re = \frac{\rho_L v_L}{\mu_L} \quad \text{and} \quad Fr = \frac{v^2}{gL}$$

where $v = ND$ is a characteristic velocity (related to tip speed) and $L = D$ is a characteristic length.

In geometrically similar systems (ratios of geometric dimensions are equal but the scales are different), the power number depends only on the Reynolds and Froude numbers:

$$N_{po} = f_3\left(Re, Fr\right) \qquad (10.8)$$

Furthermore, for stirred tanks in which the liquid surface is relatively flat (such as baffled systems) the gravitational acceleration has a negligible effect on power demand, and so

$$N_{po} = f_4\left(Re\right) \qquad (10.9)$$

Unbaffled systems, in which a central vortex forms, retain the general dependence of the power number on the Froude number (equation (10.8)), although the influence of the Reynolds number is predominant. This is because gravitational acceleration affects the formation of the surface vortex.

A complete power characteristic for various impeller types is presented in Fig. 10.11. At low Reynolds numbers there is no difference in the N_{po}–Re relationship between unbaffled and baffled systems using the same impeller. However, at high Reynolds numbers (transitional and turbulent flow), baffled systems draw considerably more power than unbaffled, indicating higher intensities of turbulence and improved mixing rates.

The power number can be shown to be analogous to a drag coefficient for the rotating impeller blades (Uhl and Gray, 1966, Vol. 1, Ch. 4). Therefore, it is not surprising that for laminar flows ($Re < 10$) the power number is inversely proportional to the Reynolds number: that is, equation (10.9) becomes

$$N_{po} = \frac{A}{Re} \qquad (10.10)$$

where A is a constant that depends on impeller type. Edwards and Ayazi-Shamlou (1983) presented the following correlations for laminar flows, which allow for variations in impeller geometry:
Helical ribbon

$$N_{po} = \frac{150}{Re}\left(\frac{C}{D}\right)^{-0.28}\left(\frac{p}{D}\right)^{-0.53}\left(\frac{h}{D}\right)\left(\frac{W}{D}\right)^{0.33} n_b^{0.54} \qquad (10.11)$$

Anchor

$$N_{po} = \frac{85}{Re}\left(\frac{C}{T}\right)^{-0.31}\left(\frac{h}{D}\right)^{0.48} \qquad (10.12)$$

where C is the clearance to the wall, D is the outside diameter of the impeller, p is the pitch, h is the height of the impeller, W is the blade width and n_b is the number of blades.

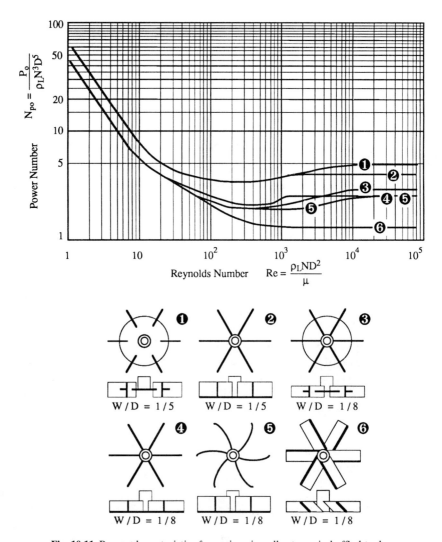

Fig. 10.11 Power characteristics for various impeller types in baffled tanks.

At high Reynolds numbers ($Re > 10^4$) the flow is turbulent, and the power number is a constant that depends only on impeller type and tank geometry:

$$N_{po} = \Phi = \text{constant} \qquad (10.13)$$

Values of the constant power number Φ for common impeller types are presented in Table 10.2 (see also Uhl and Gray, 1966, Vol. I, Ch. 3).

In the transition regime, few correlations exist for the N_{po}–Re relationship, and most results are presented graphically. Nagata (1975, Ch. 1)

Table 10.2 Constant power numbers for various standard impellers (Bates *et al.*, 1963) (n_b is the number of blades and n_B is the number of baffles)

Turbine	$\dfrac{D}{W}$	n_b	$\dfrac{D}{T}$	$\dfrac{C}{T}$	n_B	$\dfrac{B}{T}$	Φ
Flat blade	0.125	6	0.33	0.33	4	0.083	2.6
Flat blade	0.20	6	0.33	0.33	4	0.083	4.0
Rushton disc turbine ($L/D = 0.25$)	0.20	6	0.33	0.33	4	0.10	5.0
Rushton disc turbine ($L/D = 0.5$)	0.125	6	0.33	0.33	4	0.083	3.0
Curved blade	0.125	6	0.33	0.33	4	0.083	2.6
45° Pitched blade	0.125	6	0.33	0.33	4	0.083	1.3

combines the forms of equations (10.10) and (10.13) for the transition regime as

$$N_{po} = \frac{A}{Re} + B \tag{10.14}$$

and gives expressions for the constants A and B in terms of impeller and tank geometric ratios.

10.3.2 Non-Newtonian liquids

The power input to a non-Newtonian liquid may be estimated, based on an 'apparent' viscosity μ_a (Metzner and Otto, 1957). This method assumes that there is a representative 'average shear rate' $\dot\gamma$, which, by dimensional analysis, should depend only on the impeller speed (for a given impeller type and fixed geometry at any scale):

$$\dot\gamma = \beta N \tag{10.15}$$

where β is a dimensionless shear rate constant. For a power-law fluid (Chapter 5) the shear stress is

$$\tau = K\dot\gamma^n \tag{10.16}$$

where K is the consistency index and n is the power-law exponent, or

$$\mu_a = \frac{\tau}{\dot\gamma} = K\dot\gamma^{n-1} \tag{10.17}$$

From equations (10.15) and (10.17):

$$\mu_a = K\left(\beta N\right)^{n-1} \tag{10.18}$$

and the Reynolds number (see equation (10.1)) becomes

$$Re = \frac{\rho_L N D^2}{\mu_a} = \frac{\rho_L D^2}{K\beta^{n-1}N^{n-2}} \tag{10.19}$$

Metzner and Otto (1957) demonstrated that the relationship of Newtonian power number to Reynolds number also held for non-Newtonian fluids,

Table 10.3 Dimensionless shear rate constants for pseudo-plastic liquids

Impeller	Shear rate constant, β	Source
Six-bladed disc turbine	11.5 ± 1.5	Metzner and Otto (1957)
Six-bladed 45° pitched turbine	13 ± 2	Metzner and Otto (1957)
Marine propeller	10 ± 0.9	Metzner and Otto (1957)
Helical ribbon	$34 - 114\left(\dfrac{C}{D}\right)$ for $0.026 < \left(\dfrac{C}{D}\right) < 0.164$	Edwards and Shamlou (1983)
Anchor	$33 - 172\left(\dfrac{C}{T}\right)$ for $0.02 < \left(\dfrac{C}{T}\right) < 0.13$	Edwards and Shamlou (1983)

defining the Reynolds number using equation (10.19). Values for the shear rate constant β for shear-thinning fluids ($n < 1$) in standard-geometry vessels are presented in Table 10.3 (consult original references for full details of impeller and tank geometries).

To calculate the power input to a non-Newtonian liquid using a standard impeller type the following procedure should be followed.

1. Measure the shear stress versus rate of strain relationship for the non-Newtonian process fluid and fit the constants in equation (10.16) using linear regression of a log–log plot.
2. Calculate the modified Reynolds number from equation (10.19) using the value of the shear rate constant β from Table 10.3, at the required impeller speed.
3. Use an equation or graph for the N_{po}–Re relationship for the same impeller to calculate the power number.
4. Back-calculate the power using the definition of N_{po} in equation (10.6).

Note that an analogous method may be derived for non-Newtonian liquids, which obey different constitutive equations. Calculations for non-standard impellers require measurements of power consumption to be made at a pilot scale using both Newtonian and non-Newtonian fluids, covering the same range of Reynolds numbers as the full-scale design.

10.4   Miscible liquid blending operations

10.4.1   Blending of low-viscosity liquids

A large category of food-mixing operations fall into the category of liquid blending (for example, mixing of sugar syrups, water, fruit pulp and minor ingredients in the manufacture of soft drinks). For low-viscosity Newtonian liquids the process result may be achieved with a small diameter impeller (such as a Rushton turbine, pitched-blade turbine, propeller or hydrofoil), operated at high speed, but using a fairly low specific power input (typically ~0.2 kW m^{-3}; Edwards, 1985). Usually the flow is in the turbulent regime.

One design requirement is to predict the impeller speed to mix the tank contents, to a given degree of homogeneity, in a given time. Then, for a known impeller speed, tank geometry and fluid properties, the power consumption for mixing can be calculated using the methods in section 10.3. Even for single-phase operations, the fluid flow patterns in a stirred tank are sufficiently complex to preclude an a priori prediction of the mixing time for a given impeller speed. Instead, previous workers have measured mixing times experimentally and used dimensional analysis to correlate their results.

Mixing times may be measured by releasing a tracer liquid into the flow and following the time history of concentration fluctuations; ideally, the tracer liquid should have the same density and viscosity as the bulk liquid. Experimental techniques for measuring the tracer concentration include: visual observation of a coloured dye; light absorption using a dyed tracer; changes of refractive index; temperature variations of a hot or cold tracer; acid–base reactions using a coloured pH indicator; and conductivity using a salt tracer. Figure 10.12 shows the dimensionless tracer concentration c^* as a function of time from release of the tracer. These results were measured using a sodium chloride tracer, which was detected by a microconductivity probe located in the discharge stream of a Rushton disc turbine. The measured concentration (or conductivity, which is a linear function of concentration) is made dimensionless using the initial tracer concentration in

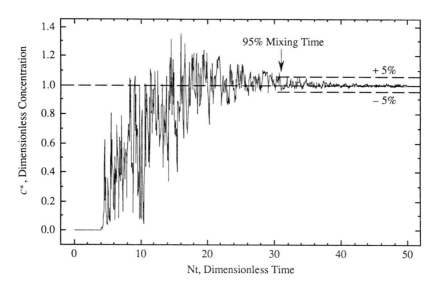

Fig. 10.12 Concentration time history.

the tank before the start of the experiment, c_0, (usually zero) and the final tank concentration, c_∞, when the contents are fully mixed.

$$c* = \frac{c(t) - c_0}{c_\infty - c_0} \tag{10.20}$$

That is,

$$c*(t = 0) = 0 \quad \text{and} \quad c*(t \to \infty) = 1$$

Time may be made dimensionless by defining

$$t* = Nt \tag{10.21}$$

A 95% mixing time, θ_{95}, may be defined as the time for the concentration to fall within ±5% of the final concentration. That is,

$$0.95 \leqslant c* \leqslant 1.05 \quad \text{for all } t \geqslant \theta_{95}$$

Similarly 90% and 99% mixing times may be defined, 99% implying a greater degree of homogeneity than 95% and consequently a longer mixing time; for most practical purposes a 95% mixing time is sufficient. Rielly and Pandit (1988) demonstrated that the mixing time is independent of the position of the detection device for fairly stringent criteria of mixedness, such as 95%; a mass balance applied to any element of the flow shows that as the mixedness criterion approaches 100%, mixing times measured at any position within the tank should be equal.

If simultaneous measurements of the tracer concentration can be made at several positions in the tank, a mixing time can be defined in terms of the decrease in concentration variance. For n detectors the variance σ^2 is defined by

$$\sigma^2(t) = \frac{1}{n-1} \sum_{i=1}^{n} \left(c_i^*(t) - \bar{c}^* \right)^2 \tag{10.22}$$

Note that $\bar{c}^* = 1$ is the tank **average** concentration at all times, $t > 0$ and that $\sigma(t)$ decays with time. The mixing time may defined as the time when $\sigma \leqslant 0.05$ (say). This latter method has the advantage that measurements are taken at many points in the flow and may well show up stagnant regions. However, it is a much more difficult technique to use in practice as it requires recording of many signals simultaneously.

10.4.2 Dimensional analysis of liquid blend times

The previous section shows that several definitions of mixing time are in common use and that they use an arbitrary criterion for mixedness. Whatever definition is used, the mixing time depends on the following parameters:

$$\theta = f_1\left(\rho_L, \mu_L, N, T, D, g, \mathcal{D}, L_d, \frac{\text{tank and impeller}}{\text{geometric dimensions}}\right) \qquad (10.23)$$

where $\mathcal{D}$ is the liquid molecular diffusion coefficient ($m^2 s^{-1}$) and L_d is the probe resolution length scale (m). The length scale L_d is associated with the scale of scrutiny of the detector and is determined by its physical size and its ability to respond to rapidly fluctuating concentrations. Concentration fluctuations that are much smaller than L_d are not detected and the mixture appears well homogeneous. Many workers omit full details of the scale of scrutiny of their measurement device, making their results unreliable for scale-up. Typically, as the scale of scrutiny of the detector increases, the response to small-scale rapid concentration fluctuations is attenuated and shorter mixing times are measured.

Forming dimensionless groups from equation (10.23):

$$N\theta = f_2\left(\frac{\rho_L N^2 D}{\mu_L}, \frac{ND^2}{g}, \frac{\mu_L}{\rho_L \mathcal{D}}, \frac{T}{D}, \frac{L_d}{T}, \text{ geometric ratios}\right) \qquad (10.24)$$

or

$$N\theta = f_2\left(Re,\ Fr,\ Sc,\ \frac{T}{D}, \text{ geometric ratios}\right) \qquad (10.25)$$

Here the Reynolds and Froude numbers are given by equations (10.1) and (10.7), and Sc is the **Schmidt number**:

$$Sc = \frac{\mu_L}{\rho_L \mathcal{D}} \qquad (10.26)$$

which is the ratio of momentum to mass diffusivity.

For baffled systems, the free surface is relatively flat and the Froude number has a negligible effect on the dimensionless mixing time $N\theta$. However, for unbaffled systems $N\theta$ retains the general dependence of equation (10.25).

The Schmidt number Sc in equation (10.25) includes the effects of the molecular diffusivity $\mathcal{D}$. The smallest practical detectors have a length scale of around 1 mm, yet on these scales molecular effects act only very slowly and hence the Schmidt number may be neglected in the analysis of macro-mixing phenomena. Moreover, the molecular diffusivities of most solutes in low-viscosity solvents have the same order of magnitude $\mathcal{D} \sim 10^{-9}\,m^2 s^{-1}$ and Sc of the order of 10^3.

At large Reynolds numbers (low-viscosity, high-speed agitation), $Re > 10^4$, the flow is turbulent and the dimensionless mixing time depends only on the tank geometry and impeller type. Literature reports of scale dependency of $N\theta$ might be attributable to incorrect scaling of the detector scale of scrutiny. Thus

$$N\theta = f_3\left(\text{impeller type, geometric ratios, } \frac{L_d}{T}\right) \tag{10.27}$$

Correlations for constant $N\theta$ values ($Re > 10^4$) for the standard impeller types are given below (Prochazka and Landau, 1961). The disc turbine conformed to the standard geometry, the propeller had a constant pitch equal to diameter, and the pitched-bladed turbine had $4 \times 45°$ blades, with projected height of $0.177\,D$. The tank geometry was: $H = T$; $B = T/12$; $C = T/2$; $n_B = 4$.

Propeller:

$$N\theta = 3.48\left(\frac{T}{D}\right)^{2.05} \log_{10}\left(\frac{2}{X}\right) \tag{10.28}$$

Pitched-bladed turbine:

$$N\theta = 2.02\left(\frac{T}{D}\right)^{2.20} \log_{10}\left(\frac{2}{X}\right) \tag{10.29}$$

Disc turbine:

$$N\theta = 0.905\left(\frac{T}{D}\right)^{2.57} \log_{10}\left(\frac{2}{X}\right) \tag{10.30}$$

The variable X is the mixedness fraction: for example, $X = 0.05$ for the 95% mixing time.

10.4.3 Blending of viscous liquids

As discussed in section 10.2.2, small-diameter impellers do not give adequate mixing in viscous liquids. Large-diameter impellers, which sweep a large proportion of the tank volume, are used at low speed; typical power inputs are of the order of $2\,\text{kW m}^{-3}$ (that is, fairly intense agitation, and under normal operating conditions the flow is laminar). Hoogendoorn and den Hartog (1967) showed that for helical ribbons and marine impellers or helical screws in draught tubes, the dimensionless mixing time $N\theta_{75}$ was approximately constant, independent of the impeller speed and liquid viscosity in the laminar regime. The values of $N\theta_{75}$ for disc turbines and anchor impellers were found to decrease with increasing Reynolds number; these authors noted that the latter impellers gave very poor mixing performance at low Reynolds numbers. Nagata (1975, Ch. 4) and Hoogendoorn and den Hartog (1967) reported values of $N\theta_{70} = 33$ and $N\theta_{75} = 65$ respectively for helical ribbon agitators, and found no effect of tank diameter on these values. Figure 10.13 illustrates the dependence of $N\theta_{75}$ on the Reynolds number for viscous fluids with a variety of impellers.

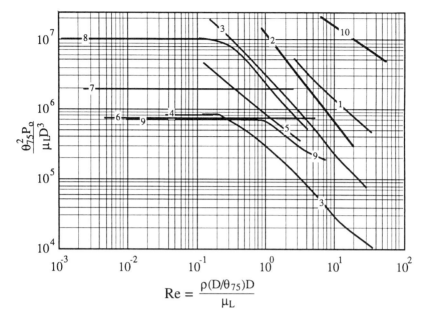

$$Re = \frac{\rho(D/\theta_{75})D}{\mu_L}$$

Fig. 10.13 Dimensionless mixing time versus Reynolds number for various impellers in viscous liquids. The tanks were unbaffled, unless otherwise stated. 1, turbine (baffled); 2, turbine; 3, three inclined-blade paddles; 4, three inclined-blade paddles (with draught tube); 5, screw; 6, screw plus draught tube; 7, ribbon; 8, propeller A plus draught tube; 9, propeller B plus draught tube; 10, anchor. (Hoogendorn and den Hartog, 1967).

10.4.4 Problems with blending non-Newtonian liquids

It has already been stated that in viscous liquids the inertia imparted by the impeller is damped out by viscous effects. The flow in regions distant from the blades is weak and mixing is poor. Bingham plastic fluids (Chapter 5, section 5.1.1) can also pose significant mixing problems when agitated by a small-diameter impeller. A cavern of well-mixed (often turbulent) fluid forms in the high-stress regions around the impeller, yet away from the impeller the fluid is stagnant (see Fig. 10.14). The boundary surface of the well-mixed cavern is where the local stress equals the fluid yield stress (recall that there is only shear in a Bingham plastic when the fluid stress exceeds the yield stress). Figure 10.14 shows that as the impeller speed increases, the size of the cavity grows until eventually the whole of the tank contents are well mixed (the usual operating condition). Nienow and Elson (1988) used X-ray flow visualization to reveal the size of cavities in opaque plastic fluids and proposed a model to predict cavity diameter D_c as a function of impeller speed N, power number N_{po} and fluid yield stress τ_y:

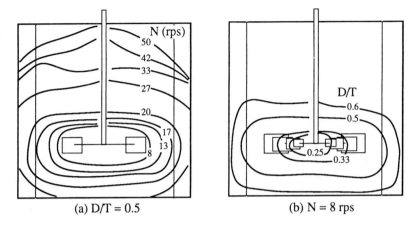

(a) D/T = 0.5   (b) N = 8 rps

Fig. 10.14 Cavern formation in a yield stress fluid (Nienow and Elson, 1988): (a) effect of
impeller speed, (b) effect of impeller size on cavern size in xanthan gum.

$$\left(\frac{D_c}{D}\right)^3 = \left(\frac{1.36}{\pi^2}\right)\left(\frac{N_{po}\rho_L N^2 D^2}{\tau_y}\right) \tag{10.31}$$

Here the height of the cylindrical cavity is assumed to be 40% of its diameter. Equation (10.31) allows calculation of the impeller speed to give a
cavity equal to the tank diameter, ensuring good mixing throughout the
vessel and no dead zones.

Different mixing problems may be found with fluids that exhibit
viscoelastic behaviour. Elastic effects cause large normal forces to be generated within the fluid, as well as the usual shear forces due to viscous
effects. Normal forces oppose the formation of a central vortex around a
rotating shaft and can actually cause the fluid to climb. This phenomenon is
known as the **Weissenberg effect** and can result in the fluid climbing as high
as the shaft seals or gearbox. At low impeller speed these normal forces can
also cause flow reversal, i.e. the flow is in the opposite direction to that
observed for inelastic fluids at similar Reynolds numbers.

10.5   Gas–liquid mixing

10.5.1   Surface aeration phenomena in stirred tanks

In many food-processing applications it is important to avoid entraining air
during the mixing process, as this causes spoilage during product storage.
Many workers have noted that in the absence of gas sparging, surface
aeration occurs above a minimum impeller speed, denoted by N_{SA}. The
forced/free vortex model illustrated in Fig. 10.9 for flow in an unbaffled tank

may be used to predict the point at which the free surface reaches the impeller; typically, for a Rushton turbine the change from forced to free vortex flow occurs at a radius of $3D/8$. Greaves and Kobbacy (1981) gave a qualitative description of the aeration phenomena from the free surface in baffled tanks, at $N > N_{SA}$. Strong eddies (A in Fig. 10.15), formed by the interaction of the discharge flow from the impeller with the baffles, induce other strong eddies (B in Fig. 8.15), which precess slowly around the impeller shaft and form a hollow vortex at the surface. At sufficiently high impeller speeds gas bubbles enter the liquid through the surface vortex B and are carried down to the impeller by the circulating liquid.

Van Dierendonck et $al.$ (1968) have correlated N_{SA}, the critical speed for the onset of aeration against physical properties and geometric parameters. Van Dierendonck's correlation for a standard disc turbine in a baffled tank is

$$\left(\frac{\mu_L N_{SA} D^2}{T\sigma}\right)\left(\frac{\rho_L \sigma^3}{g\mu_L^4}\right)^{1/4} = 2.0\left(\frac{H-C}{C}\right)^{1/2} \tag{10.32}$$

which is restricted to

$$0.10 \leqslant \frac{H-C}{T} \leqslant 0.20 + 1.75\frac{D}{T}$$

10.5.2 Aerated impeller power consumption and gas flow patterns

The effect of sparging gas bubbles into a stirred tank is to reduce substantially the power consumption of the impeller. In gas–liquid applications the

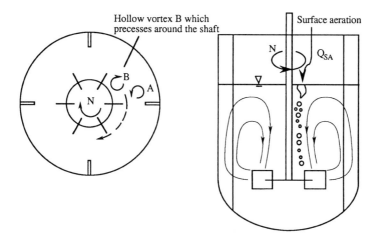

Fig. 10.15 Surface entrainment mechanism in baffled tanks.

gassed power input is fairly high ($\sim$1–2 kW m^{-3}) since large energy dissipation rates are required to produce small bubbles and large interfacial areas. Uhl and Gray (1966, Vol. I, pp. 145–148), Nagata (1975, Ch. 8) and Greaves and Barigou (1986) have reviewed the literature on power consumption under aerated conditions. The best-known correlation is by Michel and Miller (1962):

$$P_g = C\left(\frac{P_o^2 ND^3}{Q_g^{0.56}}\right)^{0.45} \tag{10.33}$$

where C is a constant with values between 0.63 and 1.19, depending on tank diameter and geometry (all units are in SI). Mann (1983) gives $C = 0.72$, but notes that equation (10.33) fails as the sparged gas volumetric flowrate $Q_g \to 0$ and as $Q_g \to \infty$; therefore caution should be exercised in using this method for scale-up.

More recently, workers have expressed their results in dimensionless terms by plotting the gassed power ratio P_g/P_o (taking values in the range 0–1) against the aeration number $N_A = Q_g/ND^3$, at constant impeller speed, as shown in Fig. 10.16. This figure is for a standard geometry disc turbine, but data are available in the literature for many other impeller designs. As the power input partly determines rates of mass transfer in gas–liquid dispersions, it is important that the gassed power number does not drop off too rapidly as the aeration number increases. The Rushton turbine was

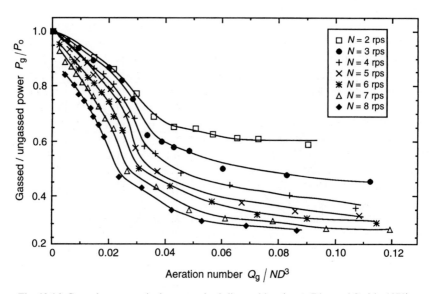

Fig. 10.16 Gassed power ratio for a standard disc turbine (van't Riet and Smith, 1973).

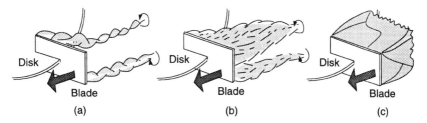

Disk   Disk   Disk

Blade   Blade   Blade

(a)   (b)   (c)

Fig. 10.17 Cavity shapes formed on blades during gas–liquid dispersion: (a) vortex cavities; (b) clinging cavities; (c) large cavities.

formerly regarded as an efficient gas disperser; however, it has a large ungassed power number, and the power decreases by as much as 60% on aeration. Modern developments in gas–liquid agitator design have concentrated on impellers that maintain a value of P_g/P_o close to 1 over the operating range of aeration numbers.

Bruijn *et al.* (1974) and van't Riet and Smith (1973) explained the decrease in gassed power consumption as a consequence of the formation of stable 'gas cavities' behind the blades. Gas sparged into the vessel is trapped in trailing vortices behind each impeller blade and may remain there for several revolutions before being dispersed as small bubbles in the highly turbulent wake of each cavity. For a continuous flow of gas, at a sufficiently high impeller speed, stable gas cavities form behind each blade; the size and shape of these cavities depends on gas volumetric flowrate and impeller speed, as illustrated by Fig. 10.17. At low gas flowrates the bubbles are trapped in the trailing vortex system behind each blade and form so-called **vortex cavities**. As the sparged gas flowrate is increased the attached cavity size increases, forming clinging and then large cavities. Smith and Warmoeskerken (1986) have published flow regime maps, of which Fig. 10.18 is an example, showing cavity types as a function of the Froude and the aeration numbers. For $N_A > {\sim}0.06$ the cavities form themselves into a three–three configuration for six-bladed impellers: that is, there are large and small cavities on alternate blades. For five-bladed impellers the three–three configuration tries to form, but the large or small cavity precesses from blade to blade. The size of the attached cavity determines the drag coefficient for the blade, and thus the precessing cavity causes a fluctuating load on the blade and an imbalance of the forces acting on the shaft. It was quite common for the shafts of five-bladed impellers to break in gas–liquid operation, and their use is avoided today.

The presence of these cavities alters the liquid streamlines around the blade, so that the separation point occurs further downstream from the leading edge of the blade. Form drag on the impeller is decreased, as the wake volume behind each blade is reduced by the presence of the gas cavity. Consequently there is a reduction in power consumption in the presence of gas, which depends on the size and shape of the gas cavities.

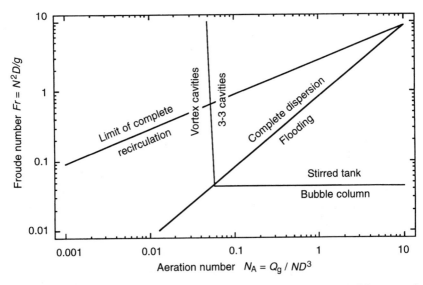

Fig. 10.18 Gas flow map for standard disc turbine, showing regions of different cavity formation.

Figure 10.19 demonstrates the effect on gas flow patterns in a gas–liquid stirred tank of gradually increasing the gas throughput or decreasing the impeller speed (Nienow *et al.*, 1978). At low gas flowrates and high impeller speeds the bubbles are well dispersed above and below the impeller; with increasing gas flow, the gas dispersion becomes worse. Nienow *et al.* (1978) defined a critical speed for complete dispersion, N_{CD}, at the change from conditions (c) to (d) in Fig. 10.19. For $H = T$, $C = T/4$, six-bladed disc turbines (valid for $T < 1.8$ m), Nienow *et al.* (1978) correlated their results by Pipe spargers:

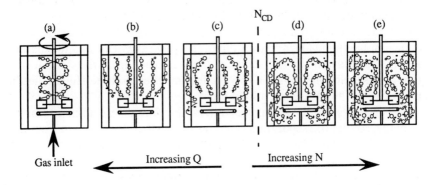

Fig. 10.19 Gas flow patterns as a function of impeller speed and gas flowrate.

$$N_{CD} = 4 \frac{Q_g^{0.5} T^{0.25}}{D^2} \tag{10.34}$$

Ring spargers:

$$N_{CD} = 3 \frac{Q_g^{0.5} T^{0.25}}{D^2} \tag{10.35}$$

Here Q_g is the volumetric flowrate of gas and all quantities are in SI units. These equations predict conservative values of N_{CD} for non-coalescing systems and turbines with more than six blades (Middleton, 1985).

Figure 10.16 shows that at constant impeller speed the gassed power ratio becomes fairly constant at large values of aeration number N_A. Under these conditions the cavities have grown to their maximum size; further increasing the gas throughput leads to 'flooding', corresponding to (a) in Fig. 10.19. In the flooded condition, not all the gas passes through the gas cavities and some is not dispersed by the impeller. At this point the impeller virtually stops pumping in the radial direction, and a bulk liquid circulation is set up by the rising bubbles (Warmoeskerken and Smith, 1984). These workers showed theoretically that at the flooding point

$$\frac{Q_g}{N_F D^3} = 1.2 \frac{N_F^2 D}{g} \tag{10.36}$$

where N_F is the critical impeller speed for flooding at a given gas volumetric flowrate Q_g. Clearly, flooding is an undesirable condition, which should be avoided in practice as liquid-phase mixing, gas dispersion and gas–liquid mass transfer are all adversely affected.

In many gas–liquid operations the process objective is to maintain the same level of power input at different gas inputs: that is, to have a gassed power curve which is relatively flat, without much reduction in the ratio P_g/P_o. This ensures that bubble sizes and mass transfer coefficients are not impaired (see sections 10.5.3 and 10.5.4). Recent developments in impeller design have shown that large numbers of blades (12 or 18) or concave blades give this type of behaviour (Middleton, 1985).

10.5.3   Gas voidage fraction and interfacial area in stirred tanks

In designing gas–liquid reactors or fermenters it is necessary to know the gas volume fraction held up in the liquid, so that the overall volume of the vessel may be calculated. The mean gas voidage fraction ε is defined as

$$\varepsilon = \frac{V_G}{V_G + V_L} \tag{10.37}$$

where V_G and V_L are the gas and liquid volumes in the stirred tank, respectively. A large number of purely empirical correlations have been proposed for the gas voidage fraction in terms of the gas flowrate and impeller speed. Calderbank (1958) presented a semi-theoretical method for predicting the mean gas voidage fraction; the method is based on Kolmogoroff's theory of local isotropic turbulence, which is valid only at high Reynolds numbers. The analysis shows that the **largest** bubble size that can exist in a given turbulent flow depends on the power input per unit volume, (P_g/V), the fluid density ρ_L and the surface tension σ:

$$d_{max} \propto \frac{\sigma^{0.6}}{\rho_L^{0.2}\left(P_g/V\right)^{0.4}}$$

(10.38)

Calderbank correlated the Sauter **mean** bubble diameter d_{32} (a surface area, volume mean) data from stirred-tank experiments using the expression

$$d_{32} = 4.15\left[\frac{\sigma^{0.6}}{\rho_L^{0.2}\left(P_g/V\right)^{0.4}}\right]\varepsilon^{1/2} + 9\times10^{-4} \text{ m}$$

(10.39)

Using similar arguments Calderbank also proposed that the interfacial area per unit volume was given by

$$a = 1.44\left[\frac{\rho_L^{0.2}\left(P_g/V\right)^{0.4}}{\sigma^{0.6}}\right]\left(\frac{v_g}{V_\infty}\right)^{1/2}$$

(10.40)

where V_∞ is the terminal rise velocity of a single bubble and v_g is the superficial gas velocity. The interfacial area and gas voidage fraction are related by

$$d_{32} = \frac{6\varepsilon}{a}$$

(10.41)

for spherical bubbles, where d_{32} is a Sauter mean diameter. The important feature of equations (10.39) and (10.40) is that both the bubble size and specific interfacial area depend on the power input per unit volume. Clearly then the rate of mass transfer also depends on P_g/V, so that it is a requirement of any gas–liquid impeller that the gassed power is almost independent of the gas flowrate. Then the expression for the voidage fraction becomes (using equations (10.39)–(10.41))

$$\varepsilon = \left(\frac{v_g\varepsilon}{V_\infty}\right)^{1/2} + 2.16\times10^{-4}\left[\frac{\rho_L^{0.2}\left(P_g/V\right)^{0.4}}{\sigma^{0.6}}\right]\left(\frac{v_g}{V_\infty}\right)^{1/2}$$

(10.42)

Calderbank's method is only approximate, as it is well known that the power input to the tank is not dissipated uniformly (Laufhutte and Mersmann, 1985): more energy is dissipated in the vicinity of the impeller than in the bulk circulation. Consequently there is a distribution of bubble sizes and voidage fractions throughout the vessel. A further drawback to these equations is that the **gassed** power consumption is required; section 10.5.2 has already shown that this is not a straightforward quantity to calculate.

An alternative to Calderbank's method is to use a purely empirical correlation that covers a wide range of variables. Smith *et al.* (1977) proposed that for

Coalescing systems:

$$\varepsilon = 0.02 \left(\frac{P_g}{V_L} \right)^{0.475} \left(v_g \right)^{0.4} \tag{10.43a}$$

for

$$0.005 \leqslant v_g \leqslant 0.05 \, \text{m s}^{-1}$$

and

$$1 \leqslant \left(\frac{P_g}{V_L} \right) \leqslant 5 \, \text{kW m}^{-3}$$

Non-coalescing systems:

$$\varepsilon = 0.04 \left(\frac{P_g}{V_L} \right)^{0.475} \left(v_g \right)^{0.4} \tag{10.43b}$$

for

$$0.004 \leqslant v_g \leqslant 0.02 \, \text{m s}^{-1}$$

and

$$100 \leqslant \left(\frac{P_g}{V_L} \right) \leqslant 750 \, \text{W m}^{-3}$$

All quantities are in SI units. The results were obtained on tanks up to 1.8 m diameter, but equations (10.43a) and (10.43b) do however contain dimensional constants, which may change on scale-up.

10.5.4 *Gas–liquid mass transfer*

Many mixing problems involve the transfer of a solute gas into the liquid phase for subsequent chemical reaction (as in aerobic fermentations, for example). This process has been introduced in section 4.9.1. The process objectives of these operations are to disperse the sparged gas as small bubbles (and therefore create gas–liquid interfacial area) and to generate turbulence to increase mass transfer rates. Large interfacial areas require small bubble sizes and large gas voidage fractions (see equation (10.41)). The general equation for mass transfer between a liquid and a gas (where chemical reaction kinetics are not rate determining) is

$$J = K_L a \left(c_L^* - c_L \right) V \tag{10.44}$$

where J is the molar transfer rate of species A per unit volume; K_L is the overall liquid phase mass transfer coefficient; a is the interfacial area per unit volume; c_L is the liquid-phase molar composition; c_L^* is the equilibrium liquid-phase molar composition; and V is the volume of the dispersion. In some cases the liquid-phase resistance predominates, and the overall mass transfer coefficient K_L is equal to the liquid film coefficient k_L (see Kay and Nedderman, 1985, Ch. 18). Experimental techniques do not usually allow separate determination of k_L and a, and so most workers have measured the product $k_L a$. For example, in air–water and air–electrolyte solutions (Smith et al., 1977):

Coalescing systems:

$$k_L a = 0.01 \left(\frac{P_g}{V_L} \right)^{0.475} \left(v_g \right)^{0.4} \tag{10.45a}$$

Non-coalescing systems:

$$k_L a = 0.02 \left(\frac{P_g}{V_L} \right)^{0.475} \left(v_g \right)^{0.4} \tag{10.45b}$$

where v_g is the gas superficial velocity ($v_g = 4Q_g/\pi T^2$).

The units are SI and the ranges of applicability are the same as for equations (10.43a) and (10.43b). Note that addition of surface active agents (such as anti-foam) significantly affects the value of the interfacial area per unit volume and therefore has a large effect on mass transfer.

Measurements of mass transfer rates in agitated vessels are not easy to make and considerable controversy surrounds the interpretation of data from oxygen or carbon dioxide absorption tests or from chemical absorption tests. That, together with obtaining data on real fermentation systems, makes the design of gas–liquid reactors a difficult art.

10.6 Liquid–liquid dispersions and the creation of emulsions

The two properties of liquid–liquid mixtures or emulsions that are of particular relevance to the food industry are rheology and stability. In liquid–liquid extractions, the formation of a droplet dispersion is an intermediate processing step in which stability is only required over a sufficiently long period to allow phase equilibrium to be established. Subsequent processing requires that the mixture be separated by coalescence of the droplets and so long-term stability would actually hinder the process. A second category of liquid–liquid processes is the manufacture of stable emulsions (for example, the manufacture of margarines and spreads): emulsion rheology gives consistency and texture to the product, while stability ensures that the material does not separate during a long shelf-life. Both these properties are related to droplet size, dispersed phase volume, interfacial tension, and attractive/repulsive forces between droplets. During production of emulsions, surface-active ingredients (emulsifiers) are often added to reduce interfacial tension and to prevent coalescence of droplets.

Stresses in the fluid due to motion of the impeller cause primary drops to elongate and finally break up into droplets and much smaller satellite droplets. These events occur many times, until an equilibrium is established between the rates of break-up and coalescence. Thus during a batch-mixing operation the mean droplet size decreases to a steady value, and thereafter remains approximately constant. Theoretical methods exist to predict the break-up of droplets in idealized flow conditions, but not in realistic mixer geometries: the dynamics of droplet break-up are complex and are outside the scope of this chapter [refer to Donaldson (1985) for introductory material]. Many emulsifications take place under turbulent flow conditions; approximate models based on Kolmogoroff's theory of local isotropic turbulence yield that the maximum droplet diameter depends on the surface tension σ, continuous phase density ρ_c and the specific power input per unit volume (P/V), in an analogous way to the break-up of gas bubbles (see section 10.5.3):

$$d_{max} \propto \frac{\sigma^{0.6}}{\rho_c^{0.2}\left(P/V\right)^{0.4}} \qquad (10.46)$$

where the constant of proportionality depends on the tank and impeller geometry. Alternatively, this may be written in terms of a critical **Weber number** for the maximum droplet size We_c:

$$We_c = 2.0 \frac{\rho_c^{1/3} d_{max}^{5/3} \left(P/V\right)^{2/3}}{\sigma} \qquad (10.47)$$

Again, the value of the critical Weber number depends on tank and impeller geometry. The local specific power input in the vicinity of the impeller (where fluid stresses are largest and droplet break-up occurs) may be many times the average value of P/V. McManamey (1979) assumed that the power input was dissipated in the volume swept out by the impeller and correlated a variety of data for the Sauter mean diameter d_{32} from different impeller systems by

$$d_{32} = C_1 \left[\frac{4}{\pi} N_{po} \frac{D}{W}\right]^{-0.4} We^{-0.6} \qquad (10.48)$$

where

$$We = \textbf{impeller Weber number} = \frac{\rho_c N^2 D^3}{\sigma} \qquad (10.49)$$

Here the constant C_1 has a value of $0.22 \pm 20\%$, independent of impeller type. Equation (10.48) applies to systems with a low volume fraction of dispersed phase, where coalescence does not occur as droplets move away from the impeller region. Lee *et al.* (1984) examined the effect of phase volume fraction ϕ on the Sauter mean drop size in stabilized systems, and proposed a correlation of the form

$$\frac{d_{32}}{D} = k_1 \left(1 + k_2 \phi\right) We^{-0.6} \qquad (10.50)$$

where *We* is given by equation (10.49), and the constants k_1 and k_2 depend on agitator design and the liquid–liquid system.

10.7 Solids suspension and solid–liquid mass transfer

In solid–liquid stirred-tank applications the process objectives fall into the following categories:

- suspension of particles initially resting on the bottom of the tank, so as to expose the maximum solid–liquid surface area for mass transfer;
- formation and maintenance of a homogeneous suspension of particles (this is a particular requirement of continuous systems with draw-off of liquid–solid mixture);
- suspension of particles in order to obtain flocculation (this requires gentle agitation to suspend the solids and promote collisions between particles, but without excessive shear, which breaks weak flocs).

Typical solid–liquid operations are dissolution (formation of sucrose syrups, for example), fermentations (suspension of cell cultures and growth media, for example), crystallization, and continuous slurry draw-offs from stirred tanks, used as premixers or holding vessels. In the latter case the objective is to keep the solids in suspension, avoiding sedimentation and segregation. Drawing off product from a mixture that is not fully suspended or has axial concentration gradients would give varying solids fractions as the vessel was emptied.

The usual criterion for **complete suspension** is that 'no particle should remain on the bottom of the tank for more than 1–2 s' (Zwietering, 1958). Measurements of the 'just suspended' impeller speed N_{JS} or impeller power P_{JS} are obtained by gradually increasing and decreasing the impeller speed in a transparent tank until the criterion is satisfied. Although this is a subjective measurement, the results are fairly reproducible because the last particles to be suspended are usually trapped in the relatively stagnant

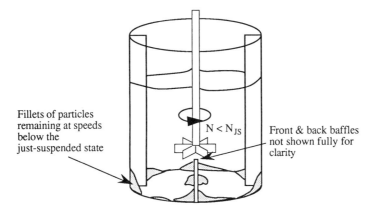

Fig. 10.20 Stagnant regions near corners and baffles, where fillets of solids collect. These are usually the last particles to be suspended.

zones located directly beneath the impeller or behind the baffles on the base of the tank (see Fig. 10.20).

A less rigorous definition of the just-suspended condition allows a small fraction of particles to remain as fillets in these stagnant regions (Fig. 10.20) but no other particles rest on the tank bottom for more than 1–2 s. This type of suspension results in considerable savings in power input (and hence agitator and shaft size) compared with satisfying Zwietering's criterion, which generally requires intense agitation ($\sim$1–2 kW m^{-3}; Nienow, 1985). If only a small fraction of particles remain motionless, then the solid–liquid mass transfer area is only slightly reduced.

Homogeneous suspension requires that no solids concentration gradients are present within the vessel: that is, the solids are uniformly distributed. The impeller speed to obtain homogeneous suspension is considerably higher than for complete suspension and operation under these conditions is not usually economically feasible. The homogeneous condition is difficult to determine experimentally; a common technique is to sample the mixture at various heights in the vessel. However, it is difficult to ensure representative, isokinetic sampling: in most regions of the tank there is relative motion between the particles and the liquid and therefore the sample withdrawal velocity cannot be made equal to the velocity of the flowing mixture.

For the case where samples can be obtained isokinetically from all parts of the tank, the homogeneous condition may be defined in terms of a mixing index M:

$$M = \frac{\sigma}{\bar{x}} = \frac{\sqrt{\displaystyle\sum_{i=1}^{n} \frac{\left(x_i - \bar{x}\right)^2}{\left(n-1\right)}}}{\bar{x}} \tag{10.51}$$

where x_i is the solids concentration of sample i (kg solids/kg mix); σ^2 is the variance of solids concentration $(kg/kg)^2$; n = number of samples; and

$$\bar{x} = \text{mean solids concentration in tank} = \sum_{i=1}^{n} \frac{x_i}{n} \quad (kg/kg) \quad (10.52)$$

For a perfectly homogeneous tank the mixing index would be zero; typically, the tank could be said to be homogeneous when $M \leqslant 0.05$. This method requires a large number of samples to be withdrawn from the tank during operation and analysed, for example, by separating the liquid and solid phases, and drying.

Many authors have measured the impeller speed to obtain the 'just suspended' state. Zwietering's (1958) correlation covers the widest range of fluid properties, particle size, concentration and properties, and tank geometric parameters:

$$N_{JS} = s v_L^{0.1} d_p^{0.2} \left(\frac{g \Delta \rho}{\rho_L} \right)^{0.45} D^{-0.85} x^{0.13} \quad (10.53)$$

The dimensionless constant s in equation (10.53) depends on impeller type, clearance ratio T/C, and diameter ratio T/D. Zwietering (1958) and Nienow (1968) presented graphs of s versus T/D at various T/C for propellers, disc turbines, vaned discs and flat blades. These data may be correlated using expressions of the form

$$s = a \left(\frac{T}{D} \right)^b \quad (10.54)$$

where a and b are constants that depend on T/C and impeller type.

The correlation in equation (10.53) is dimensionless and is generally accepted as giving a conservative estimate for N_{JS}. Nienow (1968) confirmed the exponents and constants in Zwietering's correlation using data obtained in an independent study.

For dissolution of solid particles (without chemical reaction) the rate of mass transfer $(kmol\,s^{-1})$ is given by

$$J = k_s A \left(c_s - c_\infty \right) \quad (10.55)$$

where A is the exposed solid–liquid contact area and k_s is the mass transfer coefficient. Note that equation (10.55) applies to operations in which diffusion controls mass transfer from the particles to the bulk fluid at concentration c_∞; c_s is the saturation concentration at the surface of the particles. The dissolution of solid particles should be carried out at an impeller speed in excess of N_{JS}, such that the maximum liquid–solid surface area is exposed. Operation at high impeller speeds $(N > N_{SA})$ leads to entrainment of air from the free surface, which blankets the particle surfaces, and mass transfer rates remain approximately constant, independent of speed.

Nienow and Miles (1978) showed that the diffusion-controlled mass transfer coefficient k_{JS} at the just-suspended speed N_{JS} was independent of the impeller and tank configuration (that is, k_{JS} does not depend on the specific power input P/V). In this case the impeller and tank configuration should be chosen to be the most economic in terms of power consumption and the impeller speed should be in the range $N_{JS} < N < N_{SA}$. In this range of speeds, the mass transfer coefficient varies as

$$k_s \propto N^a \qquad \text{where } a = 0.4\text{–}0.6 \tag{10.56}$$

To achieve the just-suspended condition often requires large specific power inputs: increasing the impeller speed leads to small increases in the mass transfer coefficient (equation (10.56)), but large increases in power demand ($P \propto N^3$). Thus operating much above the just-suspended condition may be uneconomic (Nienow, 1985).

The mass transfer coefficient may be predicted from a correlation similar to the Froessling equation for particle–fluid systems [Rowe et al., 1965 and equation (4.23)]:

$$Sh = 2 + 0.72 Re_p^{1/2} Sc^{1/3} \tag{10.57}$$

The Schmidt number is

$$Sc = \frac{\mu_L}{\rho_L \mathcal{D}} \tag{10.26}$$

and the Sherwood number is

$$Sh = \frac{k_s d_{32}}{\mathcal{D}} \tag{10.58}$$

In equation (10.57) d_{32} is the mean particle diameter, $\mathcal{D}$ is the liquid phase diffusion coefficient and the particle Reynolds number is

$$Re_p = \frac{\rho_L d_{32} v_s}{\mu_L} \tag{10.59}$$

where v_s is the slip velocity between the particle and liquid. Clearly, this velocity is not well defined in a complex flow such as in a stirred tank, and is difficult to calculate. One approach is based on Kolmogoroff's theory of isotropic turbulence, which shows that the Reynolds number may be written as

$$Re_p = \frac{\varepsilon_T d_{32}^4}{v_L^3}$$

where

$$\varepsilon_T = P/\rho_L V = average \text{ specific power input } \left(W\,kg^{-1}\right)$$

$$v_L = \mu_L/\rho_L$$

A second approach described by Nienow (1985) is based on the slip velocity being approximately equal to the particle terminal velocity, but both methods have their drawbacks. Calculation of the mass transfer coefficient may be carried out using equations (10.57)–(10.60). The liquid–solid mass transfer area per unit volume is unknown and must be calculated from the Sauter mean particle size d_{32} and the volume fraction of particles in suspension, α:

$$a = \frac{6\alpha}{d_{32}} \qquad (10.61)$$

The overall mass transfer rate can now be calculated from equation (10.55), knowing the concentrations of solute material in the bulk flow and at the surface of the particle.

10.8   Scale-up of mixers from pilot trials

In many situations there is no clear-cut design method available and the only remedy is to make measurements on a pilot-scale mixer and scale up to plant-scale operation. This is not a straightforward exercise, particularly when more than one parallel or series unit operation occurs within the mixer. In the previous sections a number of design equations have been presented that should allow the engineer to make **estimates** of the speed, power and tank configuration to achieve the desired process result. Wherever possible, these equations have been given in dimensionless form: that is, they make use of the principal of similarity to ensure that geometric, dynamic or kinematic conditions remain the same, regardless of the scale of operation (Ch. 2).

Similarity	Quantities remaining constant
geometric	all geometric ratios
kinematic	velocities at geometrically similar points
dynamic	ratios of forces, e.g. equal *Re*, *Fr* or *We*

These methods allow extrapolation of results obtained on a small-scale experiment to full scale, assuming that all pertinent variables have been included in the original dimensional analysis and that the systems are fluid-dynamically similar. Design equations that contain dimensional constants should always be treated with caution; it would be unwise to extrapolate results much outside the range of the original experimental data.

There are several problems associated with maintaining similarity at different scale, as follows.

• In many operations (such as solids suspension, or gas–liquid mass transfer) the size of the particles or bubbles remains approximately constant while the dimensions of the mixer increase significantly.

- Physical constraints may preclude maintaining geometric similarity. For example, in fermenter design the ratio of reactor surface area to volume decreases with increasing scale. This means that it becomes increasingly difficult to remove the heat of reaction from the fermenter if geometric ratios remain constant. Typically, the aspect ratio of the reactor is increased at larger scales.
- The scale of scrutiny for the mixture should remain the same regardless of scale, as it is determined by the end use of the product. Therefore the range of length scales from the unmixed to mixed states may be greater at larger scales.
- Pilot-scale experiments can never be designed to cover all possible variables that might affect the process result. Therefore any model derived is likely to be incomplete in all details and some contingency should always be allowed during scale-up.
- Ensuring dynamic **and** kinematic similarity can give conflicting results. Scale-up using kinematic similarity may result in a change of flow regime, as the Reynolds number increases with increasing scale and therefore a different form of correlation might apply.

Two common scale-up rules have been widely applied in the past:
Constant power per unit volume

$$\frac{P_1}{V_1} = \frac{P_2}{V_2} \tag{10.62}$$

Constant tip speed

$$N_1 D_1 = N_2 D_2 \tag{10.63}$$

In the turbulent regime the power per unit volume varies as (see equations (10.5) and (10.13))

$$\frac{P}{V} \propto \frac{N^3 D^5}{T^3} \propto N^3 D^2 \tag{10.64}$$

so that at **constant tip speed**, equations (10.63) and (10.64) show that

$$\frac{P}{V} \propto \frac{1}{D} \tag{10.65}$$

That is, as the scale increases the specific power input decreases. Clearly then, the first rule gives a more conservative estimate of full-scale operating conditions (except for systems that might be damaged by overmixing or for liquid blending). The constant power per unit volume rule may, however, lead to a grossly oversized and uneconomic design. Table 10.4 illustrates some of the difficulties in maintaining similarity. In Table 10.4 all parameters at the pilot scale are assigned a value of 1, enabling comparison of their relative changes on scale-up. In each of the last three columns the

Table 10.4 The effect of scale-up by a factor of 5 on mixer properties (geometrically similar systems)

Property	Pilot Scale	Plant Scale		
		Constant P/V	Constant πND	Constant Re
Impeller diameter, D	1.0	5.0	5.0	5.0
Power, P	1.0	125	25	0.2
P/V	1.0	1.0	0.2	0.0016
Speed, N	1.0	0.34	0.2	0.04
Pumping capacity, Q_L	1.0	42.5	25	5.0
Tip speed, πND	1.0	1.7	1.0	0.2
Reynolds Number, $\dfrac{\rho_L ND^2}{\mu_L}$	1.0	8.5	5.0	1.0

power input per unit volume, tip speed and Reynolds number are held constant, respectively. Note that for turbulent flow, dimensionless numbers such as N_{po}, $N\theta$, N_Q are independent of Reynolds number and so dynamic similarity of Re can be relaxed. Clearly choosing one scale-up rule rather than another has a very large impact on the full-scale design, even when the scale factor is only 5.

Some operations, such as solids suspension, are notoriously difficult to scale up, and there are many conflicting rules presented in the literature: for example Voit and Mersmann (1986) report that the scale-up rule for solids suspension is $P/V \propto D^a$, where the literature values of a vary between –0.7 and +0.5! These problems are further compounded in three-phase reactors, where gas–liquid dispersion, liquid-phase mixing and solids suspension may all be required simultaneously: gas–liquid dispersion is often scaled using constant power input per unit volume, liquid blending may be scaled using equal impeller speeds ($N\theta$ = constant) for equal blend times, and there is no clear-cut method for the last operation. Usually the power requirement for scaling liquid blending on equal impeller speed is not feasible and longer blend times are used at larger scales.

It should be clear from this discussion that a great deal of art remains in overcoming the scale-up problem and that successful design depends as much on experience as on fundamental science.

10.9 Alternative mixing devices

The discussion in the previous sections of this chapter has concentrated on the design of stirred-tank mixers for low- and high-viscosity fluids. The range of mixing problems encountered in the food and chemical process industries is vast, and often more specialized mixing devices are required.

For very high-viscosity materials (such as bread or biscuit doughs, which cannot be handled by anchor or helical ribbons), **kneaders** or **Z-blade mixers** are used (see Fig. 10.21). Generally, these mixers are mounted horizontally and have two counter-rotating blades; clearances between the blades and trough are very close so as to eliminate stagnant regions and eliminate build-up of sticky material on the wall. Mixing is achieved by a combination of bulk movement and intense shearing and extensional flow as the material passes between two blades or between the wall and a blade.

Some comminution processes (such as the dispersion of fine powders or emulsifications) cannot be carried out in conventional stirred tanks because it is not possible to generate large enough shear stresses to break down agglomerates or particles. In these cases, ball mills or dispersion mills may

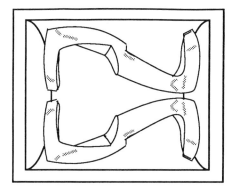

Fig. 10.21 Schematic diagram of a Z-blade mixer.

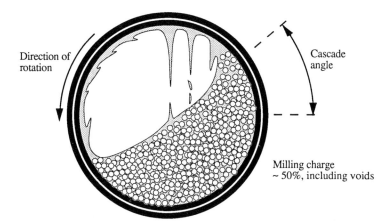

Direction of rotation

Cascade angle

Milling charge ~ 50%, including voids

Fig. 10.22 The ball mill.

be used to break aggregates or to form stable emulsions. The **ball mill** (Fig. 10.22) consists of a horizontally mounted, cylindrical drum, which is partially filled with high-density metal balls. The outer drum rotates slowly allowing the balls to roll over each other by gravity, creating very large shearing forces in the 'nip' between adjacent balls. The ball mill generally operates about half-full of balls, at a rotational speed that is about 60% of that for the balls to be thrown out to the walls by centrifugal force. This gives a cascade angle of about 20–30°. These devices are difficult to use in the food industry as the balls wear and may, in severe conditions, chip or shatter.

Dispersion mills (Fig. 10.23) make use of a very high-speed rotor blade, which moves inside a slotted stator. Close clearances between the rotor and stator give high shear stresses, which may be used for droplet or aggregate break-up, while the flow through the slots drives gross circulations within the vessel. These devices are suitable for the formation of emulsions: droplet break-up takes place in the high-energy dissipation regions close to the disperser head. The droplets are dispersed in the bulk liquid by the convective flow issuing from the head.

Screw extruders (Fig. 10.24) are often used in polymer processing and also have some applications in the food industry: for example, in the manufacture of reconstituted potato or corn snacks. Raw ingredients are added through a feed hopper and are conveyed by a rotating horizontal screw. High pressures and temperatures are generated within the barrel of the extruder, such that the food material is rapidly cooked, before being extruded through a die. Single or double counter-rotating screws are used, although the latter give more intense mixing at the expense of greater

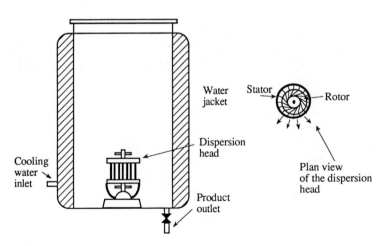

Fig. 10.23 Schematic diagram of a dispersion mill.

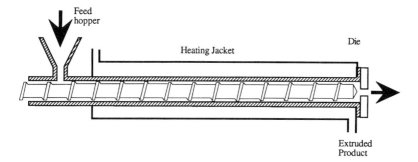

Fig. 10.24 Schematic diagram of a single-screw extruder.

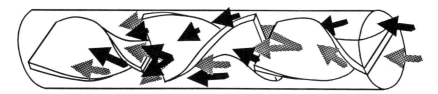

Fig. 10.25 Schematic diagram of an in-line mixer.

capital and running costs. The performance of single-screw machines can be improved by adding extra mixing heads or by using in-line static mixers.

The final category described in this section is **in-line static mixers**, so called because they have no moving parts and do not require a mechanical drive. The mixer consists of a number of mixer elements inserted in a length of straight pipe (Fig. 10.25). Mixing is achieved using the energy available in the liquid and results in a pressure loss as the process fluid passes through the mixing elements. The usual arrangement is to pump the raw ingredients through a length of pipe containing a number of static mixer elements (Fig. 10.25): the more difficult the mixing operations, the more elements are required. In the laminar regime, each static mixer element performs a cutting and twisting operation, as shown schematically in Fig. 10.5, so that after passing through a number of elements the scale of segregation (or the striation thickness) has been reduced to an acceptable level. The number of mixer elements, M, required in any application to reduce the striation thickness from δ_o to a smaller value δ is given by an expression of the form (Streiff, 1979)

$$\frac{\delta_o}{\delta} = \frac{1}{2^M}$$

(10.66)

for the mixer of Fig. 10.25, which offers *two* possible flow paths at each element.

Clearly then, static mixers are efficient for laminar blending operations, as doubling their volume squares the amount of mixing that occurs (as measured by a decrease in striation thickness).

Under turbulent flow conditions, the elements generate high turbulence intensities and promote rapid heat and mass transfer. The energy for mixing is provided by sizing the pump to give a larger pressure differential than would be required to overcome friction in an empty pipeline. Wilkinson and Cliff (1977) investigated the laminar flow pressure drop in a Kenics static mixer and proposed a modified form of the pipe flow pressure drop equation (see Ch. 2):

$$\Delta p = K \frac{4C_f \rho v^2 L}{2D} \tag{10.67}$$

where v is the velocity in the empty pipe, L is the length of the mixer and D is the internal diameter of the empty pipe. The factor K is the modification factor, which depends on Reynolds number and type of mixer elements.

These mixers are used for blending viscous materials [often with very different fluid properties, see Streiff (1979)], liquid–liquid droplet dispersion and incorporation of powders into liquids to form pastes. The essential difference between these devices and the mixers discussed previously is that in-line static mixers are intended to operate in continuous processes. Although the mixing within the elements is intense, the quality of the product depends on the operator's ability to ensure that the raw ingredients are supplied at the correct flowrates and in the right proportions. Therefore, if metering of the ingredients to the mixer is poor, the product will be homogeneous but may not match the required specification.

The design of static mixers (the number and type of mixing elements, and the pressure drop) have been much studied in the open literature, and much commercial information is available from mixer vendors (for example, Sulzer or Chemineer Kenics). A detailed description of the various types of in-line mixer is outside the scope of this chapter.

10.10 Mixing of particulate materials

In contrast to the fluid-mixing operations previously discussed, the mixing of solids is not an irreversible process. Mixtures of particles have a tendency to segregate or unmix owing mainly to differences in size between components; differences in density, shape, roughness and coefficient of restitution can also have a minor effect on segregation. Segregation occurs mainly because of the percolation of fine particles within the mixture: fines fall into gaps between large particles, slowly percolating to the bottom of the mixture, while large particles tend to rise to the top. Percolation segregation is surprisingly effective even when there are only small differences (~20%) in particles size. Examples of this situation are:

- **Vibration of a solid mixture.** This is the mechanism that results in the nuts and raisins (large particles) moving to the top of a pack of muesli, during transit.
- **Shearing of a solid mixture.** One layer of particles moves at a different velocity from another layer: small particles tend to percolate into the lower layer.
- **During pouring or discharge from a vessel or hopper into a heap.** Large particles roll down the surface of the heap, while smaller particles percolate through the surface layer into the stationary bulk. This method is used to separate coarser table sugar from caster sugar, using the difference in particle size.

Segregation can also occur because of differences in particle trajectories, during free fall or horizontal motion. These effects are a result of the particles having different drag coefficients (which depend on the particle Reynolds number) and different inertia.

The other significant difference between solids and fluid mixing is that there is no equivalent molecular diffusion effect in powder mixtures. In fluid mixtures this mechanism brings about complete homogenization, if given sufficient time and is particularly important in the final stages of mixing. In solids mixing, however, motion of the particles can only be achieved by input of energy to the system, and the final equilibrium state is determined by the mixer design and the particle-segregating properties.

10.10.1 The nature of particulate materials

Granular materials may be broadly grouped into two categories: (a) **free-flowing** or **cohesionless powders** and (b) **cohesive powders**. These characteristics may be easily identified by observing the discharge of a granular material from a hopper. The free-flowing material discharges smoothly, at a constant flowrate, whereas the cohesive powder discharges intermittently or not at all because of bridging within the hopper. Cohesion within a material is caused by interparticulate bonding forces due to moisture (formation of liquid bridges between particles or the overlap of adsorbed moisture layers on the surfaces of adjacent particles), electrostatic attractions, and van der Waals forces. The latter are only significant for particles less than about 1 μm diameter. In general, these bonding forces become less significant as the particle size increases. As a rough rule of thumb, particles with sizes greater than about 100 μm behave as free-flowing powders and are likely to segregate if components with different sizes are present. Particles with sizes less than 10 μm behave as cohesional mixtures and do not segregate easily, but may form agglomerates or aggregates. Geldart (1973) has presented a more detailed method of classifying powders according to their fluidization behaviour.

10.10.2 Solids mixers

There is a wide variety of solids mixers available. Harnby (1985) categorizes these mixers according to their mixing action.

Tumbler mixers. The particulates to be mixed are charged into a full enclosed vessel (typical designs are the roto-cube, double cone, Y- or V-shaped mixer: see Fig. 10.26). The vessel is filled to about half its total capacity and is rotated on an axis between two bearings, causing the solid particles to roll or tumble over each other continuously. The rotational speed is about half the critical speed at which centrifugal forces throw the solids out to the extremities of the container, and there is no relative motion of the particles. At the completion of mixing, the vessel may be removed from the mixer stand and transported to the next stage of the batch process.

Convective mixers. The solids are mixed in a stationary vessel by a rotating impeller or screw, which convects particles within the mixture. Examples of this type are:

- the **ribbon blender**, in which a helical blade (or Z blade) sweeps through a horizontal open trough or closed cylindrical vessel (Fig. 10.27). The

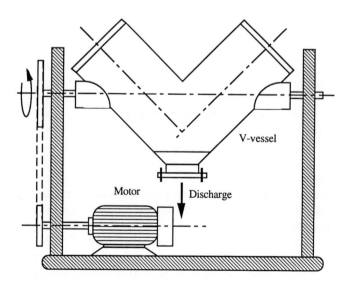

Fig. 10.26 V-shaped tumbler for solid–solid mixing.

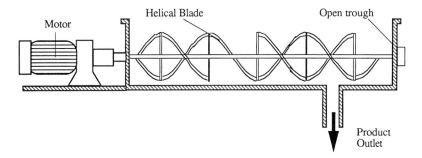

Fig. 10.27 Schematic diagram of a ribbon blender in an open trough.

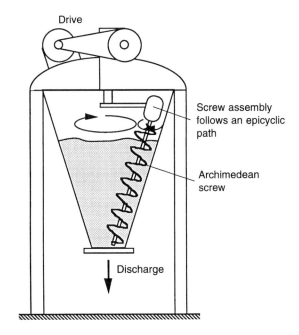

Fig. 10.28 The Nautamix convective mixer for solid–solid mixing.

mixer speed is generally low (<60 rpm) to minimize power input, heating of the mixture and particle degradation.
• the **Nautamix**, in which a small-diameter Archimedean screw rotates within a vertical, conical hopper (Fig. 10.28). Only particles in the vicinity of the screw are convected, but the driving action describes an epicyclic path within the hopper so that the blade progressively sweeps through all parts of the mixture.

Table 10.5 Selection of powder mixers

	Tumbler mixers	Convective mixers	Recirculating hoppers
Cleaning/sterility	Fully enclosed batch vessel, which may be constructed with smooth corners and with a polished surface finish or any other lining. No contact of the powder mixture with bearings or any other moving parts.	Bearings are in contact with the solids and there is a potential lubricant contamination problem. Vessels can have corners that are difficult to clean. Open troughs or vessels can disperse fine particles into the atmosphere: a dust hazard.	Difficult to flush out complete system between batches or if product specification changes frequently.
Particle degradation	Gentle action and low power input does not give comminution. Can only be used to mix weakly cohesive mixtures.	Low speed: little comminution. High speed: may be used to break down granules or agglomerates. Suitable for cohesive mixtures.	Negligible if recycle is by pneumatic conveying. Not suitable for strongly cohesive powders.
Controlled additions and heat transfer	Difficult to add materials during the mix without stopping the mixer. Addition of moisture creates large agglomerates, which are not easily broken. Difficult to use a cooling jacket.	Easily achieved, particularly with open troughs or vessels. Vessels may be jacketed to remove heat generated during mixing.	Easily achieved.
Batch or continuous operation	Not easily adapted for continuous use.	Possible to use as a batch or continuous mixer, although sufficient residence time must be allowed in the mixer to give the required degree of back-mixing. The amount of back-mixing depends on the impeller design.	Possible to use as a batch or continuous mixer.
Segregation	Rolling or tumbling motion promotes segregation and gives poor mixture quality (Harnby, 1967).	Large-scale circulation patterns reduce the amount of segregation. Good mixture quality achieved for strongly segregating materials (Harnby, 1967).	Segregation may occur due to percolation of small particles as the recycle flow pours onto a heap at the top of the hopper, or due to shear within the bulk flow.

Hopper mixers. During the discharge of a granular material from a hopper there are significant relative motions of the particles because of velocity gradients near the outlet orifice. Radial and axial mixing of different particulate components may be achieved by recycling the discharged material to the top of the hopper. This method relies on the powders being free-flowing and can be improved by collecting the discharge from several outlet locations within the hopper and combining them for recycling.

Table 10.5 summarizes the features of these mixer types and their suitability for various food-mixing operations.

Conclusions

There is surely no need to stress the importance of mixing operations, and their importance, for food processing. This chapter has introduced some of the key engineering aspects of such operations, covering the mixing of homogeneous liquids, liquid/liquid systems – including the formation of emulsions – gas/liquid systems, solid/liquid systems and solid mixtures. The chapter also outlines the design methods for these different operations, where they exist.

After reading this chapter you should know how to assess mixing quality and understand the mechanisms of mixing in the various operations and regimes described above. You will have encountered methods and correlations to estimate the power requirements for mixing in liquid-based systems. You should also understand the rules governing scale-up of mixing operations: this is particularly important since *ab initio* design methods for mixing processes are, as yet, far from completely developed.

The main emphasis in the chapter is, since this is the area where the science is best developed, on the design and selection of stirred mixing devices for fluids, but you should also understand the basic principles and selection criteria for other types of fluid mixing and for mixing dry or cohesive powders. A key theme of the chapter is the interrelationship between the material properties, the mechanisms of mixing, and the type of unit which is most appropriate for the particular mixing operation.

References and further reading

Bates, R.L., Fondy, P.L. and Corpstein, R.R. (1963) An examination of some geometric parameters of impeller power. *Industrial and Engineering Chemistry, Process Design and Development,* **2**, 310–314.

Bruijn, W., Van't Riet, K. and Smith, J.M. (1974) Power consumption with aerated Rushton turbines. *Transactions of the Institution of Chemical Engineers,* **52**, 88–104.

Calderbank, P.H. (1958) Physical rate processes in industrial fermentation. *Transactions of the Institution of Chemical Engineers,* **36**, 443–463.

Danckwerts, P.V. (1953) The definition and measurement of some characteristics of mixtures. *Applied Scientific Research,* **3**, 279–296.

Donaldson, R. (1985) in *Mixing in the Process Industries* (eds N. Harnby, M.F. Edwards and A.W. Nienow), Butterworth, London, Ch. 15.

Edwards, M.F. (1985) in *Mixing in the Process Industries* (eds N. Harnby, M.F. Edwards and A.W. Nienow), Butterworth, London, Ch. 7.

Edwards, M.F. and Ayazi-Shamlou, P. (1983) in *Low Reynolds Number Flow Heat Exchangers* (ed. Spacek, S), Hemisphere.

Geldart, D. (1973) Types of gas fluidisation. *Powder Technology*, **7**, 285–292.

Greaves, M. and Barigou, M. (1986) Estimation of gas holdup and impeller power in a stirred vessel, in *Fluid Mixing III*, Institution of Chemical Engineers Symposium Series 108, pp. 235–256.

Greaves, M. and Kobbacy, K.A.H. (1981) Power consumption and impeller dispersion efficiency in gas-liquid mixing, in *Fluid Mixing I*, Institution of Chemical Engineers Symposium Series 64, paper L1–L23.

Harnby, N. (1967) A comparison of the performance of industrial solids mixers using segregating materials. *Powder Technology*, **1**, 94–102.

Harnby, N. (1985) in *Mixing in the Process Industries* (eds N. Harnby, M.F. Edwards and A.W. Nienow), Butterworth, London, Ch. 3.

Hoogendorn, C.J. and den Hartog, A.P. (1967) Model studies on mixers in the viscous flow region. *Chemical Engineering Science*, **22**, 1689–1699.

Joshi, J.B., Pandit, A.B. and Sharma, M.M. (1982) Mechanically agitated gas–liquid reactors. *Chemical Engineering Science*, **37**, 813–844.

Kay, J.M. and Nedderman, R.M. (1985) *Fluid Mechanics and Heat Transfer*, Cambridge University Press, Cambridge.

Laufhutte, H.D. and Mersmann, A.B. (1985) Dissipation of power in stirred vessels, in *Proceedings Fifth European Conference on Mixing*, BHRA Fluid Engineering, Cranfield, paper 33, 331–340.

Lee, J.C., Tasakorn, P. and Belghazi, A. (1984) Fundamentals of drop breakage in the formation of liquid-liquid dispersions, in *Proceedings Institution of Chemical Engineers Symposium on Formation of Liquid–Liquid Dispersions*, London.

Mann, R. (1983) Gas–liquid contacting in mixing vessels. Institution of Chemical Engineers Research Fellowship report, Rugby.

McManamey, W.J. (1979) Sauter mean and maximum drop diameters of liquid–liquid dispersions in turbulent agitated vessels at low dispersed phase hold up. *Chemical Engineering Science*, **34**, 432–433.

Metzner, A.B. and Otto, R.E. (1957) Agitation of non-Newtonian fluids. *American Institution of Chemical Engineers Journal*, **3**, 3–10.

Michel, B.J. and Miller, S.A. (1962) Power requirements of gas–liquid agitated systems. *American Institution of Chemical Engineers Journal*, **8**, 262–271.

Middleton, J.C. (1985) in *Mixing in the Process Industries* (eds N. Harnby, M.F. Edwards and A.W. Nienow), Butterworth, London, Ch. 17.

Nagata, S. (1975) *Mixing. Principles and Applications*, Halsted Press, Tokyo.

Nienow, A.W. (1968) Suspension of solid particles in turbine agitated baffled vessels. *Chemical Engineering Science*, **23**, 1453–1459.

Nienow, A.W. (1985) in *Mixing in the Process Industries* (eds N. Harnby, M.F. Edwards and A.W. Nienow), Butterworth, London, Ch. 16.

Nienow, A.W. and Elson, T.P. (1988) Aspects of mixing in rheologically complex fluids. *Chemical Engineering Research and Design*, **66**, 16–21.

Nienow, A.W. and Miles, D. (1968) The effect of impeller/tank configurations on fluid-particle mass transfer. *Chemical Engineering Journal*, **15**, 13–24.

Nienow, A.W., Wisdom, D.J. and Middleton, J.C. (1978) The effect of scale and geometry on flooding, recirculation and power in gassed, stirred vessels, in *Second European Conference on Mixing*, BHRA Fluid Engineering, Cranfield, pp. F1–F16.

Poux, M., Fayolle, P., Bertrand, J. and Bridoux, D. (1991) Powder mixing: some practical rules applied to agitated systems. *Powder Technology*, **68**, 213–234.

Prochazka, J. and Landau, J. (1961) Homogenisation of miscible liquids in the turbulent regime. *Collection of Czech Chemical Communications*, **26**, 2961–2973.

Revill, B.K. (1982) Pumping capacity of disc turbine agitators – a literature review. *Fourth European Conference on Mixing*, BHRA Fluid Engineering, Cranfield, paper R1, 11–24.

Rielly, C.D. and Pandit A.B. (1988) Mixing of Newtonian liquids with large density and viscosity differences in mechanically agitated contactors, in *Sixth European Conference on Mixing*, BHRA Fluid Engineering, Cranfield, pp. 69–71.

Rowe, P.N., Claxton, K.T. and Lewis, J.B. (1965) Heat and Mass transfer from a single sphere in an extensive flowing fluid. *Transactions of the Institution of Chemical Engineers*, **43**, T14–T31.

Smith, J.M. & Warmoeskerken, M.M.C.G. (1986) The dispersion of gases in liquids with turbines, in *Fifth European Conference on Mixing*, BHRA Fluid Engineering, Cranfield, paper 13, 115–126.

Smith, J.M., Middleton, J.C. and van't Riet, K. (1977) in *Second European Conference on Mixing*, BHRA Fluid Engineering, Cranfield, paper F4, 51–66.

Streiff, F.A. (1979) Adapted motionless mixer design, in *Third European Conference on Mixing*, BHRA Fluid Engineering, Cranfield, pp. 171–188.

Uhl, V.W. and Gray, J.B. (1966) *Mixing Theory and Practice*, Vols I and II, Academic Press.

Van Dierendonck, L.L., Fortuin, J.M.H. and Venderbos, D. (1968) The specific contact area in gas–liquid reactors. *Fourth European Conference on Chemical Reactor Engineering*, pp. 205–215.

Van't Riet, K. and Smith, J.M. (1973) *Chemical Engineering Science*, **28**, 1031.

Voit, H. and Mersmann, A.B. (1986) General statement for the minimum stirrer speed during suspension. *German Chemical Engineering*, **9**, 101–106.

Warmoeskerken, M.M.C.G. and Smith, J.M. (1984) The flooding transition with gassed Rushton turbines, in *Fluid Mixing II*, Institution of Chemical Engineers Symposium Series 89, 59–67.

Wilkinson, W.L. and Cliff, M.J. (1977) An investigation into the performance of a static in-line mixer, in *Proceedings Second European Conference on Mixing*, BHRA Fluid Engineering, Cranfield, paper A2–A15.

Zwietering, T.N. (1958) Suspending of solid particles in liquid by agitators. *Chemical Engineering Science*, **8**, 244–253.

11 Process design: an exercise and simulation examples

C.A. ZAROR and D.L. PYLE

Introduction

One aim of process engineering is the design of process equipment and process flowsheets. The previous chapters in this book have described the scientific and engineering fundamentals of the design of process plant. This chapter allows the reader to develop the skills demonstrated previously, by carrying out a design exercise.

The example chosen is of a plant to manufacture a range of products from milk: cheese, whey protein concentrate, butter and alcohol. The stages of the design follow the stages discussed throughout the book.

It is first necessary to develop the flowsheet, using the ideas of Chapter 1 to follow the flows of all the streams through the system, and to identify areas where heat or cooling is required.

Once the basic flowsheet has been developed, and individual stream flowrates quantified, individual plant items can be designed. The techniques outlined elsewhere in this book can be used to estimate the size of the plant. Specific examples are shown of a tubular pasteurizer (Chapters 3 and 9) and the alcohol producing fermenter (Chapters 8 and 10). Simulations are provided on the enclosed computer disk of the operation both of the whole flowsheet and of these plant items. Computer modelling and computer-aided design is very important in the process industries; the programs given here are very simple, but illustrate the type of problem which can be solved and the use of computers to solve those problems. The simulations also allow an estimate of the cost of the plant and its profitability to be made.

This chapter is divided into two sections. The first outlines an extended design exercise, which is complemented by a spreadsheet program. The second includes details of several simulation exercises, which are also included in the computer disk with this book.

If you work through the design exercise and the accompanying computer-based problems you will learn how to:

Chemical Engineering for the Food Industry. Edited by P.J. Fryer, D.L. Pyle and C.D. Rielly. Published in 1997 by Blackie A & P, an imprint of Chapman & Hall, London. ISBN 0 412 49500 7.

- develop a mass balance within and around a complete process;
- develop energy balances around key operations;
- make a preliminary design of selected operations, including simple heat exchangers (with and without fouling), a spray drier and a fermenter;
- make an overall assessment of the process economics.

11.1   An integrated cheese plant: a design exercise

In this section we outline a more substantial problem, which readers should find a useful exercise in the application of some of the elementary design principles developed in the book. The exercise is based on a published account of an existing plant; in preparing the exercise we have made several simplifying assumptions, both about the process and about some of the basic data, and the reader should not assume that the design here is an accurate representation of the real process. We recommend the reader to attempt to follow through the design stages outlined below, before consulting our 'model' solution, as the point of the exercise is to provide an opportunity for 'learning by doing'.

The solutions to the mass balance and a simplified version of the economic analysis, and solutions to individual designs of a pasteurizer, a spray drier and a fermenter are also provided in a spreadsheet version on the accompanying computer disk. These programs will also provide an opportunity for the reader to explore the consequences of changing selected engineering and economic parameters, such as the feed composition, process efficiencies, product specifications, unit prices and heat transfer coefficients.

Tutors may also find the example, or variations on it, a useful one to adopt for class or group teaching. We have used this example as the basis of an extended preliminary design exercise (over around 10 hours) in our courses using the material in this book.

11.1.1   Process outline

This exercise is based on an extended description of the Golden Cheese Plant of California (see *Chilton's Food Engineering*, March 1986). The reader is strongly urged to read that article in order to gain a full understanding of the process. The process is highly integrated across the various stages of the operation, and it was justifiably recognized in *Food Engineering* as the Plant of the Year in 1985. Our version of the flowsheet incorporates several simplifications to help in the analysis, and we hope that those responsible for the process will be tolerant of our simplifications and any (unintended) misrepresentations.

Equally important, in compiling data and information for the design exercise we have made many assumptions about data and process efficiency, and we must emphasize that these are not meant to represent the actual plant. Wherever possible, we have tried to ensure that our assumptions are reasonable.

A simplified process flowsheet showing only the principal operations and process streams is given in Fig. 11.1. A more detailed flowsheet will be found in the journal article, but it is convenient to give a simplified description of the process based on our flowsheet.

The plant produces four main products from the milk feed: a hard (cheddar) cheese; whey butter; a whey protein concentrate; and concentrated distilled alcohol (ethanol). In addition there are a few additional liquid and gaseous effluent streams. Our calculations do not include the waste treatment of these streams, which is not to deny the considerable importance of this aspect.

We suggest that the process calculations assume a continuous feed based on a daily input of 1500 tonnes of milk to the plant. The milk is held in an intermediate cold store at 4 °C before being fed to the pasteurizer (essentially a heat exchanger operating at around 65–68 °C), and then to a cooler to reduce its temperature at the inlet to the cheese vat to 30 °C. Starter culture and rennin are added in small proportions to the contents of the vat; the cheese-making process results in the solidifying curd, which is salted during the later stages of the process, and an aqueous whey stream, comprising unconsumed proteins, fat, lactose and ash – i.e. mineral salts). The cheese is formed into blocks, sealed, cooled and stored to mature.

The whey stream, meanwhile, is separated into a fat-rich cream and a dilute aqueous stream containing mainly proteins, ash and lactose. The cream is pasteurized as before and used as the feed for butter-making. A stream of aqueous butter whey is a secondary by-product of this operation.

The dilute stream from the separator contains two further potentially valuable components, albeit in low concentration: whey proteins and lactose. In this process the whey proteins are concentrated, using crossflow ultrafiltration, and then spray-dried to produce solid whey protein concentrate. The liquid permeate from the ultrafilters is treated further using reverse osmosis, and some of the ash components are also removed at this stage. Demineralized water is a valuable by-product of this part of the operation, whose main objective is to produce a suitably concentrated lactose solution to serve as the feed to a (batch) fermenter. The anaerobic fermentation produces ethanol in solution, a carbon-dioxide-rich gas stream, and biomass (i.e. spent yeast) for disposal. The ethanol solution is concentrated by distillation to spirit-grade levels; the dilute aqueous bottom product from the distillation process must be treated before final disposal.

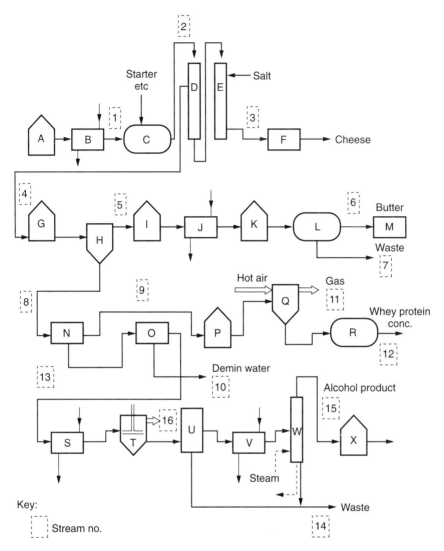

Fig. 11.1 Simplified flowsheet of cheese-making plant: A, milk storage; B, pasteurizer; C, cheese vat; D, cheddar tower; E, block former; F, sealing, cooling and storage; G, whey storage; H, cream separator; I, cream storage; J, pasteurizer; K, cream storage; L, whey butter maker; M, whey butter packaging and storage; N, ultrafiltration plant; O, reverse osmosis plant; P, retentate storage; Q, spray drier; R, whey protein concentrate packaging and storage; S, cooling; T, fermenters; U, broth separator; V, heat exchanger; W, distillation plant; X, azeotropic alcohol storage.

The actual plant has a reported annual intake of 800 million lb (360 million kg) of milk, and produces 80 million lb (36 million kg) of cheese, 5 million lb (2.3 million kg) of whey protein concentrate (containing 50–75% protein), 2.2 million lb of butter and 2.2 million lb of alcohol (1 million kg each).

11.1.2   Suggested design procedure

In reality the first stage in the design process would be the production of a detailed flowsheet showing all the major plant items and the principal flows of materials and services, such as steam and cooling water, and the waste treatment systems. In this case the flowsheet provided may be taken as the basis for the calculations; the reader should first ensure that he or she thoroughly understands the process and the rationale behind the sequence of operations.

Then, the following stages should be attempted.

1. *Material balance over the process.* You should build up a comprehensive mass balance over the whole process in order to define all flows and compositions through the plant. To assist in this process the main streams are indicated on the flowsheet (1, 2 etc.), and the mass balance should encompass all the streams. Section 11.1.3 gives details of input flows and compositions and, where necessary, indicates the suggested assumptions to be made in order to complete the balance over the process units.
2. *Energy balance.* The major energy-requiring operations should be identified and a preliminary estimate should be made of the energy requirements for the plant as a whole.
3. *Detailed unit design.* We have also given additional information on two plant items: the first pasteurizer and the fermenter. This is a sufficient basis for a more detailed process design of these units, including estimation of the equipment size and, in the case of the fermenter, of the power requirements for mixing.
4. *Process economics.* The completed mass and energy balances together with the economic data in the datasheet will allow you to do a preliminary (and very notional) economic appraisal of the plant as you have designed it.

As noted earlier, compiled versions of spreadsheet calculations, which will allow you to check some of your calculations and to carry out some simple sensitivity calculations, are given with this text. In particular, the material balance and economic analyses are contained in the programme CHEESE.XLS. Sample pasteurizer and fermenter designs are contained in PASTEUR.XLS, and CSTR.XLS respectively; an additional program, RECYCLE.XLS, complements the last program by including the possibility of cell recycle to the fermenter. Finally, the programme SPRAYDRY.XLS solves the simultaneous mass and energy balances around a spray drier.

11.1.3   Design data

Suggested values of key parameters needed to complete the material and energy balances are given below. Although the values do not necessarily correspond to the actual values in the Golden Cheese Plant, they are reasonable in the context of this process. You can vary any of the parameters in order to study the sensitivity of the design to the principal assumptions, provided the fundamental constraints (for example, that the components of a mixture must sum to 100%) are not violated.

Suggested design basis: 1500 tonne/day milk

Compositions, yields etc.   All compositions are in wt% unless otherwise noted.

1.   *Milk composition* (= feed to cheese vat, stream 1)

Component	Weight (%)
Water	87.2
Fat	3.9
Protein:	(3.3)
Casein	2.7
Whey proteins	0.6
Lactose	4.9
Ash	0.7

2.   *Starter.*   Take this to be 1 wt% of milk feed.

3.   *Rennin.*   Take this to be 0.01 wt% of milk feed.
(Note: in the calculations count items 2 and 3 as if they were water).

4.   *The cheese-maker.*   Assume that the following fractions of these components in the milk feed are retained in the cheese product, stream 3:

Component	Component in cheese / component in milk
Fat	0.89
Casein	0.94
Whey proteins	0.04

Also, assume that the fat content of the unsalted cheese = 33.1%.

Lactose and ash are incorporated into the aqueous component of the cheese in the same proportions as they occur in the feed milk.

You may compare your results with the following typical approximate compositions:

Cheddar		Sweet whey	
Component	(wt %)	Component	(wt %)
Water	36.8	Total solids	6.5
Protein	24.9	Protein	<1
Fat	33.1	Fat	0.3
C/hydrate	1.3	Lactose	5.8
Ash	3.9	Ash	0.5
		BOD	c. $30000\,\mathrm{mg\,l^{-1}}$

5. *Salt.* Assume that this is added so as to make 1.5 wt% of the cheese product.

6. *Cream separator.* Assume that the cream (stream 5) is 35 wt% fat and that the bottom product (stream 8, to whey processing) is 0.05% fat.

Assume all other dissolved components in the water phase are distributed between the top and bottom products from the separator in the same proportions as they exist in the feed to the separator.

7. *Whey butter (stream 6).* Assume 95% of fat in the cream is retained in the butter; also assume the butter is 81% fat.

8. *Buttermilk (stream 7).* Neglect any additional wash water added during the butter-making process.

9. *Ultrafilter (unit N).* Assume all the protein is retained in the retentate, stream 9, and that the retentate is 30% protein. Also assume that all the fat is in this stream, and neglect any ash and lactose.

10. *Demineralization and reverse osmosis.* Assume that the units operate so that the feed to the fermenter (stream 13) is <0.5% ash and >4.6% lactose (a reasonable value for this is around 6%). This fixes the amount of water and ash to be removed at this stage.

11. *Spray drier: whey protein concentrate.* Assume that the final product (stream 12) contains 4% moisture.

For comparison with your answer, a typical WPC composition is in the range: 50–85% protein; 1.2–4% fat; 4% + lactose.

12. Feed to fermenter (stream 13)

Lactose	>4.6% (assume 6%)
Protein	<1%
Ash	<0.5%
Yeast extract	$10 \, gl^{-1}$
Phosphate	$1 \, gl^{-1}$
Mg sulphate	$0.5 \, gl^{-1}$
Amm. sulphate	$1 \, gl^{-1}$
pH	6–6.4

13. Fermentation.

Assume that in this case the fermentation uses the GRAS yeast *Kluyveromyces fragilis*, operating at pH 4 and 38 °C.

	Yield coefficients
$Y_{p/s}$	0.49 kg ethanol/kg lactose consumed
$Y_{x/s}$	0.1 kg cells/kg lactose consumed
$Y_{CO_2/s}$	0.47 kg CO_2/kg lactose consumed

Assume that 98% of the lactose in the feed is consumed in the fermentation. To simplify the calculation assume that all the supplements are utilized.

In sizing the fermenter assume Monod kinetics (Chapter 8) with $\mu_m = 0.3$–$0.4 \, h^{-1}$, with lactose as the limiting substrate and $K_m = 0.1 \, kg \, m^{-3}$.

14. Ethanol product (stream 15).

Assume that this product is concentrated to 95% (i.e. the azeotrope).

15. Disposal (stream 14).

This will include the spent yeast and the dilute bottom product from the distillation column.

16. Some physical and thermal properties

Milk

Density: $1032 \, kg \, m^{-3}$ at 20 °C
Viscosity: $1.42 \, mN \, s \, m^{-2}$
Mean heat capacity: $3768 \, J \, kg^{-1} \, K^{-1}$
Thermal conductivity: $0.58 \, W \, m^{-1} \, K^{-1}$

Whey: viscosity = $1.16\,mN\,s\,m^{-2}$ at 25 °C
Fat: mean heat capacity $2010\,J\,kg^{-1}\,K^{-1}$
Cream: density = $900\,kg\,m^{-3}$ at 40 °C
Butter: mean heat capacity = $1382\,J\,kg^{-1}\,K^{-1}$
Cheese: mean heat capacity = $2093\,J\,kg^{-1}\,K^{-1}$

17. Some approximate economic data

Installed capital cost (K): £100 million
Maintenance (annual cost): 5% K p.a.
Discount rate: 10% plus

Unit costs:
Labour: £12000 pa per worker (166 total)
Milk: £0.14/kg
Starter: £0.5/kg
Salt: £20/tonne
Steam: £0.8/tonne*
Electricity: £0.056/kWh*
Power, overall: £60/MWh*
Cooling water: £0.006/tonne*
Waste treatment: £0.2/kg BOD removed
or: £2/m³ effluent treated

*Note: assume total daily energy and cooling requirements = 60 MWh

Unit prices of products:
Cheese: £1400–1800/tonne
Cream: £1600/tonne
Whey butter: £1400/tonne
WPC: £400–800/tonne
Demin water: £0.4/tonne
Alcohol: £1000/tonne
Spent yeast: £100–300/tonne

11.1.4   Integrated cheese plant: commentary on solution

To help the reader to understand the solution presented in the attached spreadsheet, some notes on the method and assumptions used are presented below. These should, of course, be read in conjunction with the problem statement and the design data above. The programs are written using default values for the major parameters. Most of these can be changed, but we recommend that you save the default version of the programs.

  1. *Cheese vat (streams 1–4).*   The unsalted cheese and whey compositions are calculated by assuming that the input comprises milk, starter and

rennin (counting the last two as water). The information that 89% of the fat, 94% of the casein and 4% of the whey protein are retained in the cheese allows their masses in the cheese to be calculated directly. The fat is 33.1% of the cheese, so the total weight of cheese can then be calculated. Finally, we assume that the other components (water, lactose and ash) (making up 66.9% of the cheese) are in the same proportion as in the liquid feed to the cheese vat. Thus the quantity and composition of stream 2 can be calculated. The composition of the whey stream (stream 4) now follows directly, from mass balances over the vat on each component.

The composition of the salted cheese (stream 3) differs only from stream 2 by the addition of salt.

2. Cream separator (calculation of streams 5 and 8). There are two steps in this calculation.

The first stage is to calculate the flow split across the separator. To illustrate the method, let the total feed be F and its fat content be f. Let the top and bottom output flows be T and B, with fat contents x ($= 0.35$) and y ($= 0.0005$) respectively.

Then mass balances give:

$$\text{Overall:} \quad F = T + B$$
$$\text{Fat:} \quad Ff = Tx + By$$

Knowing F, f, x and y the two equations can be solved for T and B, and the quantities of fat in each calculated.

The remainder of these streams is the water phase, containing lactose, ash etc. in the same ratios, that is, on a fat-free basis, as in the feed F (see Example 1.2, Chapter 1). Then the aqueous phase components can be computed using a fat-free basis for this part of the calculation.

3. Whey butter production (calculation of streams 6 and 7). This involves a similar calculation: knowing that 95% of the fat in stream 5 (the feed) is retained in the butter, and that this is 81% fat, allows one to calculate the fat in the butter, the total butter and, by difference, the sweet whey stream. The composition of the aqueous phases in these two is calculated as in the previous section.

4. Ultrafiltration and demineralization plant (calculation of streams 9, 10 and 13). The retentate (9) is calculated directly, knowing that it contains all the protein and that the protein is 30% of the stream. We have assumed that the retentate contains all the fat from stream 8 but no lactose and ash.

Stream 13 contains all the lactose from stream 8; knowing its concentration (here 6%), allows one to calculate the total of stream 13.

We have also assumed that stream 10 from the reverse osmosis plant is pure water plus an ash-rich stream (which for mass balance purposes only are shown as if they were one stream); the ash in this stream must be sufficient to ensure that stream 13 (whose total is already calculated) contains 0.5% ash.

5.   *Spray drier (streams 11 and 12).*   Stream 9 is the feed. All the protein ends up in the dried concentrate; the total concentrate is readily calculated as it has a moisture content of 4%. The air requirements are not included in the calculation. However, see also section 11.2.6.

6.   *Fermenter (streams 14–16).*   The composition of the inlet stream (13) assumes a lactose concentration of 6% and an ash content of 0.5%; the other supplements are added in the concentrations specified on the datasheet. The calculation assumes that 98% of the lactose is consumed.

The gas stream may be calculated by assuming that it contains all the carbon dioxide produced (knowing that 0.47 kg are produced per kg of lactose used up). The composition of the liquid stream from the fermenter follows by a similar process of calculation, assuming that all the supplements are used up.

The waste streams are calculated by assuming that they together include all the yeast biomass, any residual components (such as lactose) and water. The ethanol concentration in the waste stream has been assumed to be zero in this calculation.

11.2   Computer simulations

11.2.1   Introduction

The computer simulations included on the disk are designed to illustrate selected aspects of the material in this book and, in particular, aspects of process design and control.

No previous knowledge of computer operations is required to run the programs, which run under DOS.

Most simulations presented here are written in Excel. You need this spreadsheet program, or one compatible with it, on your hard disk to run the programs. Instructions on how to load the main program and the simulations are given below. One simulation concerned with process dynamics and control has been written in TurboBASIC and can be called up directly once the computer is switched on and the operating system loaded.

Each simulation is briefly described below.

Spreadsheet simulations.   Copies of several spreadsheet simulations are on the disk. Each is described in some detail in the following sections.

To load the programs

- Load the disk in the floppy drive (e.g. drive A)
- Open Excel
- Open the desired program from drive A.

Programs included (entitled NAME.XLS)

- CHEESE: This is a simplified model of the integrated cheese-making plant described in section 11.1. It features the unit-by-unit and overall material balances and an economic evaluation.
- PASTEUR: This is a steady-state design of a continuous shell-in-tube heat exchanger to be used for milk pasteurization, with either steam or hot water as the heating fluid. It corresponds approximately to the pasteurizer (plant item B) in the cheese-making plant.
- CSTR: This simulates the operation of a perfectly mixed continuous anaerobic fermenter with Monod kinetics.
- RECYCLE: This simulates the continuous fermenter with cell recycle. This and the previous program can be used to design the alcohol fermenter in the cheese plant.
- SPRAYDRY: This simulates the steady-state operation of a spray drier, based on simultaneous mass and energy balances. It can be used to carry out a preliminary design of the spray drier used for whey protein concentrate production in the cheese plant.

Process dynamics and control simulation.   This simulation is written in TurboBASIC and is compiled to run directly under DOS without the need of any other program. The program is called CONTROL and is a simulation of a feedback temperature control system in a continuous liquid heater tank. It shows the dynamic response of the system to a step change in the feed temperature. Two control laws (P and PI) can be selected and the effect of time delays can be studied.

The program can be loaded directly from the floppy drive (e.g. drive A) by typing **A:CONTROL**.

11.2.2   Integrated cheese production simulation

Program: CHEESE.XLS.   This spreadsheet simulates a mass balance and an economic analysis for the main components in the integrated cheese plant described in detail in the design exercise presented in section 11.1. The program is preloaded with default parameters and design assumptions (see sections 11.1.3 and 11.1.4 for details) but you can change many of these, just as with the other spreadsheet programs. Data can be entered only in unprotected cells, which are highlighted on the screen. Process data, such as compositions, process unit parameters etc. can be input into screen 1;

economic data and parameters can be entered via screens 4 and 5. The program can be used to estimate the effect of changes in these parameters on the engineering and economic performance. The feasibility of the project is measured in terms of its net present value and internal rate of return.

11.2.3   Heat exchanger simulation

Program: PASTEUR.XLS.   This simulation solves the steady-state design equations for a shell-in-tube heat exchanger. The heat exchanger is to be used for the pasteurization of a milk stream using either steam or hot water as the heating medium. This operation involves heating up the milk to the pasteurization temperature and then maintaining the fluid under adiabatic conditions for the prescribed pasteurization time, usually in a well-insulated section at the heater outlet.

A preliminary design of an appropriate shell-and-tube heat exchanger to heat up the milk to the pasteurization temperature is simulated here. It is required to estimate the heat load and heat transfer area necessary, together with an estimate of the number and length of tubes and the pressure drop on the tube side. Typical fouling resistances can be incorporated in the calculation; by comparing the sizes of the exchanger that result, some estimates of a design fouling resistance and final heat exchanger size can be made.

Default values for all the parameters have been saved into this program, so that the program will produce a filled screen. Data input by the user is allowed in those cells that are highlighted on your screen; the contents of some cells, especially those containing formulae, are protected and should not be changed. If you try to enter new data into these cells a message that the cell is protected will appear. The user can specify the principal operating parameters, such as flowrates, pipe diameter, the fluid velocity in the pipe, all temperatures and the steam and water film heat transfer coefficients.

Design equations.   The equations used are based on the heat exchanger design in Chapter 3, namely:

$$Q = Wc_p\Delta T = AU\Delta T_{lm} \tag{3.25}$$

where W and ΔT are the flowrate and temperature increase of the milk stream. The overall heat transfer coefficient, assuming thin-walled tubes, is given (see section 3.3.3) by

$$\frac{1}{U} = \frac{1}{h_1} + \frac{1}{h_2} + R_F \tag{9.42}$$

where h_1 and h_2 are the process (i.e. milk) and heating-side heat transfer coefficients, and R_F is the fouling resistance. The process or tube-side coefficient is given by the Dittus–Boelter equation:

$$Nu = 0.023 \, Re^{0.8} Pr^{0.4} \tag{3.18}$$

The shell-side coefficient depends on the heating fluid; either steam or water can be chosen. In the first case, the user specifies the steam-side temperature. With water as heating fluid, the inlet and outlet temperatures can be specified. The user can also supply values for the shell-side coefficient, for which representative default values are given in the program. The user can also supply values of the fouling resistance R_F.

Data. Assume a milk flowrate of 1500 tonnes day^{-1}, at an inlet temperature of 4 °C. Assume a single-pass exchanger. The manufacturers recommend tube-side operating velocities of ca. 1.5 m s^{-1} inside 2.5 cm external diameter tubes of 1.6 mm wall thickness. Saturated steam at 3 bar is available; this can be used directly or to heat water to 80 °C.

Suggested shell-side heat transfer coefficients are: 4 kW m^{-2} K^{-1} if steam is used, 1.5 kW m^{-2} K^{-1} for water. Estimates of fouling resistance: at $t = 0$, exchanger is clean; final resistance to be between 10^{-4} and 2×10^{-3} m^2 K W^{-1}.

Mean thermophysical properties of milk:

Density, ρ: 1032 kg m^{-3}
Specific heat capacity, c_P: 3.768 kJ kg^{-1} K^{-1}
Thermal conductivity, λ: 0.58 W m^{-1} K^{-1}
Viscosity, μ: 1.42 mN s m^{-2}

Assume a pasteurization temperature of 68 °C.

The simulation assumes a single pass exchanger; choosing a multi-pass exchanger (which is possible in the spreadsheet) will reduce the length of the exchanger. However, for simplicity, we have not incorporated the true effect of multi-pass operation on the overall heat transfer.

Calculation procedure

- Given the flowrate, mean velocity and tube diameter, calculate the number of tubes, Re, Pr, Nu (from equation (3.18)) and thus the tube-side heat transfer coefficient.
- Given the shell-side coefficient and fouling resistance, calculate the overall heat transfer coefficient U from equation (9.42).
- Given the milk flowrate and temperature rise, calculate the heat duty, log mean temperature difference ΔT_{lm} and, from equation (3.26), heat transfer area tube area, and thus tube length.
- Finally, given the tube-side conditions, calculate the friction factor and tube-side pressure drop from equations (2.70) and (2.74).

This last step is NOT included in the spreadsheet.

11.2.4   Steady-state simulation of a bioreactor

Program: CSTR.XLS.   This spreadsheet simulates the performance of a continuous well-mixed fermenter with Monod kinetics and constant yield coefficient, and provides the basis for the design of a continuous fermenter similar to the one used in the alcohol production stage of the cheese production plant.

The simulation assumes Monod growth kinetics (see Chapter 8) with the following constant parameters:

$$\mu_m = 0.4\,h^{-1}$$
$$K_m = 0.1\,kg\,m^{-3}$$
$$Y_{xs} = 0.1\ kg\,cells\ (kg\,substrate)^{-1}$$

The yield coefficient Y is defined in Chapter 1. These parameters are fixed.

Assuming Monod kinetics (equation (8.13)), the equations for the outlet substrate and cell concentrations for a continuous steady well-mixed reactor (section 8.3.4) with sterile feed are

$$c = \frac{K_m D}{\mu_m - D}$$

and

$$x = Y_{xs}\left(c_i - c\right)$$

The user can explore the consequences on c and x of changing the inlet substrate concentration c_i, feed flowrate and fermenter volume (i.e. dilution rate, $D = Q/V$). It is also interesting to study how the productivity P (i.e. production rate of cells per unit volume of fermenter) varies with dilution rate (i.e. residence time). The productivity is given by

$$P = Dx$$

Based on the simulation here you are recommended to undertake a specific exercise to design a continuous fermenter to convert the lactose stream to ethanol in the continuous cheese-making plant. For this, assume a liquid feed (stream 13 in the flowsheet) of 1150 m³/day, with a lactose (i.e. substrate concentration) of 6 wt%. You may also assume a yield coefficient $Y_{ps} = 0.5\,kg$ ethanol/kg lactose consumed; also assume that the ethanol production is growth-related (that is, the rate of ethanol production is directly proportional to the rate of cell production). The maximum productivity for ethanol production thus corresponds to the point of maximum cell productivity. The design process involves:

- the choice of optimum dilution rate D (which should be chosen to maximize productivity);

- estimation of the fermenter volume, for the specified flowrate;
- assuming a standard configuration, calculation of the fermenter dimensions;
- calculation of the input and output concentrations, flowrates and ethanol productivity.

Having sized the fermenter you can then estimate the mixing power requirements. Assuming a standard fermenter configuration, you should calculate the power requirements for selected Reynolds numbers using the power number/Reynolds number curve (Fig. 10.11). For each condition you can calculate the stirrer-tip speed and the characteristic mixing time in the fermenter. On the basis of this information, recommend a suitable set of conditions. Assume that the broth properties are the same as water.

Note that only the cell growth part of this exercise is included in the spreadsheet.

11.2.5 Steady-state simulation of bioreactor with cell recycle

Program: RECYCLE.XLS. This spreadsheet, like CSTR.XLS, simulates the performance of a well-mixed fermenter, assuming Monod growth kinetics. Unlike the previous spreadsheet, however, this program includes the possibility of cell recycle. A flowsheet, on which the nomenclature is also defined, is given in Fig. 11.2.

The simulation assumes Monod growth kinetics (see Chapter 8) with the following default values (all of which can be changed):

$$\mu_m = 0.5 \, h^{-1}$$
$$K_m = 0.5 \, kg \, m^{-3}$$
$$Y_{xs} = 0.4 \, kg \, cells \, (kg \, substrate)^{-1}$$

The yield coefficient Y_{xs} is defined in Chapter 1.

Process model. The reader should derive the steady-state equations for the system. The following assumptions have been made in the model simulated here:

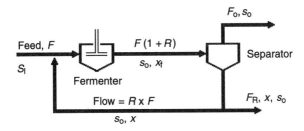

Fig. 11.2 Fermenter with cell recycle.

- steady-state behaviour;
- no reaction outside the fermenter;
- no cells in separator overflow, F_o;
- cell concentration x identical in the recycle stream and in the product stream F_R ($F_R = F - F_o$).

Note that the cell concentration leaving the fermenter, x_F, and the concentration in the recycle (or product) stream, x, are related by

$$x_F(1+R) F = x\left[(1+R)F - F_o\right]$$

Calculation procedure. The program is preloaded with the default parameters listed in the table below. All these parameters may subsequently be changed.

Parameter	Default value
Feed flowrate, F	$1000\,\mathrm{m^3\,h^{-1}}$
Substrate concentration, c_i	$30\,\mathrm{kg\,m^{-3}}$
Overflow, F_o	$0.95F = 950\,\mathrm{m^3\,h^{-1}}$
Recycle ratio, R	0.5
(Recycle $= R \times F$)	(recycle flow $= 500\,\mathrm{m^3\,h^{-1}}$)
Volume, V	$1000\,\mathrm{m^3}$
Specific growth rate, μ_m	$0.5\,\mathrm{h^{-1}}$
Growth yield, Y_{xs}	0.4 kg cells/kg substrate consumed
K_m	$0.5\,\mathrm{kg\,m^{-3}}$

It is suggested that readers study the effect of varying the key recycle parameters on the fermenter performance and, in particular, compare its performance (cell concentration, substrate utilization and productivity, shift in washout conditions) with the fermenter without recycle. The simulation reduces to Example 11.8 by setting R and $F_o = 0$.

Finally, the system design for the lactose conversion stage in the cheese-making plant can also be developed here, for comparison with the design in the previous simulation. This program also allows easy changes in the growth kinetic parameters, and you may like to explore the sensitivity of the design to the chosen parameters whose default values are slightly different across these examples.

11.2.6 Mass and energy balance over a spray drier

Program: SPRAYDRY.XLS. This spreadsheet is based on the mass and energy balances developed in Example 1.11 to represent the input/output performance of a spray drier to provide a dried milk product. The default values are close to those used in Example 1.11. The simulation calculates the input air flow, output flows of gas and solid and their compositions when the following parameters are defined:

- input flowrate, solids content and temperature of liquid milk;
- inlet air temperature and humidity;
- outlet solids temperature and moisture content;
- outlet air temperature.

You can readily examine the range of feasible operation and the variation in the input air flowrate with changes in the design conditions.

When you have familiarized yourself with the program, you should then attempt to establish the likely operating conditions for the spray drier in the whey-processing line of the cheese-making plant (i.e. stream 9, the retentate stream from the ultrafiltration plant). The whey protein concentrate will normally be at least 70 wt% solids. You should assume that the thermal properties of the dilute whey stream are the same as those built into the program as default values.

You should also calculate the energy input (i.e. as hot air) into the process in order to study how this varies with the design conditions. This calculation must be performed manually.

11.2.7 Simulation of the dynamics and feedback control of a simple process

Program: CONTROL.EXE. This simulation is compiled and, therefore, can be run directly from the operating system. Simply type the command **CONTROL**, making sure that the current drive corresponds to that where the CONTROL.EXE file is located: for example, if your disk is loaded in drive A type **A:CONTROL**.

The simulation is based on a dynamic model of a stirred continuous heat exchanger with feedback temperature control.

The process model is a set of ordinary differential equations representing the mass and energy balance around the heater:

Mass balance:

$$\frac{dV}{dt} = F - F_i$$

Energy balance:

$$\frac{d(V\rho c_p T)}{dt} = F_i T_i - FT + Q$$

where V is the heater liquid volume, F is the volumetric flowrate, T is the temperature, ρ is the liquid density, c_p is the liquid specific heat capacity (both are assumed independent of temperature); the subscript i denotes feed conditions. The steady-state model parameters give an open-loop time constant of 10 min. Q is the rate of heat input, controlled by a feedback temperature controller, and is a function of the deviation between the outlet temperature and the temperature set point (T_{sp}):

$$Q = Q_o + f\left(T - T_{sp}\right)$$

Q_o is the steady-state heat input, while the function $f(\cdot)$ depends on the type of controller used. The simulation allows the selection of either a proportional (P) or a proportional + integral (P + I) control law:

Controller	Control law $= f(T - T_{sp})$
P	$K_c(T - T_{sp})$
P + I	$K_c\{(T - T_{sp}) + (1/\tau_I) \int (T - T_{sp})dt\}$

where K_c is the proportional gain and τ_I is the reset or integral action time.

The program also enables the user to incorporate a pure time delay in the system response, to illustrate the effect of transmission lags, for example.

After typing in the command **CONTROL**, the user is asked to select either a P or a P + I controller. Next, the parameters for the P or P + I law will be requested. Finally, the user can incorporate a time delay in the system.

The program will then run, illustrating the dynamic response of the system to a step change in the inlet temperature.

Initially, study the dynamic 'open loop' response of the outlet temperature, without control action (that is, select proportional control and set gain = 0 and time delay = 0).

Then compare responses for different values of the controller parameters. Work using P control first and, later, use P + I. Initially, consider the system without time delay. Large values of the proportional gain or small values of the reset time will be seen to correspond to a 'stronger' control action. It will be seen that incorporation of the integral term eliminates offset but, with decreasing reset time, at the expense of an increasingly oscillatory response.

The best set of control parameters would be those that lead to an acceptable level of offset, give a quick return to the set-point temperature, and do not show undue oscillation in the response. By varying the parameters you can select and compare the best set of parameters for both P and P + I control, with and without a system time delay. You will also find that the control loop can become unstable at certain values of the control parameters, and that this problem is made worse by increasing the time delay.

If the program crashes because of an inappropriate input, simply load it again and retry.

To return to the operating system, key simultaneously CTRL-BREAK.

Conclusions

The core of this final chapter is the extended design exercise, which should help put in context much of the material that was treated more formally in earlier chapters. If you have worked through the exercise you should have a good grasp of the methods, and also the difficulties and limitations, of setting up material, energy and economic balances. In addition, the spreadsheet solution which we have provided should have given you the opportunity to assess the sensitivity of the results to the conditions or principal assumptions. We hope, too, that the exercise provides a good model for the important process of checking the consistency and plausibility of descriptions of technologies and processes.

The more detailed examples contained on the disk and outlined in the text should also have provided an opportunity to put into practice some of the material contained in this book.

Overall conclusions

We noted at the outset that this book was neither an attempt to describe all, nor indeed many, of the processes which are used in the food industry, nor to describe the whole of chemical engineering. Instead, we have tried to outline the key physical and physico-chemical principles which underpin food processes, and we have then tried to show how simple (for the most part) mathematical descriptions – models – can be developed and interpreted on the basis of these principles. The overall intention has been to demonstrate how quantitative understanding is important for process selection, design and operation.

We have laid great stress on the development and use of simplified models. There are several reasons for this emphasis. First, we believe, and have tried to show, that simplified models can provide a very good first basis for assessing processes and their efficiency. Often, a good estimate is sufficient to answer a technical question about the feasibility of a particular process or the advantages of one process technology over another. Even where simplified descriptions are no longer adequate you will find it useful to be able to produce order of magnitude estimates as a check. This is perhaps even more important today when highly sophisticated computer programmes are used routinely for process design and analysis: apparent sophistication or impressively presented results are, in themselves, no guarantee of reliability. Second, there are many food processes where the data available – such as physical properties – are poor. Models are no better than the data they rely on. On the other hand, rough models which recognize the limitations of their data can be very useful. Finally, recognizing that often mathematics can be off-putting, we have tried to minimize the amount of mathematics used in the text. We hope that those who persevere with the mathematics will find that this book gives them a set of tools with which food processes can be analysed.

Having said all that, we hope that the text will prove useful not only to students and professionals in the food industry, but also to chemical engineers. For the latter group we hope that the book will awaken an interest in the problems and challenges posed by food processing, which is after all the largest sector of manufacturing industry and, arguably, the one with most direct impact on our quality of life.

We will be very pleased to receive comments and suggestions on the text. Even though the process of bringing the book to completion has been desperately slow, we are conscious of the many inadequacies that still remain.

Index

Page numbers appearing in **bold** refer to figures and page numbers appearing in *italics* refer to tables.